Licia Bertani
Director of the Museum

SAN LORENZO
THE MEDICI CHAPELS
and the Laurentian Library

BECOCCI
SCALA

CONTENTS

© 1998 SCALA, Istituto Fotografico Editoriale S.p.A., Antella (Florence)
and Editrice Giusti di Becocci s.r.l., Florence
Photographs: Scala Archives, except pp. 12, 52 e 60 Becocci Archives (Paolo Nannoni)
Layout and cover: C.D.&V., Florence
Translation: Susan Scott
Editing: Patrizia Bevilacqua
Printed in Italy by: "Arti Grafiche" Stampa Nazionale, Calenzano (Florence) 1998

Plan of the San Lorenzo Complex

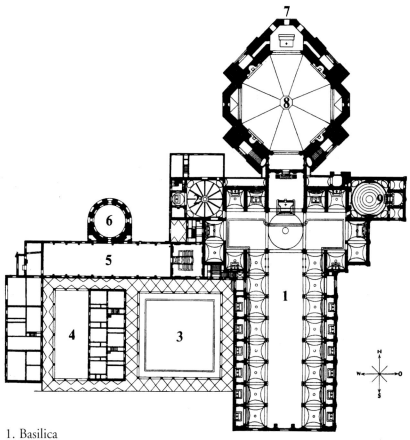

1. Basilica
2. Old Sacristy
3. Brunelleschi's Cloister
4. Second Cloister
5. Laurentian Library
6. Tribuna d'Elci
7. Entrance to the Medici Chapels
8. Chapel of the Princes
9. New Sacristy

View of the San Lorenzo complex

The Architectural Genesis of the San Lorenzo Complex

In the IVth century A.D., when Florence still preserved its Roman urban structure and was enclosed within its first circle of brick walls built some four hundred years earlier, if we came out the northern gate facing *ad Aquilonem*, we would have found one of those typical suburban neighborhoods that arose with the city's expansion in Hadrianic times (IInd century A.D.). Probably there were thermal baths here, as there were on the southern side of the walls facing the Arno river, also dating back to the Empire. Certainly this populous, noisy quarter was well supplied with *tabernae*, serving also the numerous foreigners who came and went from *Florentia* on their various kinds of business.

In the second half of that century, however, the Christianity that by then had spread to and was becoming more and more ingrained in this principal city of Tuscia was not totally faithful to the orthodoxy dictated by Rome. In some of its outlying neighborhoods (especially on the other side of the Arno *ad pontem*, the only way then to get across the river) the Arian heresy had caught hold. For this reason, among others, the bishop of Milan, Ambrose, fervent defender of the Roman creed and fierce adversary of Arianism, in 393 paid a visit to Florence to reaffirm the primacy of Rome in those crowded, lower class areas outside the walls. He stopped *ad Petram Planam* (at Pietrapiana, where today stands the church of Sant'Ambrogio, on the eastern side of the city, along the *decumanus* which was a principal artery in the subdivision of the territory) and, near the northern *cardus*, consecrated the church of San Lorenzo, willed into being by Giuliana, a Florentine matron of Jewish origin. The church was built - according to tradition - on top of a modest *monticulus* along the side of the suburban road, not far from those taverns mentioned above where, perhaps, already existed also tombs and chapels following the Roman funerary custom.

During the XIth century, in the climate of fervor and rebirth marking those years, the primitive church of San Lorenzo was restored, remodeled, and enlarged (the first documents concerning the new building go back to 1060). The church was built on the usual basilica plan, with three nave aisles divided by columns, a chancel in the domed apse, trussed roof, and a porch in front of the facade, an aspect documented as late as the XVth century in a codex by Marco di Bartolomeo Rustici. To the left of the church were the cloister and rectory.

During the XIVth century, behind the church was erected the graceful belltower, lighted by biforate windows and crowned with a delicate railing pierced with a Gothic flower pattern. The beginning of that century (1300-1302) saw the construction of a new sacristy on the west side, behind the belltower, whose appearance is documented by Pietro del Massaio, later transformed by Brunelleschi into the chapel of Marco di Luca (currently the Corsi chapel).

The original aspect of San Lorenzo as documented in a codex by Marco di Bartolomeo Rustici.
Florence, Library of the "Seminario Maggiore"

Detail of the fresco by Giorgio Vasari and Marco da Faenza portraying Brunelleschi and Ghiberti showing the model of the church of San Lorenzo to Cosimo the Elder. Florence, Palazzo Vecchio

Detail of the XIXth century copy of the Carta della Catena (ca. 1470) showing the church of San Lorenzo. Museum of Firenze com'era

Only in the fifteenth century, however, was the spark lit igniting the vital process of regenerating the entire organism, which in the course of two centuries would make it one of the most significant complexes in Italian sacred art. In 1415 Giovanni de' Medici, called Giovanni di Bicci, a resident of the San Lorenzo quarter and patron of the church, commissioned Filippo Brunelleschi (1377-1446) to enlarge the basilica, as a sign of his family's growing economic and political power in the city. This project involved adding a new 'modern' choir to replace the old Romanesque apse, raised above the level of the floor of the preceding nave, with square chapels, a shape borrowed from those in the Gothic church of Santa Trinita; subsequently this shape of chapel would become an unmistakable characteristic of all the Renaissance religious architecture springing from the line of Brunelleschi and Michelozzo.

From 1422 to 1428 construction went on of the central plan Medici mausoleum, a sort of family 'pantheon' located to the left of the new choir (later it would be called the Old Sacristy). The great ribbed (commonly called umbrella) dome characterizing it, however, is not yet an evident mark of the Renaissance, at least in the philological meaning impressed on it by the 'school' of Alberti, as we find here reminiscences of Byzantine architecture and references to the Gothic style deriving from the apses with radiating chapels and ribbed vaults of the great medieval cathedrals. The twelve (like the Apostles) sections of the dome enclose the space of the white cube, harmonically accented by the counterpoint of the *pietra serena* ribs, the polychrome *Seraphim* by Luca della Robbia (*ca.* 1399-1482), and the great spandrel medallions of the *Evangelists* by Donatello (1386?-1466).

Work on the choir commissioned by Giovanni di Bicci went on until 1429,

the year of his death; it was subsequently resumed in 1434 under his son
Cosimo the Elder, but according to a new concept that showed the influence of Michelozzo. The plan for the choir was substantially reduced in
depth, and was flattened even more by the elimination of the chapels
planned for the side nearest the nave. While in the transept the chapels, outlined by large round arches resting on an entablature supported by grooved
Corinthian pilasters, continued to be conceived on the central plan, the
new plan for the side naves called for chapels (*tribunalia*) which would be
hemispheric on their interior, as in Santo Spirito, but here inserted into
walls whose exterior was flat (as opposed to Brunelleschi's plan for the
church across the Arno). In this project, which for the moment remained
on paper (precedence was being given to Donatello's decoration of the Old
Sacristy), we can perceive a sort of rejection of Brunelleschian connotations
in the plans for San Lorenzo, perhaps willed by Michelozzo (1369-1472),
and an approach to Albertian *latinitas*. The years 1440-1451 (Brunelleschi
died in 1446, with Michelozzo definitively replacing him on the project)
saw the completion of a large part of the work, with the construction of the
transept at the head of the church and the first section of the nave, three
bays (1450), characterized by imposing sandstone Corinthian columns,
whose capitals, topped by original dosserets (or 'dadoes') carved with the
Laurentian symbol of the grill, support round arches decorated with acanthus leaves in the lintels and various types of moldings in the intrados.

It was from 1455 to 1460, however, under the direction of Antonio Manetti
Ciaccheri (1423-1497), an architect who started out as a 'woodcutter' as
was the custom of the times, that the building project took a decisive turn
in the direction of Albertian principles. Firstly, a hemispheric dome was set
over the crossing, at the intersection of the transept with the nave, where
Brunelleschi's original plan probably called for a sail vault, his preferred
type, or an umbrella vault as in the Old Sacristy. The insertion of this dome
is of fundamental significance: in fact, it constituted an element that was
decisively more 'modern' (in the sense of more avant-garde) precisely
because it was more classical with respect to the still Gothic umbrella vault
used by Brunelleschi. Furthermore, five more bays were planned for the
nave, marked off by Corinthian columns but with numerous variations and
a more rigid sculptural rendering of the capitals at the hands of the workshops of Antonio Rossellino (1427-1479) and Pagno di Lapo Portigiani
(1408-1470). The length of the nave was thus given a greater continuity,
cancelling out the sharp break planned by Brunelleschi between the new
chancel area and the lower level of the earlier church. Chapels were inserted lateral to the side aisles, no longer on a square but now on a rectangular
plan and markedly Albertian in type (as he had theorized for the so-called
Etruscan temple and realized in the Tempio Malatestiano in Rimini and the
church of Sant'Andrea in Mantua).

In 1464 Cosimo died, and work continued under Piero, who between 1465
and 1480 had the triple nave built. In 1465 the old belltower was also torn
down, a prelude to the transformations conceived by the new Signore of

The right side of the church

Florence, Lorenzo the Magnificent, a man deeply enamored of Greek and Roman classicism and the urban and architectural magnificence of the Empire. His favorite architect, Giuliano da Sangallo (1443-1515), who faithfully carried out his wishes, began the work with the intent of making the church one of the vital centers of the new Florence, the 'ideal' city. Behind the church on the right Giuliano began a new Medici chapel (later to be called the New Sacristy), also on the central plan, facing it on the exterior with *pietra forte* (the local tan-colored stone), continuing the stone facing along the right side of the church and decorating it with large blind arches framed by slender pilaster strips, a motif borrowed - as in so many of Sangallo's works for Lorenzo - from the facades of imperial Roman theatres and amphitheatres. Work, however, was halted by the death of Lorenzo in 1492, and only after the brief moment of the Republic under Savonarola was it taken up again with the return of the Medici in 1512.

In 1515 the Medici pope Leo X announced a competition for the design of a facade for the church, in which the most important minds of the Renaissance took part, from Raphael (1483-1520) to Michelangelo (1475-1564), including Sangallo himself who had returned to Florence from his 'exile' in Rome and who presented a proposal, new to Florence, of a facade flanked by two symmetrical belltowers. Unfortunately, none of these splen-

Wooden model of the facade planned by Michelangelo for the church of San Lorenzo, executed by Pietro Urbano. Florence, Casa Buonarroti

did projects was carried out, but in 1519 work resumed on the New Sacristy, entrusted to Michelangelo, and continued intermittently until 1533-34.

Michelangelo left his mark also inside the church, on the inner facade dominated by the Savoy coat-of-arms, where he created the solemn Tribune of the Relics (1530), used to exhibit to the faithful the relics housed behind its three doors.

The end of the XVIth and all of the XVIIth centuries passed in the construction of the third Medici chapel (the so-called Medici Chapels), of which we shall speak further on; the last descendant of the Medici family, the Electress Palatine Anna Maria Luisa, was mainly responsible for the works realized in the eighteenth century, which act as an ethical and cultural testament to an epoch that ended with the dynasty to which she belonged. She had Ferdinando Ruggieri (1691-1741) and then his brother Giuseppe consolidate the space under the church (now used in part for temporary exhibitions) and build the turret covering the exterior of the dome over the crossing, as well as the small but graceful belltower to the side of the New Sacristy. She also asked them to create a new, and once again unrealized, model for the facade.

Another attempt was made in the XIXth century to solve the by now centuries-old problem of the church facade, entrusting the project (1837) to the neoclassical architect Pasquale Poccianti (1774-1858), and again on the occasion of a new competition in 1900, won on the second round (1905)

View of the actual facade of the church

by the Roman Cesare Bazzani (1873-1939), the author in Florence of the building housing the Biblioteca Nazionale along the Arno. Despite all this throng of artists and ideas the facade would never be built, remaining a rough stone surface, furrowed by the thin shadows of the projections in the rows of building blocks and eroded by time, a romantic connotation common to many XIXth century Florentine religious buildings.

The last significant architectural and decorative work done in the church was the remodeling of the choir and the creation of neo-Quattrocento altars in the chapels, work carried out in 1860 in part by the architect Gaetano Baccani (1792-1867) in a climate of historicism and late romanticism.

On the exterior, instead, the last fundamental urbanistic undertaking took place in the XXth century: the creation of the short flight of steps leading up to the church, and in 1933-35 the demolition of houses adjoining the northern side of the church and chancel, near the New Sacristy, conforming to the theories of urban renewal of the time, which revolved around the idea of 'thinning out' the architecture around the major monuments in order to make them stand out against a centuries-old built environment that was considered of 'lesser' importance.

THE ARTISTIC DECORATION OF THE CHURCH

Right Aisle

In the FIRST CHAPEL, earlier under Medici patronage, Jacopo Chimenti called "Empoli" painted between 1580 and 1590 a panel of *The Martyrdom of Saint Sebastian,* in which the face of the saint is a portrait of the senator Leone Nerli. The work dates from the least fertile period of the artist's activity, but is nonetheless marked by a naturalistic arrangement of the figures; in the center background the Albertian rotunda of the church of Santissima Annunziata can be recognized among the classical columns and buildings. The panel was originally on the sixth altar on the left, under the patronage of the Aldobrandini family.

In the SECOND CHAPEL, formerly patronized by the Ginori family, is the original panel by Rosso Fiorentino dated 1523, representing *The Marriage of the Virgin.* Commissioned by Carlo Ginori when the artist was not yet thirty years old, it was painted at the end of Rosso's stay in Florence, before he left for Rome. Vasari calls it a "beautiful thing," and in fact it is distinguished by the richness of its inventions, brilliant and lively shot colors, and the rare beauty of the figures, which are sometimes dressed in a bizarre manner. The entire composition betrays Rosso's adoption of suggestions from

View of the interior of the church looking towards the inner facade

Jacopo Chimenti called "Empoli", The Martyrdom of Saint Sebastian

Rosso Fiorentino, The Marriage of the Virgin

Raphael, above all in his *School of Athens*. The scene, crowded with figures (which can be glimpsed fading all the way into the dark background) arranged in two semicircles meeting in the center, commences from the bottom with two women seated on the steps. On the right, the younger one holds an open book and wears a dress whose light color changes from yellow to light green clinging to her body. In the center, surrounded by a group of onlookers, dominate the group of the priest blessing the marriage, Mary dressed in a pearl grey surcoat over a pink tunic and Joseph here shown in

Niccolò Lapi, Saint Lawrence among the Souls in Purgatory

Michele di Ridolfo del Ghirlandaio, The Assumption of the Virgin

all his youthful boldness, in a sort of defiance of the tradition that represented the Virgin's husband as an old man.

On the left wall is a tomb slab with the effigy of the musician Francesco Landini, the "blind organist," who died in 1397, while a nineteenth century inscription commemorates three sixteenth century musicians who belonged to the Chapter of San Lorenzo: Francesco Corteccia, Luca Bati, and Marco da Galliano.

The THIRD CHAPEL, formerly patronized by the Inghirami family and dedicated to Saint Lawrence, holds a canvas by the Florentine painter Niccolò Lapi (1661-1732), of 1716, with *Saint Lawrence among the Souls in Purgatory*. Notable here are a richness and attractiveness of invention united with a creative facility very close to the 'proto-eighteenth century' idiom of Luca Giordano, and his use of lively shot colors.

In the FOURTH CHAPEL, under Martelli patronage and dedicated to Saint Sigismund in memory of Sigismondo Martelli who died at 25 (1547), is a charming panel by the Florentine Michele Tosini, called Michele di Ridolfo del Ghirlandaio (1503-1577), datable around 1572, representing *The Assumption of the Virgin*. Here earlier was a canvas by Vasari of *Saint Sigismund*, completely destroyed in 1712 and replaced by this one, brought here from the high altar of the church of San Miniato al Ceppo, on via San Gallo, and donated to the Martelli family by Niccolò Malvezzi, an organist at San Lorenzo.

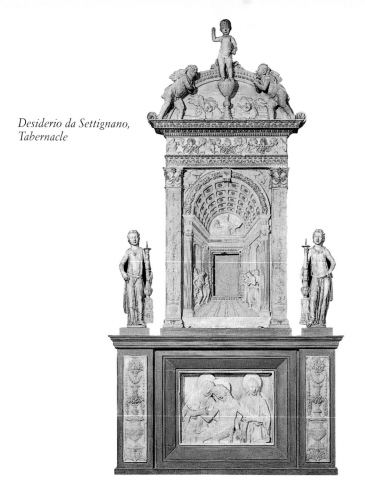

Desiderio da Settignano,
Tabernacle

In the FIFTH CHAPEL, formerly under Ginori patronage and dedicated to Saint Jerome, is a canvas by Ottaviano Dandini (?-1750), representing *The Crucifixion with Saints Jerome, Francis, and Mary Magdalene* replacing a lost *Crucifixion with Saints* by Filippo Lippi.

In the SIXTH CHAPEL, formerly under Medici patronage, is a panel of *The Adoration of the Magi* by Girolamo Macchietti (1535-1592). A follower of Vasari active also in the Studiolo of Francesco I, he represents the more academic and virtuosistic line of Mannerism.

After this chapel, we find on the wall along the right aisle of the nave a marble ALTAR TABERNACLE by Desiderio da Settignano (1430-1464). Set in 1461 in the wall of the chapel of the Holy Sacrament, patronized by the Medici, at the head of the left transept - but certainly executed before the *Funerary Monument to Carlo Marsuppini* in Santa Croce, datable to 1453-1455 - it was moved in 1677 to the opposite side, in the Neroni Altoviti chapel. Just after the end of World War II it was placed in its current, incongruous location. The aedicula of the ciborium is formed by two pilaster strips topped by an entablature; the pilaster strips frame a rectangular area represented in perspective and made up of a series of pilasters between which open arched doors, with in the back a rectangular architraved opening that held the now lost door of the ciborium, topped by a lunette with a

Donatello, Pulpit

blessing God the Father. As was the Renaissance custom in similar objects, the virtual space is covered by a classical barrel vault with coffers that in their perspectival progression towards a vanishing point trace out rayed concentric arches, representing in sculpted relief a space similar to that of the baths of imperial Rome as evoked by Alberti, rendered through a calculated and precise study of perspective. The aedicula is flanked by two wingless angels holding candles.

Above is a lunette with at its sides two winged cherubs in adoration of the Christ Child standing on the chalice of the Eucharist, His right hand raised in blessing and His left holding the signs, now lost, of His Passion. In the base of the aedicula is a *pietra serena* panel of the *Pietà*, flanked by marble candelabra. Sources assign the entire composition to Desiderio da Settignano; noteworthy is the subtle modelling clearly derived from Donatello, along with a soft, almost sensuous handling of light and shadow. The work is highly refined, with marble decorations in a very low relief.

The Christ Child on the chalice, whose austere figure shows Savonarolian influence, is instead, as Albertini affirmed in 1510, by Baccio da Montelupo, and as early as that date substituted the Child by Desiderio holding in His hands the globe of the earth, now displayed in the Sacristy.

In front of Desiderio's tabernacle is the first of two PULPITS by Donatello. The bronze panels making it up, originally perhaps planned for the high altar that Cosimo the Elder had wanted as the fitting crown for his burial place, but already part of a 'choir loft' at least since 1485, were assembled

Detail of Donatello's Pulpit representing The Resurrection

in their current arrangement only between 1558 and 1565. Some of them were in reality not done by the artist, who interrupted his work on the pulpit in 1465; they were inserted as late as between 1616 and 1634 and executed in wood in imitation of bronze. Mounted on elegant Ionic marble columns of different colors, the panels represent *Scenes from the Life of Christ* (*The Three Maries at the Tomb; The Descent into Limbo; Christ Crowned with Thorns*, this latter a seventeenth century rendition in wood, and *The Resurrection*) as well as *The Martyrdom of Saint Lawrence* and *Saint Luke* (this one too a seventeenth century image). In the creation of this work Donatello, by now old and ill, was aided by assistants, including his follower from the Veneto region Bellano and Bertoldo di Giovanni. In certain passages the working is not as careful and refined as in the master's earlier works, which is a sure sign of the intervention of a follower. The unfinished nature of the work, not understood or appreciated in the sixteenth century by, among others, Baccio Bandinelli, is today the moving witness to the last phase of the life of the great sculptor, who here left among the friezes his signature and the date, 1465.

Right Transept

Continuing our visit of the church, immediately after Desiderio's ciborium and before the end of the transept we find the SAINT JULIAN CHAPEL, formerly patronized by the Corsi family, rich in works of art. On the right wall,

Antonio del Pollaiolo, Processional Crucifix

Niccolò di Tommaso or Bonaccorso di Cino, Madonna of the Canons

The Roman sarcophagus holding the mortal remains of Niccolò Stenone

above the fragment of a sarcophagus, is a detached fresco with the *Madonna of the Canons* or the *Madonna del Parto*, a refined work attributed to Niccolò di Tommaso or Bonaccorso di Cino, Florentine painters active in the second half of the XIVth century. On the altar has been recently (in the 1980s) placed the beautiful and subtle *Processional Crucifix* in cork oak by Antonio del Pollaiolo (1431-1498). Christ, His vigorous arms stretched on

The Chapel of the Holy Sacrament

the cross and His legs bent dramatically, is captured in the moment of His death, His head bent on His breast in mute acceptance of His Father's will. It can be dated to the sixth decade of the XVth century. At one time on the altar was the wooden statue of the Virgin called "*The Bentornata*" (Welcome Madonna), now in a chapel in the left transept. A modern stained glass window, installed in 1994, represents the Danish anatomist and geologist Niels Stensen (Niccolò Stenone, 1638-1686) in an image taken from a XVII-XVIIIth century print.

On the left, a Roman sarcophagus - with high relief scenes of a funeral across the front - holds the mortal spoils of Niccolò Stenone. Converted to Catholicism and named titular bishop of Titiopolis in Greece, he was later appointed apostolic vicar for Scandinavia, with headquarters first in Hanover and later in Schwerin.

At the end of the transept is the CHAPEL OF THE HOLY SACRAMENT, formerly Neroni Altoviti, defined by a large arch, at the sides of which are two late XVIth century paintings: a small anonymous *Crucifixion* on the right, and a

School of Domenico Ghirlandaio, Adoration of the Child with Saints Mark, Francis, and a Franciscan Friar

Saint Zenobius on the left, attributed to Fabrizio Boschi (*ca.* 1570-1642).
On the baroque altar of the chapel is a *Crucifix* of the first half of the XVIIth century, close to the manner of Ferdinando Tacca.
To the side of the altar, on the right, is the *Funerary Monument to Caroline of Saxony* (who died in 1832), the first wife of Grand Duke Leopold II. Realized in *pietre dure* (inlaid semi-precious stones), it is certainly one of the last creations of the Florentine Opificio delle Pietre Dure for the Tuscan sovereigns.
On the left wall is a panel assigned to the school of Domenico Ghirlandaio (1449-1494), but some think it can be attributed to the younger David Ghirlandaio (1452-1525), representing an *Adoration of the Child with Mary and the Young Saint John the Baptist between Saints Mark, Francis, and a Franciscan*, with above *God the Father and the Dove of the Holy Spirit, surrounded by Flying Angels and Cherubim*. Although the composition is late XVth century in style, the panel can be dated to the early years of the XVIth century. The sacred scene is immersed in a hilly landscape with slender trees, scattered houses and villas, a river on the left, and on the right, with its graceful belltower, a religious building reached by a steep climb (San Salvatore al Monte?). On the road traveled by wayfarers, we can see Tobias and the Angel, wayfarers themselves. Above, God the Father with the Holy Spirit and angels are huddled together in a sort of ellipse.

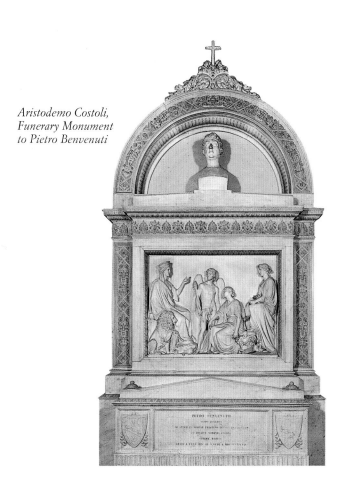

Aristodemo Costoli,
Funerary Monument
to Pietro Benvenuti

On the other side of the door leading to the New Sacristy is the CHAPEL OF SAINT BERNARD (represented in the opening of a blind window in a XVII-XVIIIth century canvas), formerly patronized by the Ciai and Ridolfi families, containing the funerary monument - executed by Aristodemo Costoli (1803-1871) in 1852 - to the painter Pietro Benvenuti from Arezzo, known also for his decorations of the vault of the Chapel of the Princes.

On the altar we can admire the late XVIIIth century canvas with a northern flavor representing *The Education of the Virgin.* On the left wall of the same chapel is the monument commemorating the goldsmith and decorator Bernardo Cennini, by Leopoldo Costoli (1850-1908).

In the following CHAPEL, patronized by the Della Stufa family, on the right wall now hangs a triptych by Puccio di Simone (active between 1335 and 1360) representing *The Annunciation between Saints Julian and John the Baptist, with donors.* Mentioned in the XVth century as being in the preceding chapel, perhaps it was originally set inside a tabernacle on the church's exterior. This hypothesis could justify the changes the panel has undergone and its unfortunate state of conservation. It can be dated no later than 1353; freed of repaintings, the work today reveals all its aristocratic beauty, certainly the expression of a refined and courtly world.

Chancel

In front of the chancel, under the patronage of the Medici, is the tomb slab of Cosimo the Elder, who is buried below within the pier supporting the floor, part of the lower structure of the church. The slab, worked in polychrome marble with a design based on a combination of geometrical shapes (circle and square), favorite symbols of the humanists, is traditionally attributed to Verrocchio. The high altar was executed in 1787 by the Opificio delle Pietre Dure on a design by Gaspare Maria Paoletti (1727-1813). In the altar frontal were inserted three panels, the central one designed by Bernardino Poccetti (1548-1612) and the side ones by Ludovico Cigoli (1559-1613), made in 1620 by Giovan Battista Sassi. Cigoli's side panels represent *Explorers in the Promised Land* and *The Sacrifice of Isaac*; the very beautiful central one by Poccetti shows *Manna from Heaven*. Set in a gilt metal frame, the scene is outlined by an elegant border also worked in *pietre dure*. In the ends of the altar, again in *pietre dure*, are the coats-of-arms of the Medici Hapsburg and the Medici Orléans families. The ciborium was executed in 1786 on a design by Cosimo Siries, while its door with the chalice and Host follows a design by Antonio Cioci.

The marble crucifix above the altar may be the work of Valerio Cioli (1529?-1599) from the end of the XVIth century, but a not completely convincing hypothesis attributes it to Baccio da Montelupo, who would however have made it in the first half of the century.

The current appearance of the choir is the nineteenth century work of Gaetano Baccani; earlier the walls had been frescoed by Pontormo (1494-1556) on a commission from Grand Duke Cosimo I. On the back wall, above the cornice, were: *The Expulsion from Paradise, Christ the Judge* and *The Creation of Eve, The Original Sin*. On the left wall, above, were *Cain and Abel, Noah, Moses*; on the right wall: *The Four Evangelists, The Sacrifice of Isaac, Adam and Eve at Work*. In the lower register were three large scenes: *The Flood* on the left; in the center, below was *The Martyrdom of San Lorenzo* and above, *The Ascent of the Souls*; on the right, *The Resurrection of the Bodies*. After Pontormo's death, Bronzino finished the side scenes. The entire cycle was destroyed in 1742 when the apse was remodeled. We have about thirty preparatory drawings and an engraving of 1598 of the choir, even if partly taken up by the decorations for the funeral services in honor of Philip II of Spain, to show us what Pontormo's paintings looked like and to make us mourn their grievous loss.

In the choir loft is a great organ, the gift of the reigning Savoy family, built in 1864 by the Serassi firm in Bergamo.

The dome over the chancel was decorated in 1742 by Vincenzo Meucci (1694-1766), on a commission from Anna Maria Luisa de' Medici, with the *Florentine Saints in Glory* and in the pendentives the *Four Doctors of the*

The chancel; in the foreground, the Tomb Slab of Cosimo the Elder, attributed to Verrocchio

The dome over the chancel with frescoes by Vincenzo Meucci

Next page: Wooden statue called "The Bentornata" dating to the middle of the XIVth century

Church (Gregory, Augustine, Jerome, and Ambrose). In these frescoes, marked by pleasing solutions and inventions, the painter reveals his predilection for delicate, shot colors combined with airy, light forms. A capable technician, Meucci, the student in Florence of Galeotti and Francesco Redi and in Bologna of Giovan Gioseffo Da Sole, was in great demand for his attractive international style.

Left Transept

In the FIRST CHAPEL to the left of the chancel, formerly patronized by the Rondinelli family, a polychrome wooden statue of the *Virgin and Child*, called "*The Bentornata*" (Welcome Virgin) stands on the altar in a glass case. Without doubt one of the church's masterpieces, it can be dated to the middle of the XIVth century; however, the pigment is not original but perhaps dates from the XVIIIth century.  An inscription on its base informs us that it was caused to be carved by Giovanni Benini and his wife Maria for devotion, as reads also the already mentioned XIXth century plaque in the Corsi chapel (right transept). On the right wall hangs a fine altarpiece representing *Saint Lawrence Enthroned between Saints Stephen and Vincent Deacons and Martyrs*. The work is attributed to Ridolfo del Ghirlandaio (1483-1561). Saint Lawrence sits on a high throne under a canopy formed by a drape of fabric worked with vegetable motifs. Above, two angels hold a precious royal crown, the prize of martyrdom. At its sides are the two saints, dressed like Lawrence in rich dalmatics with the signs of their torture. The background is a landscape with slender, delicate trees swaying in a blue sky traversed by soft clouds. A cartouche at the bottom bears the inscription A.D.M.D.XI.

On the left wall is a panel from the school of Domenico Ghirlandaio of *The Nativity with Saints Julian and Francis*, dating from the beginning of the XVIth century. The narrative tone of the scene, immersed in a real landscape with green hills and valleys, crossed by a river with high banks and slender little bridges, punctuated by religious buildings, farmhouses, and aristocratic villas, with an ideal walled Florence, on the left, contrasts with the spirituality and religious silence of the onlookers in the foreground who seem to be

School of Domenico Ghirlandaio, The Nativity with Saints Julian and Francis

David Ghirlandaio (attr.), Saint Anthony Abbot between Saints Leonard and Julian

*Giovanni Dupré,
Funerary Monument
to Berta Moltke
Withfield*

completely absorbed by the mystery of the miraculous birth of God as a baby and their hopes for future redemption.

On the altar of the next CHAPEL, earlier patronized by the Ginori family, is a panel attributed to David Ghirlandaio with *Saint Anthony Abbot between Saints Julian and Leonard* at its center. The saint sits on a polychrome marble throne in the style of a Renaissance aedicula, topped by a barrel vault and a shell motif in the background lunette that forms a concentric arch with his halo. The niche is inserted into a wall with two landscapes painted on its panels; beyond the wall emerge trees connotating symbolically a typical humanist 'garden of paradise' (cypresses, orange, pomegranate and a tree pruned in a topiary shape). The predella contains scenes from the lives of the saints represented above them.

On the left wall is set the *Funerary Monument to Berta Moltke Withfield*, carved in 1864 by Giovanni Dupré (1817-1882), in a spirit of moving, vibrant romanticism, especially in the two airy, dynamic figures of the angel

29

Early Trecento Florentine school, Nursing Madonna, set inside a canvas by Francesco Conti

and young woman with bent head and hair flying in the wind, very similar to another work by the sculptor for the tomb of Madame Favard at Rovezzano. Next, a finely worked inlaid wooden door leads to the celebrated Old Sacristy, which for the special role it plays in a visit to the church will be treated separately in the following pages.

Still within the church proper, the next stop is the CHAPEL OF SAINTS COSMAS AND DAMIAN, also called CHAPEL OF THE RELICS, patronized by the Medici and originally dedicated to the Holy Sacrament. At the sides of the entrance arch are two frescoes representing, on the right *Saints Cosmas and Damian*, and on the left, Saint Charles Borromeo, dated 1611 and attributed to Bernardino Poccetti. On the first altar we can admire a panel painting of the early Trecento Florentine school representing the *Virgin and Child*, called the *Nursing Madonna*, set inside a canvas that tradition claims was painted in just one night by Francesco Conti (1681-1760). A charming legend, supported by the inscription on the altar, says that this Madonna was kept in the bedroom of Saint Zenobius.
In front of this altar has been temporarily (1997) placed the large *Reliquary of Saint Cesonius*, coming (1785) from the royal chapel in Palazzo Pitti, datable around 1621; it is attributed, on strong evidence, to Cosimo Merlini and Andrea Tarchiani, goldsmiths in the Grand Duke's workshops. A dis-

*Dario Guidotti and
Raffaello Romanelli,
Cenotaph to Donatello*

tinguished work for its design based on the repetition of decorative motifs
and the very high quality of its workmanship, it was created for Mary
Magdalen of Austria, to whom in 1618 the body of the sainted martyr was
sent by the Jesuit priest Stefano del Bufalo. The wooden cupboards, lined
with red silk, along the chapel's three sides held the relics collected by
Lorenzo the Magnificent and Popes Leo X and Clement VII, originally preserved in the tribune on Michelangelo's inner facade of the church.
Exhibition of the relics to the faithful, which took place once a year at
Easter, followed an almost magic ritual: display of the sacred containers,
granting of plenary indulgence, while in front of the tribune a perpetual
flame was to be burning. When this ritual was suspended, part of the relics
were sent first to the Uffizi (1778) and subsequently to the Museo degli
Argenti; the church of San Lorenzo received in exchange some one hundred
reliquaries coming from the Palatine Chapel which, along with those
remaining here from the church's original holdings, were placed in these
cupboards on their elaborately carved shelves, the work of the court architect Conti. There they remained until 1945, when the most valuable pieces
(about one hundred), along with the bishop's crozier and mitre, were transferred to the Medici Chapels museum.

Next to the Chapel of the Relics is the MARTELLI CHAPEL. Its right wall holds

Filippo Lippi, The Annunciation

the Renaissance Revival *Cenotaph to Donatello* (buried underneath the church), executed by Raffaello Romanelli (1856-1928) on a design by the architect Dario Guidotti (author with Bazzanti of one of the plans for the facade of San Lorenzo). Above the altar is *The Annunciation* by the young Filippo Lippi (1406-1469), datable between 1437 and 1441. The predella with stories of Saint Nicholas of Bari is instead attributed to Fra Diamante and Francesco Pesellino (1422-1457).

The scene of the Annunciation takes place on a Renaissance porch opening onto a garden with trees, lined on either side by two long buildings rendered in perspective and marked by a recurring motif of pilaster strips on the walls; attached to the building on the right is a meticulously described vine-covered arbor under which is a well. In the far background can be glimpsed a belltower and the buildings of a city; a bright orange tower stands out. On the left are two angels symbolizing, according to the different

colors of their wings (red-orange and dark green), divine love and eternal hope, while on the right, the Annunciation Angel with his white wings represents purity. The Virgin, disturbed by the angel's words, pulls back, but at the same time accepts the divine will revealed to her through the Holy Scriptures. The panel is one of the most important works of the artist's early period, uniting the rigorous perspective of Masaccio with a warm, cordial tone conveyed by the figures' poses and even by the objects, charged with symbolic meaning - like the flask of water in the foreground representing Mary's purity - yet rendered with the realistic connotations of everyday life.

Above, in the window niche, is an expressive wooden crucifix of the German school of the XVth century. The Martelli coat-of-arms appears at the base of the mount sustaining the cross.

On the right is a marble *Funerary Monument to Niccolò and Fioretta Martelli*, in the unusual form of a woven basket, attributed to Donatello. Above it a canvas by Giuseppe Nicola Nasini (1657-1736) represents *Saint Jerome and the Angel*, painted in the first decades of the XVIIIth century.

German school of the XVth century, Crucifix

Donatello (attr.), Funerary Monument to Niccolò and Fioretta Martelli

Old Sacristy

At the end of the left transept, as we have already mentioned, a door inlaid with vegetable motifs and candelabra, topped by a shell motif in *pietra serena*, leads to the Old Sacristy.

At the center of this evocative space, under a simple altar table, is the

Old Sacristy

*Donatello, The Assumption
of Saint John the Evangelist*

Donatello, The Resurrection of Drusiana

Sarcophagus of Giovanni di Bicci - with his wife Piccarda Bueri - who commissioned the Sacristy, conceiving it as his own chapel dedicated to his patron Saint John the Evangelist.

The elegant sarcophagus is the work of Andrea di Lazzaro Cavalcanti, called Buggiano (1412-1462). Its cover is decorated with cherubs holding a garland encircling the Medici coat-of-arms; on the sides are other winged cherubs with festoons holding cartouches and the inscription.

The pendentives of the vaulted ceiling hold four medallions of *Stories of the Life of Saint John the Evangelist*. Carved by Donatello, they present boldly foreshortened architecture seen from below (note especially *The Assumption of John the Evangelist*) crowded with white figures against blue skies dotted with clouds.

In *The Resurrection of Drusiana*, the space is shown from a central perspectival standpoint; it is covered by a large barrel vault resting on matching

The dome of the Old Sacristy and the dome over the altar with the Celestial Hemisphere painted by Giuliano d'Arrigo called "Pesello"

Donatello's workshop, Lunettes with bas-reliefs portraying Saints Stephen and Lawrence; Saints Cosmas and Damian

Donatello, Bronze doors with panels portraying Martyrs and Apostles

graceful arcades connected across the back by the triple arch of an upper story portico which acts as a diaphragm between the interior and exterior. The central figure of Drusiana dressed in her black shroud stands out as she emerges from her coffin.

Centered in the lunettes are Donatello's terracotta bas reliefs of the four evangelists, seated at their writing desks clearly derived from classical Roman architecture. The terracotta frieze in the entablature running along the perimeter of the entire chapel holds a series of cherubs in round gilt frames, painted alternatively red and blue, probably the work of Luca della Robbia (*ca.* 1400-1482).

The two doors, treated architecturally as *aediculae*, were created before 1446 by Michelozzo. Above them, set inside round *pietra serena* arches, are painted terracotta bas reliefs by Donatello's workshop, representing *Saints Cosmas and Damian* and *Saints Stephen and Lawrence*. The stone frames are out-

Donatello, Saint Matthew the Evangelist

Donatello, Saint Mark the Evangelist

Andrea Verrocchio, Funerary Monument to Piero the Gouty and Giovanni de' Medici

Andrea Verrocchio and Antonio Rossellino, Basin

lined by vegetable motifs emerging from amphorae against an ochre ground. The bronze doors themselves are the work of Donatello; the panels represent *Martyrs* and *Apostles*.

In the dome over the altar, outlined by a *pietra serena* border of cable molding wrapped with a gold ribbon, Giuliano d'Arrigo called Pesello (1367-1446) has painted the celestial hemisphere with signs of the Zodiac reproducing the stellar and planetary positions in the sky over Florence the night of 4 July 1442, perhaps in reference to the arrival in the city of René of Anjou, as though to indicate that the Florentines took the side of the Angevin against the usurper of the throne of Naples, Alfonso of Aragon. The painting, unusual for a religious building, was executed on an azurite ground, with white lead, black, and touches of gold giving an effect of evanescent transparence. The altar recess is separated from the main room of the sacristy by an open-work marble rail decorated with vegetable motifs; the altar was carved by Andrea di Lazzaro Cavalcanti, mentioned earlier, and Pagno di Lapo Portigiani (1408-1470), with panels representing *The Virgin and Child* and on the sides the prophets *Ezekiel* and *Isaiah*. At the center was originally the panel with *The Sacrifice of Isaac* (now in the Museo Nazionale del Bargello) created by Brunelleschi in 1421 as his competition entry for the celebrated 'Doors of Paradise' on the Baptistery of San Giovanni. The wooden *Crucifix* on the back wall is attributed to Simone di Nanni Ferrucci (? - 1465). Datable to the first half of the XVth century, its recent restoration has revealed all its touching beauty. Until a few years ago, under the crucifix was a tabernacle triptych with two doors, by Lorenzo di Niccolò

Donatello or Desiderio da Settignano, Saint Lawrence

(doc. end of XIVth century-1412?), restored in 1996. Paid for by the Chapter between 1401 and 1405, it is without doubt one of the last works finished before the church was remodeled by Brunelleschi.

In the small room reached through the bronze door on the left is a stone *lavabo*, a wash-basin by Andrea Verrocchio and Antonio Rossellino (1427-1478/81). The basin, resting on a rectangular base, is supported by two dragons with the bodies of serpents, bat wings, and women's heads; in the center is a lion's head. Inside the basin a chalice held up by two dolphins is decorated with the Medici coat of arms and the motto "SEMPER" - the device of Piero di Cosimo de' Medici; on either side are wolf's heads, from which the water poured out. In the arched panel behind the basin, a large crown of oak leaves surrounds a green marble disc; above, a lunette holds an eagle whose claws grip a ribbon with the same motto, "SEMPER."

Facing the *lavabo*, in an elegant wooden niche painted with the signs of the Passion and on either side, in monochrome, two adoring angels, is a polychrome wooden crucifix assignable to the workshop of Baccio da Montelupo. To its sides are *The Virgin Mary* and *Saint John the Evangelist* against a background of a landscape with the sun and moon. The frieze in the entablature of the niche reads "O VOS OMNES QUI TRANSITIS PER VIAM;" both the niche and the painting can be dated around the first half of the XVIth century.

Returning to the Old Sacristy, we can admire, against the walls, the wooden cupboard, inlaid with vegetable and geometric motifs, and the wooden bench on the left, both from the second half of the XVth century. On the cupboard, on the right as you enter, is a terracotta bust of *Saint Lawrence*, assigned to Donatello, it reveals also the painterly sensibility of the works of Desiderio da Settignano, to whom it has recently been attributed.

On the wall between the Sacristy and the Chapel of the Relics is a barrel-vaulted niche closed by a metal grate imitating a rope net, inside which is the tomb of Piero the Gouty and Giovanni de' Medici, the splendid work of Andrea Verrocchio, finished in 1472. Above a marble base inscribed "PATRI PATRUOQUE" (Lorenzo the Magnificent and Giuliano's dedication to their father Piero and uncle Giovanni) rises a porphyry sarcophagus resting on elegant lion's feet laminated in bronze; bronze decorations seal the cover, made up of two very elaborate cornucopias. The lintel of the arch holds a sculpted urn and vegetable motifs.

Left Aisle

The left aisle is also graced with important art works, beginning with the large fresco by Agnolo Bronzino of *The Martyrdom of Saint Lawrence*, commissioned by Cosimo I in 1565. The scene is set in an idealized square in imperial Rome, lined by the tall Corinthian arcades of two matching buildings whose perspective converges on a flight of steps, closed across the top by a balcony rail, behind which looms an imposing central plan building. In the foreground the saint stretches across the grill (similar to the one represented in the church's Codex K, created in 1484 by Gherardo and Monte di Giovanni) surrounded by his executioners and a crowd of men and women, a sort of life study of bodies arranged in a manifestly academic

Agnolo Bronzino, The Martyrdom of Saint Lawrence

manner. Citations of Michelangelo can be seen in the choice of colors, all playing on warm tones of golden yellow, green, and violet, and in the vigorous bodies. The group of onlookers dressed in XVIth century clothes at the side of the scene appears to include portraits of real people, symbolically linking the scene of martyrdom with the contemporary world.

In front of Bronzino's fresco is the second PULPIT by Donatello, it too mounted on Ionic columns. Its panels show scenes from the *Passion of Christ: The Agony in the Garden; Christ Before Caiphas and Pilate; The Crucifixion; The Deposition from the Cross; Christ's Body Laid in the Tomb.* The *Flagellation* and the

Donatello, Pulpit

Detail of Donatello's Pulpit portraying The Deposition from the Cross

Detail of Donatello's Pulpit portraying The Agony in the Garden

representation of *Saint John the Evangelist* are here too XVIIth century works in wood made to resemble bronze. The scene of *The Agony in the Garden*, like the others, is inserted into an architectonic framework taken from classical Rome with an almost archaeological flavor, while the bare landscape setting of the episode closely recalls certain backgrounds found in Gothic paintings; other images, instead, seem to have been 'chiseled out' with a typically humanist formal serenity and precision.

Above the inlaid wooden door leading out to the cloister is the marble CHOIR LOFT, supported by elaborate consoles decorated with scrolls, acanthus leaves, and bas relief motifs (vases, cups, and candelabra). The parapet is articulated by marble panels with *pietre dure* inlays alternating with niches and lined by a series of slender columns holding up the cornice decorated with marine motifs (dolphins and shells). Attributed to Donatello, it is similar to the choir loft in Florence Cathedral. The choir loft holds the organ considered to be the oldest in Florence; its main body, by Benedetto Vantaggini, is dated 1502. It was reworked in 1783 by the Tronci family and

Foreshortened view of the left aisle with the choir loft attributed to Donatello

again later by the Paoli family of Campi Bisenzio. It was masterfully restored in 1993 for the sixteenth centennial of the church's foundation.

In the SIXTH CHAPEL, formerly Aldobrandini, is a charming painting by Pietro Annigoni (1910-1990) with *Saint Joseph the Carpenter and the Boy Jesus.*

The FIFTH CHAPEL, formerly Taddei, holds a *Crucifixion of Saint Achatius,* by Giovanni Antonio Sogliani (1492-1544), whose predella by Bachiacca (1494-1557) was transferred to the Uffizi in 1861. The panel was painted in 1521 for the church of San Salvatore at Camaldoli, commissioned by Monna Alfonsina, wife of Piero the Unlucky de' Medici. Moved during the siege of 1529 to San Giovannino on Via Martelli, it was later (1550) placed in its current location. The work, showing Achatius crucified in the center, surrounded by four other saints, is marked by unusual characteristics: the saint's body appears vigorous in contrast with his gaunt face with its full white beard. In this early work the artist reveals himself to be still faithful to the canons of the work of Fra Bartolommeo and Albertinelli.

Giovanni Antonio Sogliani,
The Crucifixion of Saint Achatius

Crucifix of the German school of the
XVth century; Grieving Figures by
Lorenzo Lippi

In the FOURTH CHAPEL, patronized by the Cambini, is a XVth century *Crucifix*, assigned to the same artist of the German school who carved the crucifix in the Martelli Chapel, flanked by *The Virgin and Saint John the Evangelist*, painted by Lorenzo Lippi (1606-1665) on silhouetted wood.

In the THIRD CHAPEL, under Altoviti patronage, is a delicate canvas by Zanobi Canovai of 1877, painted in the romantic climate of Renaissance Revival historicism; it represents the Virgin and Child seated on a marble throne between Saints Lawrence and Zenobius.

The SECOND CHAPEL, formerly under Medici patronage, holds a dramatic *Crucifixion* by Francesco Conti (*ca.* 1709). At the foot of the cross is Saint John, who looks toward the dying Christ; in the foreground the swooning Virgin is sustained by Mary Magdalene. The light breaking up the surface and colors renders the scene even more charged with pathos.

In the FIRST CHAPEL, under Ubaldini patronage, is a canvas by Pietro Marchesini (1692-1757) with *The Calling of Saint Matthew* (*ca.* 1739). This unique painter borrows XVIth and XVIIth century compositions to render scenes in an atmosphere of a return to the past.

THE CLOISTERS AND THE LAURENTIAN LIBRARY

An integral part of the Laurentian complex are also the two cloisters on the left side of the church, reached both from inside the sanctuary - from a door in the left aisle under Donatello's choir loft - and from outside, through Piazza San Lorenzo. The first cloister, larger and more harmonious in the style of Brunelleschi, is built on two levels supported by Ionic columns, and was constructed by Antonio Manetti on the basis of an earlier design by Michelozzo, continuing the earlier late XIVth century Gothic design.

The second, smaller cloister still shows its XIVth century form, perhaps a survival from the pre-Brunelleschi structure.

In the area connecting the church and the first cloister is a staircase leading up to the Laurentian Library, holding one of Italy's most fascinating and prestigious collections of ancient and illuminated manuscripts, whose architecture bears the imprint of Michelangelo's genius.

The idea of creating a library to the left of the church above the earlier rectory belongs to Pope Leo X (1519); subsequently the plan was taken up by another Medici pope, Clement VII, who assigned (1523) its design and execution to Michelangelo. The artist worked sporadically at it from 1524 to 1533, but continued to follow its construction also after his definitive departure for Rome (1534). The splendid organism represents in humanistic terms the neo-Platonic and Ficinian ascent to Light and the Peace of

View of the Brunelleschi cloister with the dome of the Chapel of the Princes

On the previous pages, the reading-room of the Laurentian Library
Above: the staircase leading to the Laurentian Library, executed by Bartolomeo Ammannati to Michelangelo's design

Knowledge (represented by the reading room with its beautiful desks designed by Michelangelo, terminating in a planned triangular secret library, a triune perfection beyond the world of common mortals) through the shadows of the *"ricetto"*, the cavernous vestibule marked by pilaster strips with a bat motif in the capitals (1526). The vestibule was left unfinished by Michelangelo and completed only in the XIXth century, and the elaborate and complex staircase leading up to the reading room, originally planned in wood, was realized by the Mannerist Ammannati in 1559 on a terracotta model provided by Michelangelo. It symbolizes the means of purification in order to pass from the darkness into the Light.

The Laurentian Library, whose original nucleus was catalogued in 1589 by Baccio Valori and Giovanni Rondinelli, holds priceless manuscripts and illuminated books, in large part the fruit of the humanistic passion of Cosimo the Elder, his son Piero, and above all his grandson Lorenzo the Magnificent, who was responsible for the presence of most of the Greek

The Library's vestibule or "Ricetto"

manuscripts now in the library. Among the holdings are Graeco-Egyptian papyruses; the Byzantine *Pandects* by Justinian; Evangelistaries, among them a Syrian one written in Mesopotamia by the monk Rabula in 586; the *Amiatinus Bible* from the VII-VIIIth centuries; books by classical writers (from Tacitus's *Annals*, a IXth century codex from the abbey of Corvey in Westphalia, to the famous *Medici Virgil*, datable around 494 - the oldest codex currently in the library - to Horace's *Odes* with Petrarch's glosses). Also there are a *Divine Comedy* annotated by Filippo Villani and the *Biadaiolo Codex*, listing expenditures for grain, charmingly illustrated with miniatures showing Florentine city life in the first half of the XIVth century. Represented, too, are *Scriptoria* from the monasteries of Santa Maria degli Angeli and San Marco. Over time the Laurentian Library was enriched by other important collections, from that of the monastery of Santa Croce to one from the Arte della Lana, the woolmakers' guild, witnessing to the Medici passion for collecting, continued later by the house of Lorraine.

THE CHAPEL OF THE PRINCES

Coming out of the church and a short walk down the street is Piazza Madonna degli Aldobrandini; along the way one can admire the statue of the *Electress Palatine*, sculpted after World War II by Raffaello Salimbeni and placed in 1995 inside a little garden adjacent to the church. In the square is the entrance to the museum complex of the Medici Chapels, a term used to indicate the Chapel of the Princes and the New Sacristy.

The Chapel of the Princes is a treasure chest containing the earthly remains of the Medici family, and represents the mausoleum of the great dynasty.

The idea of creating a third, more monumental family chapel, after the two sacristies (the Old Sacristy designed by Brunelleschi and the New Sacristy by Michelangelo), came to the first Medici Grand Duke Cosimo, who gave the assignment to his architect Giorgio Vasari (1511-1574) in the years between 1561 and 1568. Vasari planned a space entirely lined in marble and mosaics, but his design was not carried out during Cosimo's tenure as Grand Duke, and although taken up again by his son Francesco I, a great admirer of *pietre dure* inlays, work only began under Ferdinando I, in accord with his brother Don Giovanni. In 1588 were gathered together numerous masters of this form of stonework (the birth of the famous Florentine Opificio delle Pietre Dure); to underline the importance given to the decorative aspects of the plan, work began on the inlays for the walls even before a clear definitive idea was had of the architectural form of the building.

Already in 1589 the great polychrome inlaid coats-of-arms of the Tuscan cities that were bishops' sees were ready to be set into the lower register of

Raffaello Salimbeni, Statue of the Electress Palatine

the wall decorations lining the new chapel. With more or less manifest coordination by Don Giovanni, suggestions were taken from various architects of the period, from Giorgio Vasari the Younger to Santi di Tito (1536-1603), but only in 1596 did the Grand Duke give his approval to the plan presented by Alessandro Pieroni (*ca.* 1550-1607), worked out in close contact with Don Giovanni, winning out over those by Cigoli (1559-1613) and Bernardo Buontalenti (1536-1608), the eclectic and original architect who for this project invented a new saw for cutting the semi-precious stones. He, however, continued to be involved in the project, as witnessed by one of the two ciboria which he created before 1599 - the other, never installed, was the work of Matteo Nigetti (1560-1649). In this unique space, death is

Exterior view of the Chapel of the Princes with the entrance to the Medici Chapels

not contemplated so much in a Christian or in any case religious vision (for example, there are none of the skeletons so dear to the Counter-Reformation's sense of *pietas*) as it is seen as the pretext for a theatrical secular representation of the immortality of the Medici dynasty, destined to arouse wonder in those who saw it and to ratify the aristocratic pride of a triumphant power. It is an example - extremely rare for Florence - of a complex and emphatic display with multiple dynastic and allegorical meanings, glittering with the forms, figures, and colors characteristic of the Baroque.

The Chapel of the Princes was added behind the chancel and choir of the church of San Lorenzo to act, as we have said, as a sort of third sacristy. The shape chosen (perhaps already by Vasari in the 1560s) was the octagon, a symbolic reference to the Baptistry of San Giovanni, the historical and moral heart of the city, but also with its eight summits an allusion to the eight stars in the constellation of the Capricorn, Cosimo I's sign of the Zodiac.

In 1602 a competition was called, and once again the plan worked out by Don Giovanni together with Nigetti won out over the one presented by Buontalenti and Gherardo Silvani (1579-1675). The Chapel of the Princes and the crypt were begun in 1604 under Ferdinando I, but definitively finished, as we shall see, only in the XXth century.

The project was followed by Nigetti alone, as Don Giovanni was far away from Florence, engaged in the wars in Flanders that at the time were upsetting the whole shape of Europe. Don Giovanni's profession as an expert in military affairs (today we would say that he was part of the intelligence service) emerges also from the final plan for the complex, with the stairs between the crypt and the Chapel of the Princes in a shape resembling pliers, clearly betraying their military influence.

Although claiming to adhere to Don Giovanni's design, in reality Nigetti took advantage of his absence to introduce numerous variations to the plan. The building, in the intentions of the Grand Duke and its designers, was supposed to project on the outside an image of massiveness and stoniness, befitting the solid austerity of a dynasty that intended to challenge eternity, but the interior was meant to resemble a precious treasure chest, with the architectural supports reduced to a minimum and appearing only in their effects of light and shadow (thus reversing the Renaissance concepts distinguishing the church and the two Sacristies). The wall decorations thus become fundamental to the decorative plan, with their Baroque *horror vacui*, their tenaciously pursued ideal of overall polychrome decoration on a vast scale, which, at least on this dimension, is a new concept for Florence, if we exclude, but only in part, the Baptistry. To underline their virtual continuity with the Roman empire, *caput mundi*, the Medici had ancient porphyry sent up from Rome to be reutilized in the new mausoleum.

In 1608 the crypt was created underlying the Chapel of the Princes, also the work of Nigetti, who would remain involved in this project for a good 44

The sumptuous interior of the Chapel of the Princes

Pietro and Ferdinando Tacca, Cenotaph to Grand Duke Ferdinando I

years, until 1650. The crypt, which today is the first space entered by visitors to the Medici Chapel complex, is also built in the shape of an octagon, covered by massive cross vaults resting on short piers. Alternatively inserted into the walls are semipolygonal exedrae and rectangular chapels (*tribunalia*), corresponding on the exterior with rectangular buttresses into which marble panels are set.

In 1613 the encrustation of the lower register of the Chapel of the Princes

Two coats-of-arms of Tuscan cities adorning the wainscot of the Chapel of the Princes

was completed, articulated by pilaster strips between which are set the Medici cenotaphs (Cosimo I, Francesco I, Ferdinando I, Cosimo II, Ferdinando II, Cosimo III), topped by pedimented aediculae intended to hold bronze statues of the deceased Grand Dukes. Two of these were cast by Pietro (1577-1640) and Ferdinando Tacca (*ca.* 1616-1686) between 1626 and the mid 1640s, representing Ferdinando I and Cosimo II dressed in the rich damask robes and ermine cape of the Grand Masters of the knightly Order of Saint Stephen I, pope and martyr. They bear the grand-ducal crown and scepter with the fleur de lys. Noteworthy are the refined use of the bronze and tactile suppleness of the material, which the two sculptors bent to their figurative needs with great skill.

Here foreign visitors were brought to marvel at the work, still unfinished and viewed under a temporary wooden roof whose skylights let fall evocative rays of light on the multicolored, highly polished slabs of semi-precious stones with their glittering decorations.

Between 1625 and 1654 the elevations were finished and the great dome covering the space; in 1629 the interior decoration was complete up to (but not including the entablature) while Nigetti was replaced by Andrea Balatri as "Architect of the Royal Chapel."

Subsequently, however, interest markedly decreased towards the conclusion of the work; as a consequence, the important architects who succeeded each other in the position (Giovan Battista Foggini and Giovacchino Fortini)

Ferdinando and Giuseppe Ruggeri,
Wooden model for the construction of
the dome of the Chapel of the Princes

The dome with frescoes by
Pietro Benvenuti
portraying Stories from the
Old and New Testaments

were not able to leave their distinct imprint on the building. In 1726 the cornice was finished economically in fake stone, and in 1729 Montesquieu, on his visit to Florence, seemed to confirm this decadence with his harsh criticism of the "vacuous" relict of what seemed almost a "cathedral in the desert" willed into being by a dynasty on the wane.

Nonetheless, it is precisely with the arrival of the new Lorraine dynasty, although still tied to the will of the last Medici descendant, the Electress Palatine, that the project was decisively reopened in 1740.

The upper part of the Chapel was finished on the exterior only around that year by Ferdinando and Giuseppe Ruggieri, who inserted the characteristic marble bell-shaped windows (substituting the earlier arched windows topped by oculi) and the corner pilaster strips, also in marble, in the octagonal *pietra forte* drum. The space was covered by a great exterior dome in red terracotta tiles which in the original project was intended to echo closely the one Brunelleschi placed over Santa Maria del Fiore (the marble ribs and lantern documented by a wooden model by the Ruggieri brothers now

in the crypt would however not be realized due to the death of the Electress Palatine in 1743).

Only at the beginning of the XIXth century would the neoclassical architect Luigi De Cambray Digny (1778-1843) top the dome with its current low lantern-skylight outlined by marble coping.

In 1821 the architect Giuseppe Cacialli (1770-1828), an exponent of the rigorous classicism of the Restoration, lined the interior of the drum, while the frescoes in the intrados, less expensive, were done only in 1828-37 by the neoclassical painter Pietro Benvenuti (1769-1843), in place of earlier plans (the mosaics originally foreseen; encrustations in sunken panels; oculi, an early XVIIIth century idea).

The painter decorated the dome with sacred stories from the Old and New Testaments. The eight trapezoidal sections include *The Creation of Adam and Eve; The Original Sin; The Death of Abel; The Flood; The Nativity; The Crucifixion; The Resurrection; The Last Judgement.* In the hexagonal panels are the four *Evangelists* and four *Prophets.* The coloristic sense and sumptu-

The large crypt housing the mortal remains of some members of the Medici family

ousness of these neoclassical images, echoing Michelangelo and certain Bolognese XVIIth century painters, do not contrast with the austere, severe atmosphere of the Chapel; lending a note of lively, transparent color to the complex, at the same time they inject a clearly religious reference into the solemnly secular tone of the monument.

In 1837 Pasquale Poccianti designed a new burial place for the reigning Lorraine dynasty inside the Old Sacristy and took up again the idea of placing the Medici in the crypt, an idea realized in part by Ferdinando III of Lorraine, who caused to be moved (1791) the remains of the Medici who were in the two sacristies and the area under the church.

In 1855, when Piazza della Madonna degli Aldobrandini was redone, the existing entrance to the crypt from the square was modeled with a neo-seventeenth century marble facade designed by Domenico Giraldi (end of XVIIIth century-after 1855). Only between 1857 and 1858, however, would Leopoldo have the mortal remains of the Medici moved definitively into the crypt, utilizing for this purpose some of the underground rooms existing at that time. The work of remodeling the space to make a sepulchre was carried out by Gaetano Baccani, the architect mentioned above, who also created the door between the Chapel of the Princes and the chancel of San Lorenzo.

Altar panels worked with inlays of semi-precious stones portraying The Supper at Emmaus by Augusto Betti and liturgical objects by Giovan Battista Giorgi

Since 1869 the Chapel of the Princes is an integral part of the museum of the Medici Chapels, inaugurated by the Regie Gallerie e Musei in the fervid, celebratory climate when Florence was briefly the capital of the Kingdom of Italy.

Between 1874 and 1882 Edoardo Marchionni began installing the flooring of the Chapel, respecting its historical aspect; the job was finished only in 1962 by the Opificio delle Pietre Dure. In 1874, too, Emilio De Fabris (1807-1883), who was responsible also for the restoration of the Old Sacristy and the plans for a new staircase for the Laurentian Library, realized the long-awaited Lorraine burial place, but by now in a newly united Italy, in the area under the church contiguous with the Medici crypt.

The last element to be finished, beween 1929 and 1940, was the high altar, for which were used pieces from the XVIIth, XVIIIth and XIXth centuries, inserted into a *faux-marbre* wooden structure designed by Amedeo Orlandini, director of the Opificio delle Pietre Dure. The altar frontal has at its center an evocative *Supper at Emmaus* by Augusto Betti, flanked by panels, also in inlaid *pietre dure*, showing liturgical objects and symbolic plants, the work of Giovan Battista Giorgi done toward the middle of the XIXth century. On the sides of the altar can be admired panels created in the XVIIth century.

The two small sacristies behind the altar contain some one hundred liturgical vases and relics from the Treasury of the church of San Lorenzo, stored here since June 1945.

Housed in "gray cases," they are offered to the inattentive and some-what profane view of the visitors to the museum of the Medici Chapels. We have already highlighted how, instead, in the festive atmosphere of the Easter of Resurrection, with a solemn ritual they were displayed for the wondering, and in some ways magical, veneration of the faithful.

These products of the goldsmith's art can be divided into three sections. The oldest core of the collection is made up of four vases of rock crystal, amethyst, and jasper, part of what remained of Lorenzo the Magnificent's treasury after it was dispersed following the expulsion of the Medici from Florence and the sack of their palace on the Via Larga (now Via Cavour).

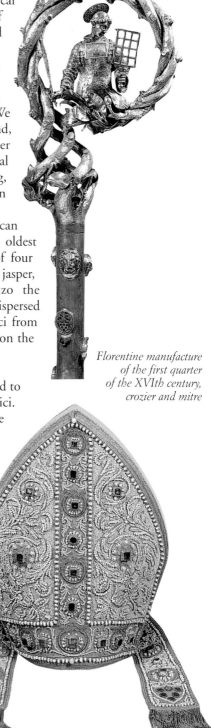

Florentine manufacture of the first quarter of the XVIth century, crozier and mitre

They contain relics bought in Constantinople and in Greece, donated to the church by Pope Leo X de' Medici. Pope Leo X added the *Crozier* (the work of a Florentine goldsmith of the first quarter of the XVIth century, made up of four pieces simulating a laurel trunk cut at the base and terminating in three intertwined branches forming a curl enclosing the bust of Saint Lawrence), a lectern drape (now in the church rectory), and perhaps the *Mitre*, Florentine manufacture of the first quarter of the XVIth century, studded with pearls and precious stones, one of the most precious works in the Treasury of San Lorenzo.

The second core is made up also of donations,

Islamic manifacture and Venetian goldsmith work, Reliquary of Saint Erina

Massimiliano Soldani Benzi, Reliquary of Saint Casmir

this time by Pope Clement VII de' Medici, who offered to the church all the relics collected by Leo X, including the beatiful vases that had belonged to Lorenzo the Magnificent. Among these we can admire the *Reliquary of Saint Erina*, in a Fatimite embossed vase with a Venetian mount in precious metal with enamels and a pearl on its lid. The handle is in the shape of a serpent, the spout that of a dragon. The pope also donated other vases of semi-precious stones. This second group is also made up of precious objects commissioned by the Grand Dukes (from Cosimo I to Christine of Lorraine to Cosimo III) from the most skillful goldsmiths of the time. Among these we can note the *Reliquary of Saint Roch* by Bernardino Baldini, dated to 1553, the gift of Cosimo I along with another Fatimite vase containing the bones of numerous martyrs, with a precious mount of 1555, also the work by Baldini. The third group of reliquaries (some belonging to Christine of Lorraine, some to Vittoria della Rovere, but mostly created for Cosimo III) arrived here from the Palatine chapel in Palazzo Pitti, and were then donated to San Lorenzo in exchange for a significant group of sacred vases now exhibited in the Museo degli Argenti.

This last section contains precious works not only of Florentine manufacture, but also of various other schools, ranging from the Roman to the German. Among these objects we should mention the *Reliquary of Saint Casmir,* by Massimiliano Soldani Benzi, who executed in 1687 on a commission from Cosimo III for the Palatine chapel. Numerous other seventeenth century reliquaries by this same artist are to be seen in the Chapel: in all these works Massimiliano Soldani Benzi masterly united work in semi-precious stones with silver and gold.

Along the corridor connecting the Chapel of the Princes with the New Sacristy one can also admire two large marble panoplies, perhaps originally destined to adorn the New Sacristy and attributed to the sculptor Silvio Cosini (*ca.* 1495-*ca.* 1549), who was a collaborator of Michelangelo.

Giuseppe Antonio Torricelli, Reliquary of Saint Emeric

THE NEW SACRISTY

The greatest jewel in the museum of the Medici Chapels, however, is without doubt the New Sacristy of the church of San Lorenzo (geometrically and symbolically the pair to Brunelleschi's Old Sacristy). This spectacular space was designed by Michelangelo to house the remains of Lorenzo the Magnificent and his brother Giuliano, inserting it into an existing structure planned by Giuliano da Sangallo. The work, however, was finished in its present form only after numerous interruptions (the first occurring in 1521 with the death of Pope Leo X), under the direction of Vasari and Buontalenti between 1554 and 1555.

The first idea was to create a central plan burial space, with on the back wall (opposite the altar niche) the tombs of Giuliano and Lorenzo the Magnificent in two sarcophagi, behind which a marble facing with hori-

The dome of the New Sacristy with the lantern

Two views of the New Sacristy

zontal coping would have been marked off by pilaster strips dividing the space vertically into three panels; those on the right and left would have had roundels above and the central one would have been a large niche, topped by a pediment, containing a celebratory statue. The preparatory drawings, now in the British Museum in London, show indisputable similarities with the plan for the facade of the church, as known to us from the wooden model in the museum of Casa Buonarroti in Florence. Unfortunately, none of this would ever come into being.

Against the two side walls, instead, the plan called for the tombs of the two 'captains,' Giuliano Duke of Nemours (died 1516) and Lorenzo Duke of Urbino (died 1519), dressed in military clothes. Behind the sarcophagi would have been placed two semi-reclining figures (two others were planned for the ends of the sarcophagi), and here too the wall would have been faced with imposing marble decorations focussing on the central niche with its statue of the 'captain' and continuing up the wall to a height slightly above what in fact actually was realized (the current marble facing is entirely contained and enclosed by the upper 'cornice' represented by the entablature separating the area between the pilaster strips and the lunette above, which Michelangelo had wanted to fill with frescoes).

The white plaster walls, representing the 'voids,' serve as background for the orchestration of the *pietra serena* architectural elements (fluted Corinthian pilaster strips, entablature, and arches, and pedimented windows of the sec-

ond story), with a harmonic play between the rigorously classical corner pilasters and the large arches and windows tapering in perspective, creating a tension that resolves itself through counterpoint (represented by the marble 'stopgap' inserts in the lower register) in the dominant solo of the massive coffered dome derived from classical Rome (the Pantheon comes to mind).

This structure contained one of the principal cycles of Michelangelo's sculpture: from the imposing statues (*ca.* 1533) of the two 'captains' to the enigmatic reclining figures of *Day* and *Night*, of *Dawn* and *Dusk*, which unite in a symbolic and arcane way the meaning of time and space and the mystery of the ages of man, so dear to the tormented Michelangelo.

Concluding the cycle are the unfinished *Virgin and Child* (1521) between *Saints Cosmas and Damian*, these last two the work of his pupils Giovannangelo da Montorsoli (1507-1563) and Raffaello da Montelupo (1505-1567), placed there to seal with the solar faith of dogma the nude parallelepiped tomb of Lorenzo the Magnificent and his brother Giuliano and the wholly 'nocturnal' and secular doubt of the artist.

Various interpretations have been given over time to the philosophical meaning of the New Sacristy. Condivi formulated the hypothesis that the monument symbolized Time which consumes Everything; Tolnay, instead, interpreted the New Sacristy in neo-Platonic, tripartite terms: an underworld where the rivers of Hades run (with the statues of river gods that Michelangelo had planned for the base of the two tombs), an earthly sphere regulated by Time and Matter, and a world beyond this one symbolized by the luminous celestial dome. The soul, which has lost its knowledge of its origin, moves through these three spheres in a path of liberation from the material sphere which oppresses it (connoted by the 'broken' arcs under the weight of the four statues signifying Time) to reach the heavenly 'home.' Others have seen in the four unrealized river allegories the representation of four geographical entities (Florence, Rome, Nemours, Urbino).

Beyond the plausible but unproven interpretations the complex might have, what remains indisputable is Michelangelo's vision of the contrast between an earthly world below, dominated by matter and the passing of time, and a luminous other world above, where the souls of the dead, liberated from matter, look at and turn to Mary and her Child, as intercessors and the path for reaching God.

On the right, the TOMB OF GIULIANO DUKE OF NEMOURS. Seated on a stool, he is shown with idealized features, dressed in the armor of a soldier of imperial Rome, his curly hair tight around his head; the ornamentation of the armor shows early hints of Mannerism. He holds the scepter of command and looks toward the Virgin. On the tomb below lie the nude figures of *Night* and *Day*. The figure of *Night*, so dear to XIXth century romanticism, is represented as a young woman asleep (iconographically close to the classical representation of the sleeping Leda or Ariadne), closed in her undefinable grief and almost as though fleeing reality. The alchemical and hermetic connection between Night and Melancholy (a motif dominating the

Michelangelo, Tomb of Giuliano Duke of Nemours

Next page: Michelangelo, Giuliano Duke of Nemours, detail

Michelangelo, Day (above); Night (below)

Michelangelo, Tomb of Lorenzo Duke of Urbino

entire sculpture cycle), ever-present in Michelangelo, appears also here to have been derived by the artist from an engraving by Dürer published in 1514, confirming a stimulating influence of the northern world on the Mediterranean one. The woman wears a crescent moon in her hair, and at her feet are a cushion and an owl, while her left shoulder rests on a mask (perhaps a self-portrait of Michelangelo) symbolizing nightmares. Her polished body gleams like snow.

Day, which has always been considered the symbol of wrath and fiery, vital rebellion against slavery (with iconographical references taken from the ancient sculpture *The Belvedere Torso*), has a vigorous, mature aspect and an unnatural position with his legs crossed and one arm bent back while the other lies forward across his chest. The surface is less polished and is of a warm golden hue in contrast with the lunar light reflected by *Night*. The barely sketched-in face still manages to express the toil of everyday living. Facing this, the TOMB OF LORENZO DUKE OF URBINO (the sarcophagus holds also the body of his son Alessandro, first duke of Florence). He too sits on a stool dressed like a Roman soldier, and he wears a strange helmet shaped like the head of a lion, borrowed from Etruscan art. While Giuliano represented, also to his contemporaries, pride and the sanguine active life, Lorenzo, his left hand resting on his face absorbed in thought, emblemizes contemplative life. The heroic aspect of the figure, nonetheless, is once again symbolic,

Michelangelo, Dawn (above and below right); Dusk (above right)

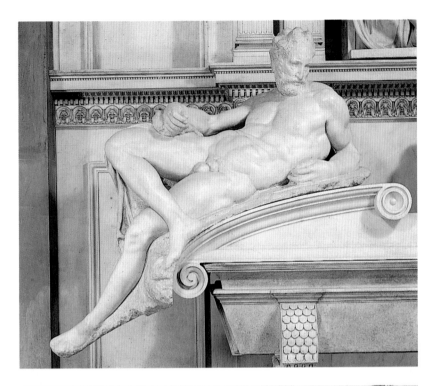

not reflecting reality, as Michelangelo here perhaps wanted to represent youth and beauty. The two reclining figures on the sarcophagus of *Dawn* and *Dusk*, taken from ancient reliefs of river and mountain deities on the Roman arch of Septiumius Severus, symbolize with their flexed bodies all of Michelangelo's pessimism: the melancholic disillusion which emerges without enthusiasm and the sadness that results from the useless daily toil of man. *Dawn*, one of the most beautiful sculptures in the cycle, is a young woman with her soft body stretched out on a blanket, her left arm bent and the other touching the veil falling from her head. *Dusk* has a barely sketched face, like the other male figure, while the rest of his body is polished to a golden shine.

The statue of the *Virgin and Child*, although part of the funerary monument to Lorenzo the Magnificent and Giuliano in an arrangement that certainly does not correspond to Michelangelo's idea for the tomb, nonetheless maintains,

Michelangelo,
Virgin and Child

Giovannangelo da Montorsoli, Saint Cosmas   *Raffaello da Montelupo, Saint Damian*

as we have said, the role of symbolic and spiritual center of the entire composition, as the great artist had planned. Iconographically it recalls the medieval theme of the *Virgin of Humility* or the *Nursing Virgin*. But here the parallels end. This Virgin sits in a rather unusual position, her legs crossed, her gaze lost in the distance and not looking at her lively Child whose dynamic twist, later so recurrent in Mannerist art, contrasts with the static pose of His mother. The rough surface shows nevertheless the subtle, delicate work of the artist's chisel, while in some parts like, for example, her hand resting on the Child's shoulder as though to brake his impetuous squirming, the sculptor uses his technique of leaving the surface unfinished. The group is flanked by the two polished statues of *Saints Cosmas and Damian*, treated with a more pictorial than plastic effect.

In front of the altar recess is a marble altar datable to the XVIth century with two marble candelabra; the one on the left was made by Silvio Cosini after a design by Michelangelo. On the base is a pelican, symbol of Christ. The other was made in 1741 (the original had been destroyed) by an artist of the school of Ticciati. On the altar are four XVIIth century brass candlesticks

Detail of the altar candelabrum designed by Michelangelo

Next page: Michelangelo, Detail of a bucrane taken from the Tomb of Lorenzo Duke of Urbino

with a *Crucifix* attributed to Giambologna (Jean de Boulogne, 1529-1608). In the altar recess were discovered in 1975-78 by Paolo Dal Poggetto, at the time director of the Medici Chapels, some drawings by Michelangelo, representing, among other things, one of the windows of the Laurentian Library and a strange inscription ("vieni a vedere" - come and see), recognized as from the actual hand of the artist.

In the basin on the left, down a steep flight of stairs, inside a recess, are some charcoal drawings, also thought to be Michelangelo's. They represent figures from the Sistine Chapel; the legs of the statue of Giuliano Duke of Nemours; the head of the celebrated Laocoon; a David (or maybe Apollo) and finally, some caricatures that may not be Michelangelo's. The drawings can be dated to the years between 1525 and 1530, thus during the time the New Sacristy was being built.

The Laurentian complex, as we have seen, offers an itinerary that is also a unique synthesis of 'the rebirth of classicism,' from the *forme antiquae*, vibrating with modernity, of Brunelleschi and Michelangelo up to neo-classicism; almost a bridge, the hinge of Western culture, between the earlier medieval culture and the tortured modern age.

Knowledge
Development
in Nursing
THEORY AND PROCESS

EDITION 9

Knowledge Development in Nursing

THEORY AND PROCESS

PEGGY L. CHINN, RN, PhD, FAAN

Professor Emerita
School of Nursing
University of Connecticut
Storrs, Connecticut

MAEONA K. KRAMER, APRN, PhD

Professor Emerita
College of Nursing
University of Utah
Salt Lake City, Utah

ELSEVIER

ELSEVIER
MOSBY

3251 Riverport Lane
St. Louis, Missouri 63043

Knowledge Development in Nursing: Theory and Process, 9e   ISBN: 978-0-323-31652-1
Copyright © 2015 by Mosby, an imprint of Elsevier Inc.
Copyright © 2011, 2008, 2004, 1999, 1995, 1991, 1987, 1983 by Mosby, Inc., an affiliate of Elsevier Inc.

Notices

Knowledge and best practice in this field are constantly changing. As new research and experience broaden our understanding, changes in research methods, professional practices, or medical treatment may become necessary.

Practitioners and researchers must always rely on their own experience and knowledge in evaluating and using any information, methods, compounds, or experiments described herein. In using such information or methods they should be mindful of their own safety and the safety of others, including parties for whom they have a professional responsibility.

With respect to any drug or pharmaceutical products identified, readers are advised to check the most current information provided (i) on procedures featured or (ii) by the manufacturer of each product to be administered, to verify the recommended dose or formula, the method and duration of administration, and contraindications. It is the responsibility of practitioners, relying on their own experience and knowledge of their patients, to make diagnoses, to determine dosages and the best treatment for each individual patient, and to take all appropriate safety precautions.

To the fullest extent of the law, neither the Publisher nor the authors, contributors, or editors, assume any liability for any injury and/or damage to persons or property as a matter of products liability, negligence or otherwise, or from any use or operation of any methods, products, instructions, or ideas contained in the material herein.

ISBN: 9780323316521

Director, Traditional Education: Kristin Geen
Content Development Manager: Laurie Gower
Content Development Specialist: Lisa Newton
Publishing Services Manager: Hemamalini Rajendrababu
Project Manager: Kiruthiga Kasthuriswamy
Designer: Teresa McBryan

Printed in United States of America

Last digit is the print number: 9   8   7   6   5   4   3   2   1

Working together
to grow libraries in
developing countries

www.elsevier.com • www.bookaid.org

Preface

A major and noticeable change for this ninth edition of our book is the title: *Knowledge Development in Nursing: Theory and Process.* The title change reflects the book's focus on the broader realm of knowledge and knowing, but it does not signal major changes within the individual chapters. In this edition, we continue to strive to improve the clarity of the text. We realize that the material we address is new to many readers, and several chapters present concepts and processes that go "against the grain" of the empiric traditions that dominate most aspects of modern life. To accomplish our goal of conveying this material as clearly and comprehensibly as possible, we have done the following:

- Continued to develop and integrate even more examples to illustrate meaning of difficult concepts. All examples of patient or client situations are fictitious and do not refer to real people or events.
- Continued to simplify the language to increase understanding of content.
- Reviewed and updated the material on Elsevier's Evolve site, which we encourage readers and faculty to access. Evolve now houses new material we retained from the book that the reviewers found useful.
- Interspersed "Think About It" questions on nursing issues and situations to expand on the narrative and add interest.
- Importantly, with this edition the animated Model for Knowledge Development on the Evolve site has been significantly improved. The graphics and animation make the model easier to follow in a more informative and aesthetic presentation.

We continue to make revisions consistent with the role of those studying for the practice doctorate as well as the traditional PhD. These changes and others reflect current trends and issues in nursing, including advances in theoretic and philosophic ideas related to evidence-informed practice.

We have updated references and citations where appropriate. We also have retained many older references we believe are important for readers to know about and access. We both are products of the "golden age" of theory in nursing, when conceptual models were being developed, used for curricular organization, and taught to learners of nursing. We have great respect for those pioneers who paved the way for our present knowledge development paths and believe current learners should have an opportunity to appreciate and understand their contributions. Moreover, in many instances, older references are still timely and current in relation to the chapter content.

Chapter 1 continues to overview nursing's fundamental patterns of knowing in addition to emancipatory knowing, a pattern we developed in the 7th edition that encompasses Barbara Carper's four fundamental patterns. We present our model of the essential interrelationships between knowing and knowledge in nursing for each pattern and as a whole. Chapter 1 provides an overview of the ontology (the "being/knowing" aspect) and epistemology (the "knowledge development" aspect) for each pattern, using our model for knowledge development as a guide. We have also included an account of the nature of *praxis* as a process integral to emancipatory knowing and knowledge.

Chapter 2 provides an overview of the historical development of nursing with a particular focus on knowledge development. We continue to integrate new information on current knowledge development trends, including translational research, evidence-informed practice, practice-based evidence, and intersectionality. In general, we reorganized and streamlined this chapter to improve its readability and flow, consistent with reviewers' comments. A significant change is a more concise review illustrating how the historical literature represents the knowing patterns; pertinent quotes are now in bulleted lists to make this information more readable.

We have retained the order of the remaining chapters as they appeared in the 7th edition, where we first introduced the pattern of emancipatory knowing. Chapters 3, 4, 5, and 6 are devoted to the less familiar but very important nonempiric patterns of knowing. Chapters 7, 8, 9, and 10 retain the classic content on empiric theory development from previous editions.

Chapter 3 describes the emancipatory knowing pattern, detailing how it interrelates with the four fundamental patterns developed by Carper. We have worked diligently to make this content more accessible by providing examples and illustrations of difficult concepts; for example, we clarify the concept of praxis as the process of emancipatory knowing. Chapter 4, devoted to ethical knowledge development, remains similar to previous editions but has been updated throughout. Chapter 5 discusses personal knowing, and Chapter 6 covers aesthetic knowing; the content in these chapters remains generally intact, but again, we have tried to simplify the language and include even more examples and illustrations.

Chapter 7 describes the processes of conceptualizing and structuring theory by creating conceptual meaning and contextualizing theory. We have included content that addresses how our approach to creating conceptual meaning differs from other approaches and is consistent with emancipatory knowing. Chapter 8 addresses the description and critical reflection of theory and remains a well-received chapter, although the distinctions among semantic and structural clarity and consistency can be confusing. Because we believe these distinctions are important, rather than consolidate these subcategories of clarity, we added narrative to clarify the distinctions. Chapter 9 focuses on confirming empiric knowledge using research that generates and examines the truth value of theoretic relationships, consistent with the underlying assumptions inherent in empiric approaches. In this edition, we do not include specific study examples of theory-testing and theory-generating research, because that content did not seem to be valuable to learners. Chapter 10 focuses on validating empiric knowledge through practice by deliberative use of empiric theory and now includes the rationale for using the term *evidence-informed nursing practice.*

This edition includes an updated glossary, which reflects the ongoing challenge of keeping word definitions current and adding newly introduced words in this edition. Appendix A of former editions—an overview of historically important broad conceptual models—remains on the Evolve site.

The "Think About It" questions in each chapter highlight the interrelatedness of all patterns of knowing, prompting the reader to consider all dimensions of knowing while focusing on the specific content of a chapter. In particular, it is our intention that the questions will sharpen the reader's understanding of the emancipatory knowing process of praxis—critical reflection and action that transforms experience.

WHO NEEDS THIS TEXT?

As authors, we believe the perspectives within this text are imperative. We are aware that in recent years, nursing education has moved away from a focus on theory and philosophic thought. This transition has many roots, including the limited time educators have to provide nursing education in the face of explosive development in practice, as well as the shifting role of advanced practice nurses to provide more and more medical care. We believe that sacrificing theoretic and philosophic foundations in graduate education is a detriment to the discipline, and that practice itself can and will be enhanced if this trend can be reversed.

Recent trends that emphasize the importance of reliable evidence for practice have created significant changes in education. Doctoral education has traditionally been founded on standards of quality that highlight scientific rigor and quality. The doctorate of nursing practice was introduced to underscore greater emphasis on advanced practice roles, leadership in practice that promotes high standards of quality in nursing care, and scholarship that provides evidence for practice. We believe that a broad understanding of knowledge and knowing is essential for preparation of advanced practice nurses and research scholars. This broad understanding that encompasses the aesthetic, personal, ethical, and emancipatory patterns of knowing is crucial for defining that which is nursing in practice and in knowledge development. Whether consciously recognized or not, those who practice nursing use these patterns, and acknowledging and attending to them can only enhance client care. If patients and clients are to be better served by their health care providers, it is essential that educators understand and help learners deliberately develop and assess knowledge within all patterns of knowing. An encouraging development in this regard is the emergence of the term *evidence-informed practice,* signaling that evidence is only a portion of knowledge and knowing for practitioners.

This text can be used by all "levels" of learners. As was our intention with the very first edition of this text, we believe that this knowledge is basic nursing knowledge and as such is essential for entry-level learners. However, the fact remains that most learners are introduced to this material in graduate education, and we fully endorse the use of this text for graduate learners. We think it is particularly important for those enrolled in programs culminating in the practice doctorate. If these practitioners are the refiners and users of knowledge that is "developed" by nursing scholars, their level of sophistication and success in validating, confirming, and refining knowledge will be directly related to how well they understand how personal, aesthetic, and ethical knowing affect those processes. Additionally, without understanding the nature and need for emancipatory knowing, practitioners and researchers alike will be less effective in their efforts to engender real praxis in our health care system.

It is our passion for the best nursing care and best nursing education possible that has energized us to produce this work; it is why we have labored to make it understandable and accessible for the beginner as well as the seasoned practitioner. Many users of this text have told us that as they have grown in their nursing experience and education, their reading and understanding of the text has markedly changed. While what they found in the text was useful as a beginning learner, as they understood more about nursing, they understood the text in deeper and more meaningful ways.

Finally, practitioners who are focused on (and rightfully so) using best evidence to inform their practice must understand how the utilization of that "best evidence" is both facilitated and impeded by the state of knowledge and the disciplinary foundation of knowing within all patterns. For these reasons, we believe a work such as this is important for all of nursing.

IN THANKS

When we first conceived the essential elements of this book, we had both recently completed our doctoral programs and were beginning our academic careers. During a 2-year period of our early academic lives, we were both employed at the University of Utah, where we collaborated professionally and discovered our mutual interests in theory and knowledge development. Despite living in different geographic locations, we have since maintained an ongoing professional association. We now have completed our active teaching careers and continue our personal growth as we begin to experience our "resignation" from formally appointed academic life. We owe so much of our ability to change and mature in our thinking to those who enrolled in our classes and labored with us to push the edges of knowledge and venture into that which is possible but not yet fully real. It is to each of you who have worked with us in classrooms that we owe our greatest debt of gratitude. Without your continual prodding for clearer explanations, your challenges to our ideas, and your insistence that we make matters of theory, knowledge, and philosophy pertinent to practice by pushing us beyond our preconceived notions, much of what has emerged in this book would not have been possible. Indeed, in the classroom you became our teachers, and we give to you our deepest appreciation.

Our many academic colleagues—within the institutions where we taught and studied as well as those around the world—have contributed to our thinking by being an informed, critical, and thoughtful audience. Our close friends and chosen families, especially Karen and Sue, have continued to provide the love and support so essential to this type of work—our deepest thanks and gratitude to you.

To the formal reviewers who thoughtfully read and commented on the 9th edition, we are grateful. Each of you provided insights that were helpful in this revision. We made many of the changes you suggested. We feel confident that your careful critique, both positive and negative, has produced a stronger volume. We truly appreciate your effort.

As much as we feel deeply the ways in which this work depends on our interactions with each of our colleagues, we acknowledge that the content of this book remains our own doing and our own responsibility. We have taken the responsibility to represent and acknowledge the work of others as openly and honestly as possible. We hope there are no errors in the text, yet we expect there will be; we are learners and make no claim to having final answers. We ask that you understand and honor our wish not to be seen as an authoritative voice, but rather a voice among many to be challenged and moved beyond. We began our professional collaboration in 1972 and continue to provide for one another the challenges and the grounding that are inherent in conceptualizing and co-writing a work of this type. It is our mutual respect and appreciation for one another, as well as our inherent differences, that sustain this type of relationship over time. We are grateful to each other for these mutual gifts. We offer this work, always in progress, to you with hope that it will continue to provide a perspective that is worthy of critique and that deepens your understanding and inspires your own thoughts and actions.

Reference

Carper, B. A. (1978). Fundamental patterns of knowing in nursing. *ANS Advances in Nursing Science, 1*(1), 13–23.

Reviewers

Janet M. Baiardi, PhD, FNP-BC
Interim Associate Dean
McAuley School of Nursing
University of Detroit Mercy
Detroit, Michigan

Jane E. Bostick, PhD, RN, PMHCNS-BC
Associate Teaching Professor
Sinclair School of Nursing
University of Missouri
Columbia, Missouri

Carey S. Clark, PhD, RN, AHN-BC, RYT
Professional Titles: Assistant Professor
University of Maine at Augusta
California Institute of Integral Studies
Augusta, Maine

Marcia Elliott, MSN, PHN, RN
Coordinator, Learning Resource Center
Charles R. Drew University of Medicine and Science
Mervyn M. Dymally School of Nursing
Los Angeles, California

Beth Rodgers, PhD, RN, FAAN
Professor and PhD Program Director
College of Nursing
Albuquerque, New Mexico

Contents

⊖ http://evolve.elsevier.com/Chinn/knowledge/

It is the general conception of any field of inquiry that ultimately determines the kind of knowledge that field aims to develop as well as the manner in which that knowledge is to be organized, tested and applied.... Such an understanding... involves critical attention to the question of what it means to know and what kinds of knowledge are held to be of most value in the discipline of nursing.

Barbara A. Carper (1978, p. 13)

This quote from Barbara A. Carper underscores that, in the field of nursing, what we believe our disciplinary focus to be will determine what we value as knowledge and how we go about developing that knowledge for our practice. At first, the quote seems to state the obvious: the things that we believe we should develop knowledge about or that we feel to be valuable will determine what our knowledge development products eventually are. The importance of the quote is that it makes what we value—not what we produce as knowledge—centrally important.

Think About It

- What do you believe nurses need to know?
- Do you find your answer to be grounded in what you value or what the profession values? Or both sets of values?
- If you believe that nurses need to know more than what they learn in books and articles, where does that knowledge come from?

This text challenges you to think broadly, to consider deliberately what you need to know to be an effective nurse, and to think about the values that ground your knowing. This chapter begins with Carper's quote and examines five patterns of knowing as a basis for considering the value of multiple forms of knowledge and knowing in nursing. It provides an overview of Carper's four fundamental patterns of knowing, in addition to discussing knowing and knowledge within the pattern of emancipatory knowing.

KNOWLEDGE FOR A PRACTICE DISCIPLINE

The patterns of knowing identified by Carper (1978) include traditional ideas of empiric knowledge as well as knowing and knowledge that are personal, ethical, and aesthetic in nature. Initially developed by Chinn and Kramer (2008), the pattern of emancipatory knowing focuses on developing an awareness of social problems and taking action to create social change (see Chapter 3). Although we believe that knowledge and knowing within all patterns are required for effective nursing care, empirics has been and continues to be a major focus for all health care disciplines, including nursing (Archibald, 2012; Mantzorou & Mastrogiannis, 2011; Thorne & Sawatzky, 2014; Paley, Cheyne, Dalgleish, Duncan, & Niven, 2007; Porter, 2010; Satterfield et al., 2009). Understanding knowledge for nursing practice as something more inclusive and broader than empirics is, in our view, critical for a practice discipline.

Nursing involves processes, dynamics, and interactions that are most effective when the five knowing patterns of empirics, ethics, aesthetics, personal knowing, and emancipatory knowing come together. Praxis is possible when all patterns of knowing are integrated in a way that supports social justice. The term *praxis* is not just a fancy word for "practice." A nurse who follows orders and thoughtfully completes an ordered treatment such as wound irrigation is practicing and indeed may be practicing well. To be engaged in praxis, however, requires the nurse to move beyond just practicing and to engage in processes that undo any social inequities that he or she finds to be present in the health care environment.

To illustrate each of the patterns of knowing, consider a young woman—we'll call her Nayan—who sustained a gunshot wound that requires extensive management, including painful cleansing irrigation. In the context of this treatment, the nurse will surely be thinking about more than just aseptically irrigating this young woman's wound (a procedure grounded in empirics). He might be wondering whether he should advise Nayan to get rid of her pistol (a move with moral/ethical implications). He questions the ethics of this because Nayan lives in a tough neighborhood where her life is endangered. Although his day is rushed because another nurse called in sick, the nurse certainly cannot in good conscience (ethics) omit this treatment any more than he can shortcut aseptic procedures. He may be keeping his feelings about guns in check, because he realizes that his biases (personal knowing) may affect his approach and the subsequent trust that Nayan has in him. This nurse is probably also considering how to finesse or carry out the treatment in the way that makes it as pain free but effective as possible, which falls within the realm of aesthetics. Aesthetic knowing would guide how vigorously he tends to the wound and how he will modify his technique in response to how Nayan responds.

Emancipatory knowing requires the nurse to reflect thoughtfully and to act in relation to a treatment and its implications in a way that makes things better for the future, not just for Nayan at this particular moment but for society in general. It is this reflection and action that we call *praxis*. In this example, the very existence of a needless gunshot wound that requires extensive care and that involves lost wages and additional expenses for this young woman is considered. Praxis means that the nurse considers the situation and does something about it. Praxis may come in the form of political action, such as joining in a letter-writing campaign or lobbying about limiting or not limiting access to guns; working to increase the safety of neighborhoods so that guns are not needed; or championing programs to promote the safe handling of guns. Thus, emancipatory knowing would lead this nurse to do something broader about gunshot wounds in an effort to stop them from occurring in the first place. We do not mean to imply that praxis should come out of each and every nursing encounter. What we do imply is that, in the context of practice and within the professional community, it is important to be aware of situations of injustice, to raise everyone's awareness of injustices, and to reflect on these situations and act to improve them whenever possible.

In the remainder of this chapter, we provide more detail about the nature of knowledge forms and about the knowing processes that are unique to each pattern. Each pattern involves distinct processes for developing knowledge. These processes are located within five dimensions: (1) critical questions and (2) creative processes that initiate and generate knowing and knowledge; (3) formal expressions and (4) integrated practice expressions of knowledge and knowing; and (5) authentication processes that are used to examine and improve knowledge for the discipline.

Although a complete understanding requires that each pattern be considered separately, we return again and again to the complementarity of the processes within each pattern and their contribution to the whole of knowing. We also shun the unquestioned use of rules, methods, and principles often associated with knowledge development and embrace perspectives that value knowledge development that is grounded in creating an envisioned future.

This chapter also presents an example of pattern disintegration that we call "patterns gone wild," which occurs when any one pattern is taken out of the context of the whole. We conclude by presenting a case for knowledge development that encompasses all knowing patterns.

KNOWING AND KNOWLEDGE

In the context of this text, the term *knowing* refers to ways of perceiving and understanding the Self and the world. The term *knowledge* refers to knowing that is expressed in a form that can be shared or communicated with others. The "knowledge of a discipline" is knowledge that has been collectively judged by standards shared by members of the disciplinary community and that is taken to be a valid and accurate understanding of elements and features that comprise the discipline. The *epistemology* of a discipline refers to the ways in which knowledge is developed. Epistemology is the "how to" of knowledge development. The types of knowledge that are taken to be most important for the discipline of nursing are epistemologic concerns.

Alternatively, knowing is a more elusive concept. Knowing is fluid, and it is internal to the knower. People know things as a result of interactions with multiple sources: from what they are taught by others, from books, from their own thinking and experiential processes, from the subconscious absorption of background societal directives (e.g., the nature of personal space), and from many other sources. People "know" more than they can ever express formally as knowledge. For example, try to explain what an onion tastes like to someone who has never eaten onions, or try to explain fully how you, as an expert nurse, managed a difficult clinical situation. Not only is your experience of onions or nursing expertise personal to you, but you also cannot fully impart the nature of these experiences to others. However, you do know what an onion tastes like, and you know that you managed a difficult nursing situation well. In this way, knowing is a concept linked to ontology, or a way of being; knowing is particular and unique to our existence and to each individual's personal reality.

As they practice, nurses make use of insights and understandings gained from a variety of sources that they often take for granted and that they do not consciously think about. Much of what they know is expressed through actions, movements, or sounds in a fluid nursing situation. What is conveyed in a nurse's actions is a simultaneous wholeness or "whole of knowing" that textbooks and theories can never portray. This whole of knowing that happens in practice can only exist in the moment, and it is typically not available to a broader audience.

To summarize, knowing is a particular and unique awareness that grounds and expresses the being and doing of a person, whereas knowledge is knowing that can be expressed and communicated to others in many forms, including principles of practice, works of art, stories, and theories. *Disciplinary* knowledge is knowledge that has been judged to be pertinent to the focus of a discipline by its members.

We believe that much of what nurses know has the potential to be more fully expressed and communicated than it has been in the past, and that this can happen when all patterns of knowing are valued. Formal descriptions and theories that are used to convey empiric knowledge will only partially reflect the whole. However, when you move beyond the traditional limits of empirics and consider representing knowing within the aesthetic, ethical, personal, and emancipatory patterns, it is possible to convey a more complete picture of what is known within the discipline as a whole. When the knowledge picture is more complete, its value can be more openly assessed and embraced.

Sharing knowledge is important because it creates a disciplinary community beyond the isolation of individual experience. When this happens, social purposes form, and knowledge development and shared social purposes can form a cyclic interrelationship that moves us toward the prospective, value-grounded change that emerges from praxis.

OVERVIEW OF NURSING'S PATTERNS OF KNOWING

Since Florence Nightingale first established formal secular education for nurses, nursing has depended on formal knowledge as a basis for practice (see Chapter 2). The nature of knowledge changes with time, but the fundamental values that guide nursing practice have remained remarkably stable (Clements & Averill, 2006; Fawcett, 2006; Gallagher, 2013; Thorne & Sawatzky, 2014).

Examination of the early nursing literature resulted in the naming of four fundamental and enduring patterns of knowing. Carper (1978) called the familiar and respected pattern of *empirics* the science of nursing. She described *ethics* as the component of moral knowledge in nursing; *personal knowing* as knowledge of the Self and others in relationship; and *aesthetics* as the art of nursing. As noted previously, we have developed the pattern of *emancipatory knowing* as a fifth pattern. The fundamental patterns of knowing as identified by Carper were valuable in that they conceptualized a broad scope of knowing that acknowledged knowing patterns beyond the limited boundaries of empirics.

The empiric knowing pattern has been a central focus for knowledge development within the nursing discipline. The emancipatory, ethical, personal, and aesthetic patterns have not been as well developed, which reflects a neglect of these patterns of knowing and an overvaluing of empirics as the knowledge of the discipline (Fawcett, 2006; Fawcett, Watson, Neuman, Walker, & Fitzpatrick, 2001). However, methods for developing knowledge related to emancipatory, ethical, personal, and aesthetic knowledge are beginning to be systematically described. The appearance of a literature devoted to additional knowing patterns underscores the value of a broader scope of knowing and knowledge in practice (Archibald, 2012; Clements & Averill, 2006; Cloutier, Duncan, & Bailey, 2007; Fiandt, Forman, Megel, Padieser, & Burge, 2003; Gramling, 2006; Lane, 2006; Mantzorou & Mastrogiannis, 2011; Porter & O'Halloran, 2009; Weis, Schank, & Matheus, 2006; Wittmann-Price & Bhattacharya, 2008). Because of this shift, in this and subsequent chapters, we first discuss emancipatory knowing; this is followed by ethics, personal knowing, and aesthetic knowing, and it ends with our conceptualization of the more traditional approaches to empiric knowledge development.

We provide an overview of our conceptualization of each of the patterns of knowing in nursing in the following sections. We have extended the understanding of Carper's descriptions on the basis of our ideas, research, and the insights of other nursing scholars. In addition, these overviews introduce the methods that we propose for the development of each of the patterns.

Emancipatory Knowing: The Praxis of Nursing

Emancipatory knowing is the human capacity to be aware of and critically reflect on the social, cultural, and political status quo and to determine how and why it came to be that way. Emancipatory knowing calls forth action in ways that reduce or eliminate inequality and injustice. Awareness and critical reflection are essential to identify the inequities that are embedded in social and political institutions, as well as to identify the cultural values and beliefs that need to change to create fair and just conditions for all. Emancipatory knowing requires an understanding of the power dynamics that create knowledge and of the social and political contexts that shape and influence prevailing epistemologies of knowledge and knowing. Emancipatory knowing seeks freedom from institutional and institutionalized social and political contexts that sustain advantage for some and disadvantage for others.

Emancipatory knowing occurs when Cherise, a nurse practitioner in a wellness clinic, becomes aware of the extent to which overweight children are seen in her practice. Emancipatory knowing would focus on understanding the social and political processes that have contributed greatly to the problem of childhood obesity, such as understanding how lack of regulation of the food industry with regard to labeling or use of harmful food ingredients is linked to capitalistic profit motives for large corporations that market to children. These understandings might lead Cherise to organize a group of parents to lobby legislators to pass legislation banning the use of harmful food ingredients that contribute to obesity.

Emancipatory knowledge, as an expression of emancipatory knowing, begins with being aware of social problems such as injustices and questioning why these exist. This questioning leads to critiques of the status quo. These critiques lead to imagining the changes that are needed to create equitable and just conditions that support all humans in reaching their full potential. Formal written expressions of emancipatory knowledge (e.g., action plans, manifestoes, critical analyses, vision statements) describe the conditions that limit human potential, the circumstances that create and sustain those conditions, what is required to change the status quo, and what needs to be created in place of the status quo. Emancipatory knowledge is also expressed in activist projects directed toward changing existing social structures and establishing practices and structures that are more equitable and favorable to human health and well-being.

The integrated expression of emancipatory knowing is praxis, which produces changes that are intended for the benefit of all. We emphasize "integrated," because the action and reflection of true praxis must be grounded in all knowing patterns to be effective. To illustrate further, we return to the nurse caring for the young woman with a gunshot wound. To have had some awareness that this situation was not only unnecessary but also unjust, the nurse had to be aware that Nayan's need for aseptic wound irrigation (which requires empiric knowing) was in part the result of the city shifting police resources from poorer to wealthier neighborhoods (an ethical issue). The nurse would have also had to know that—if he were going to have any influence on this young woman with regard to the safe handling and use of guns, removing guns from the home, or encouraging Nayan to speak out politically—his counsel and teaching would have to be performed with a consideration of Nayan's and her family's attitudes about weapon use, Nayan's safety needs (aesthetic knowing), and his own bias regarding gun control (personal knowing).

Although this is a simple example, it illustrates that emancipatory knowing is integrated with the four knowing patterns when the nurse encourages the young woman to speak out politically about the situation in her neighborhood. In addition, praxis at the community level would occur when the nurse teams up with friends and peers to work with community leaders to improve police patrol in underserved neighborhoods.

Praxis at the individual level occurs when people recognize conditions that unjustly limit their own or others' abilities and experiences, reflect on these situations with a growing realization that things could be different, and take action to change the circumstances of their own and others' lives. As actions are taken, individuals remain continually attuned to the ideals that they seek, and they continue to reflect critically and act to transform experience into the imagined ideal.

Praxis as a collective endeavor requires reflection and action in concert with others who are engaged in creating social and political change. When groups of people collectively share their individual insights and experiences, critiques and imaginings become symbiotic, and possibilities for change multiply. When members of a discipline such as nursing engage in praxis at a collective level, their cooperative reflections and actions can create substantial change. Praxis within a disciplinary collective also creates emancipatory knowledge that can be authenticated and understood by members of the discipline.

As a community of critical reflectors and actors, nurses can begin to act on their insights and move toward the goal of transforming nursing and health care. In this way, the critical reflections and actions that constitute praxis at the individual and the collective level continue to energize change in the direction of creating emancipatory knowledge to show how equitable and just social structures can be created. The cycle of praxis (i.e., action and reflection to undo unjust social practices) and the emancipatory changes that it produces are ongoing processes. As praxis produces change, this change undergoes further action and reflection in relation to the envisioned outcome.

Ethics: The Moral Component of Nursing

Ethics in nursing is focused on matters of obligation: what ought to be done. The moral component of knowing in nursing goes beyond knowledge of the norms or ethical codes of conduct: it involves making moment-to-moment judgments about what ought to be done, what is good and right, and what is responsible. Ethical knowing guides and directs how nurses morally behave in their practices, what they select as being important, where their loyalties are placed, and what priorities demand advocacy.

Ethical knowing comes into play when Juan, a nurse working in rehabilitation, learns that a young man in his care travels across state lines to purchase marijuana legally for medicinal use and then uses it for pain control in his state, where marijuana is illegal. Juan must decide whether to "play dumb" or to share this knowledge with others and run the risk that his patient's pain will not be properly controlled.

Ethical knowing also involves clarifying conflicting values and exploring alternative interests, principles, and actions. There may be no satisfactory answer to an ethical dilemma or moral distress; rather, there may only be alternatives, some of which are more satisfactory than others. Ethical knowing in nursing requires an experiential knowledge of social values and mores from which ethical reasoning arises, as well as knowledge of the formal principles and codes within the discipline (Carper, 1978).

Ethical principles and codes are formal expressions of ethical knowledge that reflect the philosophic ideals on which ethical decisions rest. Ethical knowledge does not describe or prescribe what a decision or action should be. Rather, it provides insight about which choices are possible and direction with regard to choices that are sound, good, responsible, and just.

Ethical knowledge forms are similar to empiric theory and formal descriptions in that they are expressed in language, reflect some dimensions of experience, and express relationships among phenomena. However, empiric theory relies on observations that can be tested or confirmed by others in a more or less objective manner. Ethical codes and principles cannot be tested in this sense, because the relationships expressed in codes and principles rest on underlying philosophic reasoning that leads to conclusions that concern what is right, good, responsible, or just. This means that reasoning processes—rather than an appeal to facts or observational data—authenticate ethical knowledge. The reasoning can include descriptions that substantiate an argument, but the conclusions are value statements that cannot be perceived or confirmed empirically. The integrated expression of ethical knowing is moral and ethical comportment, which requires the nurse to practice in a way that integrates disciplinary knowledge and situational factors to achieve a morally acceptable result.

Personal Knowing: The Self and Other in Nursing

Personal knowing in nursing concerns the inner experience of becoming a whole, aware, genuine Self. Personal knowing encompasses knowing one's own Self as well as the Self in relation to others. As Carper (1978, p. 18) stated, "One does not know about the self, one strives simply to know the self." It is through knowing one's Self in a nonobjectified way that people are able to know the other. Full awareness of the Self in the moment and in the context of interaction makes possible meaningful, shared human experience. Without this component of knowing, the idea of the therapeutic use of the Self in nursing would not be possible (Carper, 1978).

Personal knowing is operating when Luella, an older nurse-midwife, recognizes that she has strong negative feelings about young, single itinerant mothers that she must contain. Raised in a staunchly religious family with conservative political values, Luella is in touch with the source of her negativity and tries to channel it into accepting and understanding the perspective and situation of her young female clients.

Personal knowing is most fully communicated as an authentic, aware, genuine Self. Other people perceive the existence of a unique person by physical characteristics, but they also come to know each person as having a unique personality. As personal knowing emerges more fully throughout life, the unique or genuine Self can be more fully expressed and thus becomes accessible as a means by which deliberate action and interaction take form. A deliberate effort to understand the Self through the cultivation of personal knowing increases personal authenticity and genuineness.

Authenticity as a person is important for the provision of sound nursing care. Authenticity requires questioning, acknowledging, and understanding such factors as personal biases, strengths and weaknesses of character, feelings, values, and attitudes. After these have been acknowledged and understood, the nurse can work toward reconciling and resolving inner conflicts of the Self that compromise best nursing practices. In this way, the inner knowing of the Self grows, and authenticity increases.

For example, suppose you hold a negative bias against a certain group of persons. For this example, we will use older adults. Unless you address personal knowing by acknowledging and understanding your bias, you are forced into inauthenticity (e.g., "I'm trying to like this old person even though I don't") when in contact with frail elders. Willfully changing a bias that you have grown up with and learning to recognize actions that reflect this bias are major lifelong processes that cannot be accomplished easily. However, when you face your bias and acknowledge that it is preventing you from being genuinely present as a nurse when you care for older people, you can deliberately choose to bring forth your desire to be genuinely present with such individuals in a nursing situation. Your actions will reflect that intention, and your bias will fade into the background. When you are genuine with older people, you also come to a place where you can begin to see older people in a more positive light. You become more comfortable working with elderly persons, and as a result of your encounters with them, you continue your own self-healing journey. Your actions are motivated from an intention to provide good care. In short, the key to cultivating personal knowing is to recognize your inner Self as fully as possible and to choose those aspects of the Self that best serve your intentions as a nurse.

It is possible to describe certain aspects of the Self with the use of personal stories, which are written expressions of personal knowing. These descriptions provide sources for deep reflection and a shared understanding of how personal knowledge can be developed and used in a deliberative way. Descriptions of the Self portrayed in personal stories are limited in that they never fully reflect personal knowing, and they are retrospective in that they can describe only the Self that was. However, publicly expressed descriptions can be a tool for developing self-awareness and self-intimacy and for communicating to others valuable possibilities for developing personal knowing (Hagan, 1990; Nelson, 1994). In addition to public descriptions of personal knowing, the genuine Self is expressed through our daily living in the world. This in-person, ongoing type of expression defies complete description, but it is nonetheless a formal expression of personal knowing.

In a sense, all knowing is personal; individuals can know only through their personal experience (Bonis, 2009). For example, empiric theories can be learned, but their meaning for the individual comes from personal meaning and experience with the phenomena of the theory. Ethical codes and moral beliefs are likewise personal in nature. We recognize the broad meaning of personal knowing, but our focus is on the aspect of personal knowing that evolves from processes for knowing the Self and for developing and growing in self-knowing through healing encounters with others. It is knowing the Self that makes the therapeutic use of the Self in nursing practice possible.

Aesthetics: The Art of Nursing

Aesthetic knowing in nursing involves an appreciation of the meaning of a situation and calls forth inner resources that transform experience into what is not yet real, thus manifesting something that would not otherwise be possible. Aesthetic knowing allows one to move beyond the surface to sense the meaning of the moment and to connect with human experiences that are unique for each person: sickness, suffering, recovery, birth, and death. Aesthetic knowing in practice is expressed through the actions, bearing, conduct, attitudes, narrative, and interactions of the nurse in relation to others. It also is formally expressed in art forms such as poetry, drawings, stories, and music that reflect and communicate the symbolic meanings embedded in nursing practice.

Presley works in the orthopedic clinic of a large urban hospital and uses aesthetic knowing with each young child who comes for cast removal. It is aesthetic knowing that helps him remove the cast in the least distressing way for the child. Presley understands that this child likely sees a large person approaching her leg with an electric cutter and other tools that resemble those in her father's woodworking shop. Presley might use a combination of distraction and humor as well as careful timing to move through the required procedure in an artful way.

Aesthetic knowing is what makes possible knowing what to do and how to be in the moment, instantly, without conscious deliberation. Carper (1978) characterized aesthetic knowing as "abstracted particulars." In other words, aesthetic knowing is having an understanding of those particular features of a situation that come from a direct understanding of what is significant and meaningful in the moment. The nurse's sense of meaning in the situation is reflected in the action taken. Meaning among those in the situation is often understood and shared without a conscious exchange of words, and it may not be consciously or cognitively realized; it may be occurring in the background of the situation and may not be consciously considered.

Sometimes what a situation means to the nurse comes from the nurse's own perspectives, which makes it possible for the nurse to share new meanings and possibilities for managing a given situation with others. These new meanings and possibilities can be rehearsed, which provides experience with possible movements and verbal expressions that can be used in future situations. Within the pattern of aesthetics, the nurse's actions take on an element of artistry and create unique, meaningful, and often deeply moving interactions with others that touch the common chords of human experience. We refer to this aspect of nursing practice as the *transformative art/act*. We use the notion of art/act to convey that nursing is art in action. A nurse who practices artfully is acting in a way that transforms what is into what could be. In short, the term *art/act* is used to convey the notion that clinical nursing is simultaneously an art and acting or doing.

Aesthetic knowing is expressed in the moment of experience-action (Benner, 1984; Benner & Wrubel, 1989) in the transformative art/act. As an example, imagine a nurse who enters a clinic examination room and sees a young woman sitting on the examination table. Immediately, from an integration of contextual factors such as body language and facial expression, the nurse understands that the young woman is fearful; the nurse's facial expressions and movements confirm to the young woman that the nurse understands that she is afraid. The woman relaxes and looks at the nurse; the nurse places her hand on the young woman's shoulder and smiles. In this example, nothing was said, but the nurse entered the room and immediately grasped the meaning of the situation (i.e., the young woman's fear and the need to relieve it). The ongoing mutual reading of meanings that quickly occurred between the nurse and client resulted in the client's situation transforming from one of fear to one of safety. Transformative art/acts such as these constitute a form of performance art.

Aesthetic knowledge is formally expressed in aesthetic criticism and in works of art that symbolize experience. Aesthetic criticism is a written expression of aesthetic knowledge that conveys the artistic aspects of the art/act, the technical skill required to perform the art/act, the knowledge that informs the development of the art/act, the historical and cultural significance of specific aspects of nursing as an art, and the potential for the future development of the art form.

Empirics: The Science of Nursing

Empirics is based on the assumption that what is known is accessible through the physical senses, particularly seeing, touching, and hearing. Empirics can be traced to Florence Nightingale's precepts regarding the importance of accurate observation and record keeping. Empirics as a pattern of knowing is grounded in science and other empirically based methodologies. This means that science as a process makes use of empirically based methods to generate knowledge. Empirics assumes that an objective reality exists, and that truths about it can be understood through inferences based on observations and understandings that are verifiable or confirmable by other observers. In other words, empirics assumes that what many people observe and agree on is an objective truth.

You use empirics when you review a procedure manual and follow required aseptic procedures for inserting a catheter. Empiric knowing is also used when you review a grounded theory of hopefulness as you prepare to care for a crash victim who is now a quadriplegic patient. When you recall and use in practice what you have studied—whether about how to perform a urinary catheterization or how body language can help restore hopefulness—you are in the realm of empiric knowing.

Empiric knowing is expressed in practice as scientific competence by means of competent action grounded in empiric knowledge, including theory. Scientific competence involves conscious problem solving and logical reasoning, but much of the underlying empiric knowing that informs scientific competence remains in the background of awareness. What remains in the background usually can be brought to awareness when attention turns to the reasoning process itself. In other words, when completing the wound irrigation from our earlier example, the seasoned nurse does not consciously think about the empiric knowledge that justifies the requirement of asepsis as he performs the procedure. However, he could explain the scientific basis for asepsis if asked to do so.

Empiric knowledge is formally expressed in the form of empiric theories, statements of fact, or formalized descriptions and interpretations of empiric events or objects. The development of empiric knowledge traditionally has been accomplished by the methods of traditional science. This has often involved testing hypotheses derived from a theory that offers a tentative explanation of empiric phenomena. Many types of formal descriptions and theories that express empiric knowledge in nursing are linked to the traditional ideas about what is legitimate for developing the science of nursing. In addition, newer methods have been developed to include activities that are not strictly within the realm of traditional empiric methodologies, such as phenomenologic or ethnographic descriptions or inductive means of generating theories and formal descriptions.

It is important to remember that although each of the patterns is reviewed separately in the previous sections, in clinical situations the nurse cannot be a purist with regard to using only one from of knowing or knowledge. *All* patterns operate, to one degree or another, in all situations of patient care.

Think About It

Recall a nursing care situation in which you were recently involved. How did you draw on each of the patterns of knowing as you managed the patient's care?

PROCESSES FOR DEVELOPING NURSING KNOWLEDGE

Figures 1-1 and 1-2 illustrate the interrelationships among each of the patterns of knowing. Figure 1-1 focuses on emancipatory knowing, whereas Figure 1-2 details the four fundamental patterns that were originally described by Carper. As shown in Figure 1-1,

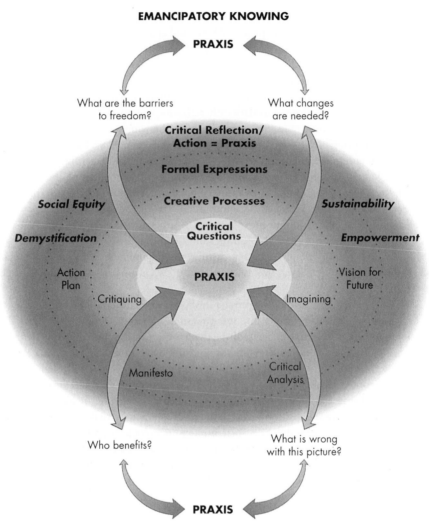

FIGURE 1-1: Emancipatory knowing and knowledge.

emancipatory knowing surrounds and connects with each of the four fundamental patterns of knowing. The four fundamental patterns are represented in the figure by the central, light-colored, irregular oval (yellow on the color plate inside the front cover) with praxis at its core. Because the pattern of emancipatory knowing focuses on matters of social justice and equality, it is configured as surrounding and encompassing ethical, personal, aesthetic, and empiric knowing. Embedding the four fundamental knowing patterns within emancipatory knowing also symbolizes the need to examine and understand both practice and disciplinary approaches to knowledge development in relation to how they enable praxis and emancipatory change.

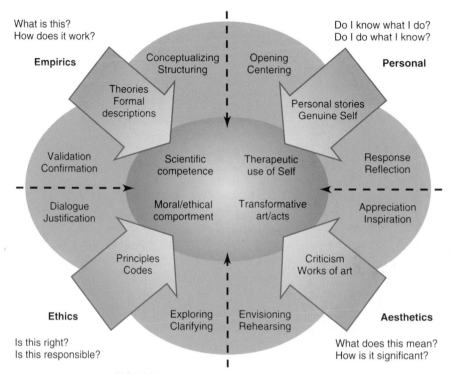

FIGURE 1-2: Fundamental patterns of knowing.

The central location of the fundamental patterns and the four large arrows that extend from the center through the outer hazy, indistinct border represent the need for an outward praxis with which the profession critically examines itself and acts in relation to the societal context in which it exists. The arrows that point inward toward the four fundamental patterns at the model's center represent the need for an inward praxis that critically reflects and acts in relation to the development of nursing knowledge and the practice of nursing. This inward view critically examines the methods used when developing and using nursing knowledge and the nature of knowledge that is considered to be authenticated. The outward view considers the social and political contexts in which nursing knowledge is developed and in which nursing is practiced, the interests that nursing serves, and the ways in which nursing shapes and is shaped by its context and history.

For each pattern, we have proposed five dimensions that are shown in both figures and that are summarized in Table 1-1:

- Critical questions
- Creative processes for developing knowledge
- Formal expressions of knowledge
- Authentication processes
- Integrated expressions of knowing in practice

TABLE 1-1 Dimensions Associated with Each of the Patterns of Knowing

Dimension	Emancipatory	Ethics	Personal	Aesthetics	Empirics
Critical questions	Who benefits? What is wrong with this picture? What are the barriers to freedom? What changes are needed?	Is this right? Is this responsible?	Do I know what I do? Do I do what I know?	What does this mean? How is this significant?	What is this? How does it work?
Creative processes	Critiquing Imagining	Clarifying Exploring	Opening Centering	Envisioning Rehearsing	Conceptualizing Structuring
Formal expressions	Action plans Manifestoes Critical analyses Visions for the future	Principles and codes	Personal stories Genuine Self	Aesthetic criticism Works of art	Facts Models Formal descriptions Theories Thematic descriptions
Authentication processes	Social equity Sustainability Empowerment Demystification	Dialogue Justification	Response Reflection	Appreciation Inspiration	Confirmation Validation
Integrated expression in practice	Praxis	Moral and ethical comportment	Therapeutic use of Self	Transformative art/acts	Scientific competence

It is through critical questions that creative processes for developing knowledge are initiated. Out of creative processes, knowledge is developed and can be formally expressed and shared with others for authentication. Each pattern of knowing is also associated with an integrated expression in practice. Although formal expressions of knowledge can be shared and presented for authentication, integrated practice expressions of knowing are a way of being that express in the moment of care what is known. The processes for each pattern are unique and particular to the pattern with which they are associated. To say that each process is unique to its individual pattern of knowing means that you cannot create empiric theory, for example, by initiating the creative processes of ethics or personal, aesthetic, or emancipatory knowing. Processes for creating, authenticating, and expressing knowledge and knowing within each pattern are detailed next.

The critical questions of emancipatory knowing in Figure 1-1 are located external to the outer boundary of the model. These queries are as follows: What are the barriers to freedom? What changes are needed? Who benefits? What is wrong with this picture? These questions focus on the social context of nursing and health care as well as on formal expressions of disciplinary knowledge and knowing in the immediate clinical situation as portrayed by the four double arrows. The critical questions awaken and sustain emancipatory awareness and suggest what needs to change. These critical questions arise from a nurse's personal experience either in practice or in some other aspect of his or her personal and professional life that affects practice. The questions are placed outside the boundaries of the model to symbolize that critical questions also come from an awareness of larger social and political contexts. The double curved configuration of the arrows also represents the ongoing, constant, and synchronous nature of praxis that arises when you or other nurses ask, reflect, and act in relation to the critical questions.

The three outer spheres that encircle the fundamental patterns of knowing represent (1) the creative processes that are used to develop emancipatory knowledge, (2) the formal expressions of emancipatory knowledge that assist and enable praxis, and (3) the authentication processes that document emancipatory change. The creative processes within the inner sphere that surrounds the central area containing the four fundamental knowing patterns are engaged to develop emancipatory knowledge. These are critiquing the status quo and imagining what might create a world that is more equitable for all. Critique can be approached with the use of one or more of several possible lenses, including the lens of race, ethnicity, socioeconomic status, sexual identity, age, culture, religious beliefs, and political orientation. Critiques uncover the subtle ways in which injustice is sustained and deepen the awareness of what needs to change. From the critique emerges an image or imagining of what could be and ideas about the actions that are needed for change. Formal expressions of the critique are shown within the middle sphere that surrounds the fundamental patterns and include critical analyses that are published in scholarly journals, action plans that are communicated electronically or in writing, manifestoes, and vision statements. Formal expressions that are communicated as emancipatory knowledge also provide insights about the processes of praxis for emancipatory change; this knowledge is useful in other situations that call for similar forms of change.

Praxis, which is the critical action/reflection dimension of emancipatory knowing, is located both outside the porous outer sphere and centrally within our model of emancipatory knowing. The central location of praxis symbolizes the local individual expression of critical reflective nursing practice; this is a place where a new awareness of problems often begins to take shape and where consciousness shifts to a realization that your experience and your situation are problematic, and you do something to begin to change it. The outer circle of the model that is open to what is beyond symbolizes that praxis is also situated in and directed to the larger social, political, and economic contexts of nursing practice.

The discipline authenticates emancipatory knowing by demonstrating that social change—and the formal disciplinary expressions that motivate and mobilize that type of change—accomplishes imagined and intended shifts that end injustices and inequities. Authentication processes examine the sustainability of the change, the presence of social equity, to what extent the demystification of processes that sustain inequities has occurred, and the degree of empowerment for those who have been unjustly treated. These authentication processes are shown in bold black type and are primarily within the two outer spheres of Figure 1-1, because these processes arise from formal expressions of emancipatory knowing that mobilize praxis. They also overlap slightly with the inner sphere of critiquing and imagining, because praxis can begin to emerge from the creative processes of emancipatory knowing.

Figure 1-2 expands on the irregular oval at the center of Figure 1-1 that represents the four fundamental patterns of knowing. We refer to the four patterns originally proposed by Carper as the "fundamental knowing patterns." In Figure 1-2, each of the fundamental patterns is represented as a quadrant. At the periphery of each quadrant are the pattern's critical questions that are asked in relation to knowledge expressions as well as in the practice moment. The large arrows that point toward the model's central core contain the formal expressions of knowledge for each pattern. The central core at the tip of each large arrow contains the in-practice or integrated practice expressions of knowing associated with each pattern. The inner sphere of Figure 1-2 is configured as a whole, without quadrant boundaries; this represents our view that, in nursing practice, knowing is experienced as an integrated whole that can never be experienced as discrete patterns. On either side of the vertical broken arrows are the creative processes for developing formal written and communicable knowledge expressions for each pattern. Above and below the broken horizontal arrows are the authentication processes used within the discipline for validating or authenticating disciplinary knowledge forms.

Knowledge and knowing come about when critical questions are asked within each of these four patterns. Personal knowing asks, "Do I know what I do?" and "Do I do what I know?" Ethics asks the critical questions "Is this right?" and "Is this responsible?" Aesthetics asks, "What does this mean?" and "How is this significant?" Finally, the critical questions for empirics are "What is this?" and "How does it work?"

These critical questions and similar queries are implicit in practice, which means that they are "asked" in the moment of care, but often not consciously or deliberately. They also are asked apart from the moment of practice to develop consciously or deliberately a better understanding of what happened in a particular situation or to initiate some form of inquiry to find an answer that seems elusive. Critical questions are also asked of the disciplinary knowledge forms located within the large arrows as a way to improve their usefulness for practice. The process of posing these questions and seeking answers or solutions improves practice and advances the knowledge on which practice is founded.

The creative processes, which are adjacent to the vertical dotted arrows in Figure 1-2, lead to formal expressions of knowledge. Opening and centering the Self creates personal knowledge. The development of ethical knowledge uses processes that clarify values, rights, and responsibilities in practice and explores alternative ethical positions and actions. Aesthetic knowledge is developed by envisioning possibilities and rehearsing art/acts that can be used to transform clinical experiences. Empiric knowledge development makes use of the reasoning processes of conceptualizing and structuring empiric phenomena.

With regard to creative inquiry processes, forms of expression evolve that can be shared with members of the discipline for authentication. The creative inquiry processes for ethics generate principles and codes as well as other expressions (e.g., precepts) that guide ethical conduct in practice. The critical questions for personal knowing generate personal stories and the lived expression of the nurse's being (i.e., who the nurse is) in nursing care situations that conveys the genuine Self. Aesthetic inquiry leads to works of art that symbolize nursing experience and to aesthetic criticism that reveals deep meaning embedded in nursing art/acts. Empiric inquiry processes produce theories, formal descriptions, models, and various other constructions (e.g., facts, thematic descriptions of experience, conceptual frameworks).

The formal expressions of each pattern, after it has been made available to the members of the discipline, make possible certain formal authentication processes that depend on the collective efforts of the discipline or the community. These authentication processes, which are adjacent to the horizontal dotted lines in Figure 1-2, begin with the critical questions for each pattern and are requisite to establishing the professional value of knowledge generated from creative inquiry processes. Ethical principles and codes are authenticated through collective dialogue and through the justification of the soundness of the principles when addressing nursing's ethical and moral dilemmas. For personal knowing, others in the discipline respond to stories and the expression of the genuine Self to discern the value and adequacy of personal insights. Questioning the meaning and significance of aesthetic criticism and works of art leads to the formation of a collective appreciation of aesthetic meanings for practice and becomes a source of inspiration for the development of transformative art/acts. In the empiric pattern, formal expressions such as theories and models that are grounded in observations and perceptions of empiric events are subjected to inquiry that can be confirmed and validated in similar but different situations.

All the processes involved in developing nursing knowledge are interactive and nonlinear, and there is no single starting point. Nurses in practice and nurses who primarily engage in the formal inquiry processes all contribute to the activities that are involved in creating nursing knowledge. Each nurse engages in activities that make possible critical reflection and action, scientific competence, moral and ethical comportment, the therapeutic use of Self, and transformative art/acts.

PATTERNS GONE WILD

When knowledge within any one pattern is not integrated within the whole of knowing, distortion—rather than understanding—is produced. Knowledge that is developed in isolation without the consideration of all patterns of knowing leads to uncritical acceptance, narrow interpretation, and partial use of knowledge. We call this situation "patterns gone wild." When this occurs, the patterns disintegrate and are used in relative isolation from one another, and the potential for the synthesis of the whole is lost.

Emancipatory knowing removed from the context of the whole of knowing produces an extreme political standpoint that is unjustly imposed on others. Even when a particular political system has the potential to benefit people and to create a more equitable social order, if it is imposed on others in the extreme, it has the potential to create another form of oppression and injustice. Failure to question your own political standpoint constantly and critically is counter to emancipatory knowing and leads to this pattern of knowing gone wild. Remaining critically reflective and open to empiric, ethical, personal, and aesthetic insights is central to emancipatory knowing.

Empirics removed from the context of the whole of knowing can lead to control and manipulation. Ironically, these have been the explicit traditional goals of the empiric sciences. When the validity of empiric knowledge is not questioned, one danger is its potential use in contexts where it does not belong. When you recognize how all the patterns contribute to the value of empirics, you begin to see the unquestioned goals of control and manipulation as a distortion or misuse of empiric knowledge.

Ethics removed from the context of the whole of knowing produces rigid doctrine and insensitivity to the rights of others. This happens when you simply set forth personal ideas about what is right or good and advocate a position on the basis of reasoning derived from personal perspectives. You may present a justification for a perspective to others but not take seriously the processes of dialogue that the justification invites. In the absence of this integrating process, an individual's position remains isolated, with little or no opportunity for empiric, personal, or aesthetic insights to give meaning and social relevance to the ideas.

Personal knowing removed from the context of the whole of knowing produces isolation and self-distortion. When this happens, the individual Self remains isolated and truncated, and knowledge of the Self comes only from what is known internally. Self-distortions can take a wide range of forms, from aggrandizement and the overestimation of the Self to destruction and the underestimation of the Self.

Aesthetics removed from the context of the whole of knowing produces indulgence in self-serving expressions and a lack of appreciation for the fullness of meaning in context. Human actions emerge from and are represented by the tastes and desires of the individual alone, without taking into account the deep cultural meanings that are inherent in an authentic art/act. Your attempts to enact art/acts are not artful but rather self-serving, shallow, arrogant, and empty. Self-serving preferences grow out of a failure to comprehend the deeper cultural, historical, and political significance of the art/act itself. Inauthentic meanings are assigned to another's experience, or a self-serving posture is assumed with respect to another person.

To illustrate patterns gone wild in a nursing situation, imagine Ruth, an elderly woman who is living in an extended-care facility. Ruth's life has been rich in experience and activities, and she verbally explores her past to make sense of what it means and how it relates to her present life. She has always been physically active, and she takes a nightly stroll before going to bed. She walks the halls, unsteady but determined, smiling and peering into other rooms. When she hears other residents talking or moaning, she sometimes goes into their rooms and tells them stories or talks with them to ease their troubled nights. She does not willingly retire to her own room, and her nightly excursions often disturb others who are trying to sleep or who want to be left alone.

Consider what might happen if one of the patterns of knowing were isolated from the context of the whole of knowing. Emancipatory knowing alone might lead you to defend Ruth's individual right to do as she wishes, regardless of how this affects others, on the basis of a liberal political philosophy of the primary rights of the individual. Ethics taken alone might impose your view of what is good for Ruth, which may lead to a prescription in her care plan that would confine her to bed after the lights are out, thus creating a rigid, rule-oriented atmosphere that is insensitive to what others see as right or good for Ruth or that Ruth sees as being beneficial for herself. Personal knowing in isolation could impose your bias that Ruth is a nuisance who is interfering with the time needed to complete the charting for the night. Aesthetics alone would impose your own tastes, preferences, and meanings on the situation. You might attempt to confine Ruth to her room and play your favorite new age music without considering whether Ruth can hear the music or whether she finds the music soothing or appealing. Empirics isolated from the other patterns of knowing might require giving Ruth a sleep-inducing drug, thereby controlling the situation and manipulating Ruth into compliance, regardless of other concerns.

When you, being the best nurse you can be, act so that emancipatory knowing, ethics, aesthetics, personal knowing, and empirics come together as a whole, your purposes for developing knowledge and your actions based on that knowledge become more responsible and humane and create liberating choices. A whole understanding of Ruth and the meaning of her life means that you have taken into account the social and political prescriptions for long-term care, Ruth's safety, the needs of other residents, Ruth's personal life history and what gives her pleasure, the ethical dimensions of moral development and caring for others, the aesthetic meanings of Ruth's actions in the cultural context of aging, and the personal perspectives of the nurses who care for Ruth. Many choices remain open when addressing Ruth's situation, but all these considerations together would lead you to nursing approaches that would differ from any of the approaches taken from one knowing perspective alone.

WHY DEVELOP NURSING'S PATTERNS OF KNOWING?

As is shown in Figures 1-1 and 1-2 and from our discussion of the knowing patterns, the fundamental reason for developing knowledge in nursing is for the purpose of creating expert and effective nursing practice. Nursing's unique perspective and the particular contributions that nurses bring to care come from the whole of knowing; this wholeness has survived despite a cultural and contextual dominance of empiric knowing (Archibald, 2012; Betts, 2009; Billay, Myrick, Luhanga, & Yonge, 2007; Clements & Averill, 2006; Fawcett et al., 2001; Mantzorou & Mastrogiannis, 2011). In a sense, the discipline of nursing can be viewed as the empiric pattern of "knowing gone wild" in that most efforts in formal knowledge development have focused on empiric methods. Moreover, knowledge has been equated with empiric forms to the exclusion of any other forms of expression, and the basis for best practices in nursing has come to be associated almost exclusively with empiric evidence.

The idea that knowledge development occurs in academic settings that are separate from practice can be seen as deriving from the dominance of empirics. Empiric knowledge is inadequate to represent the complexity of the practice world. In fact, the methods of science traditionally require controlling or eliminating the uncontrolled and unpredictable contingencies in the practice realm, which makes the findings of empirics questionable when used in a practice context. The practice implications of empiric knowledge are often not direct or immediately obvious, and empiric knowledge often makes use of a different language than that used in practice.

A shift to a balance in knowledge development to reflect each of the patterns of knowing in nursing holds potential to bring the realm of knowledge development and the realm of practice together. Methods for developing emancipatory, ethical, personal, and aesthetic knowing compel immersion within the realm of practice, and those nurses who hold the practice doctorate are well positioned to develop more comprehensive approaches to knowledge development. Giving attention to diverse aspects of knowledge development by focusing on all patterns of knowing shifts how empirics itself is viewed. Empirics becomes part of a larger whole, and its value takes on different meanings in this context. In addition, as greater attention is given to methods other than empirics, many of the traditions and assumptions that underlie empiric methods are challenged, thereby opening the way for creating empiric methods that better accommodate the contingencies of practice.

Formally expressed nursing knowledge provides professional and disciplinary identity, which in turn conveys to others what nursing contributes to the health care process (Copnell, 2008; Jackson, Clements, Averill, & Zimbro, 2009). Professional identity that evolves from distinct disciplinary knowledge provides a basis from which nurses can create certain aspects of their practice. The knowledge that forms nursing practice provides a language for talking about the nature of nursing practice and for demonstrating its effectiveness. When nursing practice is described, it is made visible. Moving to a conceptualization of knowledge that more fully embraces the whole of practice will serve to impart value to what has been intangible. In addition, when nursing's effectiveness can be shown, it can be deliberately shaped or controlled by those who practice it (Banks-Wallace, Despins, Adams-Leander, McBroom, & Tandy, 2008).

On an individual level, nursing knowledge can provide self-identity and confidence because you will have a firmer base when your ideas are questioned. As you become familiar with the language and processes of knowledge development, you can begin to think about how assumptions, definitions, and relationships within each of the patterns of knowing can be challenged. The study and understanding of knowledge development will provide a basis on which to take risks, act deliberately, and improve practice.

Imagine yourself as a nurse who is using massage to ease chronic pain for a hospitalized person. A physician notices that you are using this method of care. Because this approach is not something the physician would customarily use, she asks you about it. You explain your reasoning, which is based on nursing knowledge. You can cite research evidence of the effectiveness of massage and how you have integrated that evidence into a clinical decision to use it. You convey to the physician information about the positive results that the person is experiencing. You explain the ethical importance of providing relief from suffering, when possible without using analgesic drugs; the aesthetic components of the meaning in the situation; and what you have learned about the therapeutic use of the Self when giving a massage. You explain the societal shift toward accepting and expecting complementary therapies to be included in any approach to care and the social practices that labeled alternative practices as "quackery" that kept this valuable therapy suppressed. You also cite facts regarding the nurse practice act in your region that includes massage as a legitimate nursing care practice. Your explanation leads to an informed discussion about various approaches to caring for people with pain and why your approach seems to be effective for this person. As other practitioners learn about your knowledge in this area, they seek your consultation when caring for people with pain. Your knowledge of empiric pain theory and of what is effective when caring for people with pain—as well as your emancipatory, ethical, aesthetic, and personal knowledge—provides a valuable resource for developing and improving practice.

Nursing's formally expressed knowledge forms also provide the discipline with a coherence of purpose, and a coherence of professional purpose is closely linked to professional identity. A coherence of purpose contributes to a collective identity when nurses agree about the general practice domain. The processes for developing nursing knowledge serve as a means for resolving significant disagreements among practitioners about what is to be accomplished. Varying points of view that involve the general purpose of nursing are reflected in the following questions:

- Should nurses address the prevention of illness?
- Should nurses treat human responses to illness?
- Should educational programs be structured around the nursing process? Nursing diagnoses? Patterns of knowing? Critical thinking? Evidence-based nursing practices?
- Should nurses view health and illness as opposites?
- Can people with an illness or disease also be healthy?
- Is political activism part of nursing's responsibility to society?

As nurses develop individual and collective responses to these questions, this will help clarify our directions for developing knowledge, and in turn, our knowledge-development efforts will contribute to clarifying responses to such questions. Nursing knowledge facilitates coherence by examining such questions as a basis for deliberate choices. When nurses examine and agree about professional purposes and develop knowledge related to those purposes, the public and other practitioners will recognize nursing's expertise in relation to those arenas. The fact that nurses are responsible for certain situations will be directly and indirectly communicated to society, and professional identity and coherence of purpose will continue to evolve. By shifting to a balance in the development of all of nursing's knowledge patterns, a sense of purpose grounded in the whole of knowing can develop that shapes and directs nursing practice.

Think About It

To deepen your appreciation of the whole of knowing, consider the following questions related to the content of this chapter:

1. Recall a difficult client care situation in your own nursing experience. What contextual factors contributed to this situation? Were there institutional policies, social structures, or cultural expectations that influenced your experience? What were the ethical problems of the situation? What personal opinions or values did you bring to the situation? Were there any creative solutions or possibilities that you recognized as a nurse that might have changed the situation? Are you aware of empiric facts or theories that might explain the situation?

2. Which knowing pattern is most challenging for you in practice: scientific competence, the therapeutic use of the Self, moral and ethical comportment, transformative art/acts, or praxis? What kinds of experiences or knowledge do you need to develop more fully to meet the challenge that the pattern provides?

3. Have you experienced a situation in which one of the patterns of knowing "went wild"? Describe this experience, and discuss it with your colleagues. Identify how the whole of knowing would bring about a transformation in the situation.

REFLECTION AND DISCUSSION – SUPPLEMENT ⊖

References

Archibald, M. M. (2012). The holism of aesthetic knowing in nursing. *Nursing Philosophy, 13*(3), 179–188. http://dx.doi.org/10.1111/j.1466-769X.2012.00542.x.

Banks-Wallace, J., Despins, L., Adams-Leander, S., McBroom, L., & Tandy, L. (2008). Re/affirming and re/conceptualizing disciplinary knowledge as the foundation for doctoral education. *ANS Advances in Nursing Science, 31*, 67–78.

Benner, P. A. (1984). *From novice to expert: Excellence and power in clinical nursing practice.* Menlo Park, CA: Addison-Wesley.

Benner, P. A., & Wrubel, J. (1989). *The primacy of caring: Stress and coping in health and illness.* Menlo Park, CA: Addison-Wesley.

Betts, C. E. (2009). Nursing and the reality of politics. *Nursing Inquiry, 16*, 261–272.

Billay, D., Myrick, F., Luhanga, F., & Yonge, O. (2007). A pragmatic view of intuitive knowledge in nursing practice. *Nursing Forum, 42*, 147–155.

Bonis, S. A. (2009). Knowing in nursing: A concept analysis. *Journal of Advanced Nursing, 65*, 1328–1341.

Carper, B. A. (1978). Fundamental patterns of knowing in nursing. *ANS Advances in Nursing Science, 1*(1), 13–23.

Chinn, P. L., & Kramer, M. (2008). *Integrated theory and knowledge development in nursing* (7th ed.). St. Louis, MO: Mosby.

Clements, P. T., & Averill, J. A. (2006). Finding patterns of knowing in the work of Florence Nightingale. *Nursing Outlook, 54*, 268–274.

Cloutier, J. D., Duncan, C., & Bailey, P. H. (2007). Locating Carper's aesthetic pattern of knowing within contemporary nursing evidence, praxis and theory. *International Journal of Nursing Education Scholarship, 4*, 1–11.

Copnell, B. (2008). The knowledgeable practice of critical care nurses: A poststructural inquiry. *International Journal of Nursing Studies, 45,* 588–598.

Fawcett, J. (2006). Commentary: Finding patterns of knowing in the work of Florence Nightingale. *Nursing Outlook, 54,* 275–277.

Fawcett, J., Watson, J., Neuman, B., Walker, P. H., & Fitzpatrick, J. J. (2001). On nursing theories and evidence. *Journal of Nursing Scholarship, 33,* 115–119.

Fiandt, K., Forman, J., Megel, M. E., Padieser, R. A., & Burge, S. (2003). Integral nursing: An emerging framework for engaging the evolution of the profession. *Nursing Outlook, 51,* 130–137.

Gallagher, A. (2013). Values for contemporary nursing practice: Waving or drowning? *Nursing Ethics, 20*(6), 615–616. http://dx.doi.org/10.1177/0969733013496362.

Gramling, K. L. (2006). Sarah's story of nursing artistry. *Journal of Holistic Nursing, 24,* 140–142.

Hagan, K. L. (1990). *Internal affairs: A journalkeeping workbook for intimacy.* New York, NY: Harper & Row.

Jackson, J. R., Clements, P. T., Averill, J. B., & Zimbro, K. (2009). Patterns of knowing: Proposing a theory for nursing leadership. *Nursing Economic$, 27,* 149–159.

Lane, M. R. (2006). Arts in health care: A new paradigm for holistic nursing practice. *Journal of Holistic Nursing, 24,* 70–75.

Mantzorou, M., & Mastrogiannis, D. (2011). The value and significance of knowing the patient for professional practice, according to the Carper's patterns of knowing. *Health Science Journal, 5*(4), 251–261.

Nelson, G. L. (1994). *Writing and being: Taking back our lives through the power of language.* San Diego, CA: LuraMedia.

Paley, J., Cheyne, H., Dalgleish, L., Duncan, E. A., & Niven, C. A. (2007). Nursing's ways of knowing and dual process theories of cognition. *Journal of Advanced Nursing, 60,* 692–701.

Porter, S. (2010). Fundamental patterns of knowing in nursing: The challenge of evidence-based practice. *ANS Advances in Nursing Science, 33*(1), 1–11.

Porter, S., & O'Halloran, P. (2009). The postmodernist war on evidence-based practice. *International Journal of Nursing Studies, 46,* 740–748.

Satterfield, J. M., Spring, B., Brownson, R. C., Mullen, E. J., Newhouse, R. P., Walker, B. B., et al. (2009). Toward a transdisciplinary model of evidence-based practice. *Milbank Quarterly, 87,* 368–390.

Thorne, S. E., & Sawatzky, R. (2014). Particularizing the general: Sustaining theoretical integrity in the context of an evidence-based practice agenda. *ANS Advances in Nursing Science, 37*(1), 1–10.

Weis, D., Schank, M. J., & Matheus, R. (2006). The process of empowerment: A parish nurse perspective. *Journal of Holistic Nursing, 24,* 17–24.

Wittmann-Price, R. A., & Bhattacharya, A. (2008). Reexploring the subconcepts of the Wittmann-Price theory of emancipated decision making in women's healthcare. *ANS Advances in Nursing Science, 31,* 225–236.

The History of Knowledge Development in Nursing

⊖ http://evolve.elsevier.com/Chinn/knowledge/

Nursing history was taught, but never accorded much importance . . . a casual interlude . . . and even more disheartening not valued. Lacking historical record the profession is poorly informed . . . a void in self awareness that affects the stature and growth of nursing as a vital, essential service.

Myra Estrin Levine (1999, p. 214)

The nursing models and frameworks that have been all too often disregarded as if they were inconvenient remnants of an immature disciplinary science can instead serve as a strong philosophical foundation for expanding our understanding of the complexity, and context within which nursing enacts [its] particular role within the health care [system].

Sally Thorne and Richard Sawatzky (2014, pp. 14–15)

L evine's quote suggests that, if nurses do not know their history, they cannot value it; when nurses do not value history, they cannot learn and grow from what it teaches. Thorne and Sawatzky remind us that all too often, nurses have devalued the nursing knowledge expressed in the early nursing theories and models, and that these ideas form the important philosophic and value basis for our practice. This chapter reviews the history of nursing's knowledge development as a way to reclaim the value of nursing knowledge and to understand not only where nursing has been but also where it might go in the future.

Think About It

- To what extent does the quote from Myra Estrin Levine reflect your feelings about the study of nursing history?
- What nursing theories or models have you studied, and what do you know about the development of the ideas around which they were built?
- What do you know about Florence Nightingale and her work? Have you ever read *Notes on Nursing*? Have you read her essay titled "Cassandra"?
- Would it surprise you to know that Florence Nightingale was widely known and respected for her statistical accomplishments during her lifetime?
- What do you think nurses 50 years from now will say about what we are doing today?

The history of knowledge development in nursing is a vast subject indeed. In this chapter, we touch on some of the key events that are part of nursing's rich knowledge development heritage. Our purpose is to trace major historical trends that undergird serious inquiry surrounding each of nursing's patterns of knowing and spark interest in further study of the subject.

Well before the advent of modern nursing in the United States, which was marked by the beginning of the Nightingale era during the early 1900s, nursing existed in many forms that shared a common core. What the word *nursing* means and the functions of nurses have shifted to reflect the social order of the time and the demands placed on nurses. Despite shifts in their functions, nurses have played a role in the care of ill persons since the beginning of recorded history. Nursing has been fundamentally linked with a nurturing role toward the infirm, ill, and less fortunate. Much of nursing's history is tied to the history of medicine, which has dominated the accounts of changes in the care of the sick throughout time. Although much of nursing's unique history has been obscured or lost, substantial evidence supports the value and strength of nursing in the delivery of care and the promotion of health.

Early conceptions of nursing knowledge were grounded in a holistic view of health and healing. Nurses writing about nursing between the late 1800s and 1950s addressed all aspects of knowing, perhaps without recognizing it. These nurses wrote about the importance of observation and recording facts, the need to bring a sense of virtue to the care of sick people, and the characteristics of a good nurse. Early writings also addressed the art of nursing and called for responsible social action that would better the lot of the sick. With increasing interest in promoting the study of science during the 1950s in the United States, nursing shifted toward a focus on empirics as the primary concern of the discipline. Even during this period in nursing's history, however, threads of philosophic and practical commitment to holistic practices and to other patterns of knowing persisted. As the 21st century approached, nurses gave serious attention to holistic approaches in practice and in the methods used for the development of knowledge.

Current knowledge development approaches will undoubtedly continue to change with the times as societal values and resources are altered. Despite changes, strong evidence supports the claim that nurses have, throughout time, developed and used knowledge to improve practice. This chapter reviews some of the key events in nursing's knowledge development trajectory from antiquity to the present. It also addresses how societal values and resources operate to create nursing's history.

FROM ANTIQUITY TO NIGHTINGALE

There is ample evidence that, long before the work of Nightingale, nurses assisted with the routine care of the sick and, in some societies, independently provided healing care (Achterberg, 1991; Donahue, 2011; Ehrenreich & English, 1993). The care provided by these early nurses was influenced by the healing traditions within society. Pagan healers such as shamans, midwives, and other folk healers linked disease to influences that came from within a spirit world. These early healers used rituals, ceremonies, and charms to dispel perceived evil and to invoke good. Plants and herbal remedies also were used for healing. Nurses provided assistance to others who carried out healing traditions, but they were also independent providers of care.

Early Christian traditions often attributed disease to divine wrath, and punishment was meted out in the form of disease states for sinful transgressions. With the advent of early forms of scientific thought that dated from the mid-1500s to the mid-1700s, pagan and early religious views of illness were challenged. The work of scientists and philosophers such as Copernicus, Galileo, Bacon, and Newton began to lay the groundwork for a view of disease as the result of natural rather than spiritual causes. As society's understanding of the causes of disease changed, approaches such as invoking the spirits with charms and the idea of disease being a punishment for religious transgressions began to subside. It was nurses who were there to provide nurturing and assistive services consistent with the view that disease was linked to natural causes. The early religious orders offered a respectable avenue for nuns and monks to provide care to ill and infirm persons. In some societies, people who were being punished for civil offenses, people who were homeless and needed shelter, people who were addicted to drugs and alcohol, and women who were prostitutes also provided nursing care. Nurses also included women who bore the primary responsibility for the care of their ill family members.

NIGHTINGALE'S LEGACY

Although nursing as a nurturing, supportive activity always has existed, it was Florence Nightingale who advocated and promoted the need for a uniformly high standard of nursing care that required both education and certain personal characteristics. The recognition of nursing as a professional endeavor distinct from medicine began with Nightingale. Her actions and writings about the subject of nursing and sanitary reforms earned her recognition as the founder of modern nursing (Dossey, 2010). For our purposes, the term *modern nursing* refers to nursing that came after the work of Nightingale. Nightingale spoke with firm conviction about the nature of nursing as a profession that could provide an avenue for women to make a meaningful contribution to society (Nightingale, 1860/1969). During the mid-1800s, women cared for the sick as daughters, wives, mothers, or maids. These socially prescribed roles influenced Nightingale's conviction that nursing should be a profession for women, but this cultural tradition was secondary to her philosophy. Her primary concern was the more pervasive plight of Victorian women. Women in her era were poverty stricken and forced to work at menial labor for long hours for little or no pay, or else they were—as was the case with Nightingale—idle ornaments in the households of wealthy husbands or fathers. In either case, there was no avenue for women to use their intellect, passion, and moral activity to benefit society (Nightingale, 1852/1979).

Nightingale spent the first decade of her adult life tormented by a desire to use her productive capacities in a way that would benefit society. She eventually defied the wishes of her family and broke free of the oppressive social prescriptions for her life. She obtained training as a nurse with the protestant sisters at Kaiserswerth Hospital and subsequently agreed to serve in the Crimean War (Dossey, 2010; Nightingale, 1852/1979; Tooley, 1905; Woodham-Smith, 1983). After her service in the war, Nightingale wrote

Notes on Nursing (1860/1969), in which she set forth the basic premises on which nursing practice should be based and articulated the proper functions of nursing. Although it was written for the lay nurses of the time, *Notes on Nursing* contains timeless wisdom that is still appropriate for today's professional nurses. In Nightingale's view, nursing required the astute observation of sick patients and their environment, the recording of these observations, and the development of knowledge about the factors that promote the reparative process (Cohen, 1984; Nightingale, 1860/1969). Nightingale's framework for nursing emphasized the use of empiric knowledge. She is recognized for using the statistics that she gathered in a way that would further the cause of health care in England and throughout the world (Dossey, 2010).

Because she was firmly committed to the idea that nursing's responsibilities were distinct from those of medicine, Nightingale maintained that the knowledge developed and used by nursing must be distinct from medical knowledge. Medicine, wrote Nightingale, focused on surgical and pharmacologic "cures," which relied heavily on empiric science. Nursing, however, was broader. Nursing was meant to assist nature with the healing of the patient. This was to be accomplished by managing the internal and external environments in an assistive way that was consistent with nature's laws. Nightingale also had a great influence on nursing education; she founded St. Thomas School in London after returning from Crimea. She insisted that women who were trained nurses should control and staff early nursing schools and manage and control nursing practice in homes and hospitals to create a context that was supportive of nursing's art. Nightingale's influence on nursing education was felt within schools of nursing in all the British Commonwealth, in the United States, and in many other parts of the world. The first Nightingale schools were autonomous in their administration, and nurses held decision-making authority over nursing practice in institutions where students learned.

Instruction in Nightingale schools emphasized the powers of observation, the necessity of recording observations, and the potential for organizing the nursing knowledge that was gained through such observation and recording. Students also learned proper techniques of nursing. Nightingale's strong beliefs about the character and values that should be cultivated in nursing were reflected by the admissions standards and educational programs of the early schools (Dennis & Prescott, 1985). Nightingale regarded nursing as a calling and vehemently opposed registration practices of the day as a way to ensure the quality of practitioners. She argued that testing and subsequent registration might ensure a minimal knowledge base but would not guarantee the quality of the moral disposition within the individual nurse. Nightingale advocated that nursing was much more than knowledge of facts and techniques. These were important, but to her, nursing also required a certain ethical and moral disposition, a certain type of person, and an ability to act artfully. Nightingale also addressed emancipatory knowing and was concerned about the sociopolitical context within which nursing occurred. For example, in *Notes on Hospitals* as well as in other documents addressed to military administrators, she outlined the need to rectify unsanitary environmental conditions in hospitals to create a proper environment for healing (Nightingale, 1860/1969).

FROM NIGHTINGALE TO SCIENCE

From the beginning of the 1900s to about 1950 was a time of great change in nursing that still continues to mold and shape knowledge development processes. Three major themes mark this period and reflect societal change patterns in the United States as they pertain to hospitals, the role of women in society, and the nature of nursing education.

Loss of the Nightingale Ideal

Despite Nightingale's insistence that nurses rather than hospital administrators or physicians control nursing care, many circumstances came together in opposition to her model for schools of nursing in the United States. The medical care system developed as a capitalist, for-profit business. This system provided the context for rapid technologic development and a complex institutionalized system to support medical interventions. Early during the 1900s, the Nightingale era was ending, and medical care was taking shape as a science. Women were viewed as incapable of practicing medicine and unqualified to be scientists. With industrialization, large populations of people moved to urban areas, and the number of hospitals increased dramatically in these areas.

Physicians and hospital administrators saw women as a source of inexpensive or free nursing labor who could further their economic goals. Many women entered nursing and provided student labor for hospitals in exchange for receiving apprenticeship training to become nurses. Many of these women came from the working class and had limited opportunities for education and meaningful work. After they were trained for nursing in hospital schools, many found themselves without employment as new student recruits filled available staff positions. Nurses were exploited both as students and as experienced workers. They were treated as submissive, obedient, and humble women who were "trained" in correct procedures and techniques. Ideally, they fulfilled their responsibilities to physicians without question. Nurses' positive desire to help people in need, coupled with their relative lack of educational preparation and social or political power, led to an extended period in history when nursing was practiced primarily under the control and direction of medicine (Evans, Pereira, & Parker, 2009; Group & Roberts, 2001; Lovell, 1980; Malka, 2007).

The Entrenchment of Apprenticeship Learning

Despite strong leaders who followed the Nightingale tradition and who viewed nursing knowledge as unique, nursing knowledge has not always been regarded as distinct from medicine. The control of nursing education and practice was transferred from the profession to hospital administrators and physicians during the early 1900s, when most of the Nightingale-modeled schools in the United States were brought under the control of hospitals (Ashley, 1976). Strong efforts to move nursing to institutions of higher learning were not enough. In a manner that was consistent with the social history of women, nursing was viewed and increasingly treated as a role that supported and supplemented medicine and certainly not as one that required a unique knowledge base

(Hughes, 1980, 1990). Although training was acceptable and even necessary, true education for women and nurses was discouraged, discouraging, and limited. Indeed, education was counterproductive for women who, as nurses, were expected to follow orders and serve the needs and interests of physicians when it came to providing care (Melosh, 1982; Reverby, 1987a, 1987b).

Economic independence for women in the United States was not possible until the mid-1900s. Even a woman who earned an income was not able to have a bank account, own property, or conduct financial transactions in her own name. Normal schools were established for the training of teachers, and nursing schools were available for training nurses. To obtain long-term security, however, women were required to conform to the role of wife or daughter. Throughout the early part of the 20th century, nursing practice was based on rules, principles, and traditions that were passed along through limited apprenticeship forms of education. Nursing practice also included an ever-increasing array of delegated medical tasks that were acquired as medical knowledge expanded; these tasks were performed by nurses as extensions of physicians. Higher education for nurses was not available. What evolved as nursing knowledge was wisdom that came from years of experience.

Nursing was viewed primarily as a nurturing and technical art that required apprenticeship learning and innate personality traits that were congruent with that art (Hughes, 1990). Tradition as a basis for nursing practice was perpetuated by the nature of apprenticeship education (Ashley, 1976). Nursing students were presumed to learn at random through long hours of experience (with limited exposure to lectures or books) and to accept without question the prescriptions of practical techniques. The novice nurse acquired knowledge of what was right and wrong in practice by observing more experienced practitioners and by memorizing facts about the performance of nursing tasks. Nurse recruits also learned what sort of person a nurse should be through the imposition of rigid rules that regulated most aspects of behavior, including sleeping, eating, socializing, and dress, both inside and outside the hospital walls. Rules were strictly enforced, with severe penalties for those who strayed outside the rules' boundaries.

Persistence of Nursing Ideals

Despite social impediments to the development of nursing knowledge, nursing philosophy and ideology remained committed to the idea that nursing requires a knowledge base for practice that is distinct from that of medicine (Abdellah, 1969; Hall, 1964; Henderson, 1964, 1966; Rogers, 1970). This commitment grew from the consistent recognition that, although the goals of nursing and medicine were related, the central goals and functions of nursing required knowledge not provided by medicine or by any other single discipline outside of nursing.

Although social circumstances limited the possibilities for nursing education, early nursing leaders sustained ideals that reflected Nightingale's model of education and practice. Because most nursing service was provided as free labor by students in hospitals, those who graduated secured jobs as independent practitioners who were engaged by families to assist with the care of the sick in homes and hospitals. Many nurse leaders were active in confronting a wide range of community-based social and health issues of the time, including temperance, freedom for enslaved people, the right of disenfranchised groups to vote, and the control of venereal disease. These experiences cultivated and required a broad view of nursing knowledge and a desire to change the future of nursing; technical training was not enough for these women. Despite that training, they saw nursing as independent and vital and with a firm knowledge base.

As nurses developed community-based practices, their work and writings reflected the multiple patterns of knowing in which their efforts were grounded. There is substantial evidence that graduate nurses during the early part of the 20th century had ethical and moral commitments that contributed substantively to improving health conditions in hospitals, homes, and communities. Not only did they develop health knowledge as they practiced, but they were politically committed to finding ways to distribute this knowledge to the people who needed it (Wheeler, 1985). Consistently throughout the early 20th century, nursing leaders in the United States worked together nationally and internationally in strong connecting networks and called for a social and political ethic that would restore the control of nursing practice to nurses and promote the health and welfare of citizens.

Margaret Sanger, Lillian Wald, Lavinia Dock, Susie Walking Bear Yellowtail, Mabel Staupers, and Adah Belle Thoms are among those nurses who were challenged by specific needs in society and set about to change problematic practices that affected health care. They observed the circumstances of people in their work environment, identified health-related needs, and worked with others to meet those needs. They acted to improve health care practices by integrating ethical commitment with scientific knowledge.

For example, Sanger developed knowledge about reproduction and birth control. She fought against great odds to distribute birth control information to women who were desperate to obtain it, and she established a foundation for family-planning programs that remains viable today in the form of Planned Parenthood (Sanger, 1971). Concerned about child care and family health in the context of extremely poor sanitation in crowded immigrant tenements, Wald established the Henry Street Settlement in New York City, which is still operating today. On the basis of concepts of community health nursing and social welfare programs, Wald developed stations for distributing safe milk to families with young children and established centers for educating mothers about family care (Silverstein, 1985; Wald, 1971). Dock was an ardent suffragist and pacifist who worked for much of her professional life with Wald at the Henry Street Settlement. Dock campaigned actively for changes in labor laws that would benefit women and children. She devoted 20 years of her life to gaining the vote for women in the United States, reasoning that if women could vote, the oppressive laws that affected them could be changed (Christy, 1969).

Although much less well known, many influential nurses among minority groups in the United States also took equally significant actions to improve the health and well-being of their people. Susie Walking Bear Yellowtail was a midwife who traveled throughout North American Indian reservations to assess the health, social, and educational problems of Native Americans, and she then recommended solutions (American Nurses Association, 2009b). She was instrumental in ending the abuses of women (e.g., involuntary sterilization) that were occurring within the Indian Health Care System

(Scozzari, 2008). Mabel Staupers worked for improved access to equitable health care services for African American citizens (American Nurses Association, 2009a). Her research into the health care needs of individuals in Harlem led to the founding of the first facility there for treating tuberculosis in African Americans. Adah Belle Thoms was among the first nursing leaders to recognize public health as a new field of nursing. In 1917, she added a course on the subject to the curriculum at New York's Lincoln School for Nurses (American Nurses Association, 2008). Thoms also founded the Blue Circle Nurses, a group of African American nurses who worked with local communities and provided instruction regarding sanitation, diet, and appropriate clothing. She also organized a campaign to encourage members of the National Association of Colored Graduate Nurses to vote after the passage of the 19th Amendment, which gave women the right to vote (Thoms, 1929/1985).

Similar to contemporary scholars, these and other early nursing leaders kept alive the ideals of practice as chronicled by Nightingale, and they used multiple ways of knowing to ground improvements in health care and nursing practice. They were women of strong personal character who lived their ethical convictions that nurses can and should control nursing practice. Their ethical and moral ideals of nursing practice required making observations and organizing the resulting knowledge. Art and emancipatory knowing were central to their practices as they orchestrated complex system changes that required them to interpret and maneuver through the existing social and political environments.

KNOWING PATTERNS IN THE EARLY LITERATURE

From about 1900 to 1950, nurses and others were writing about nursing and patient care in the journals of the time. These early articles reflected all the knowing patterns, although these were not named until the publication of Barbara A. Carper's doctoral research in 1978. An examination of nursing literature published before the 1950s is rich with detail about how nursing embodies, reflects, and requires multiple ways of knowing. The following sections provide some examples of how early writings addressed each pattern of knowing, including the pattern of emancipatory knowing.

Emancipatory Knowledge and Knowing

The early literature's attention to emancipatory knowing was reflected primarily by the recognition that inequities exist as well as by descriptions of situations that create inequities and injustice. The early literature also included directives about what nurses must do to change unfair social conditions. Although nurses contributed some of these early writings, other pieces were written by physicians and non-nurse educators and published in nursing journals and books or presented to nursing audiences. The following examples illustrate our heritage of emancipatory knowing.

- Effie Taylor acknowledged the existence of social inequities in a speech given at the opening session of a national nursing organization meeting. Taylor noted that the "nations of the world are sick mentally and socially and need to be enabled to live better, think better and act better." (1934, p. 474).

- How injustices are created is embedded in an eloquent quote from Lavinia Dock (1902–1903), who noted the following in an early issue of *American Journal of Nursing*: "... after one has worked for a time healing wounds which should not have been inflicted, tending ailments which should not have developed, sending patients to hospitals who need not have gone if their homes were habitable, and bringing charitable aid to persons who would not have needed it if health had not been ruined by unwholesome conditions, one longs for preventive work ... something that will make it less easy for so many illnesses to occur, that will bring better conditions of life" (p. 532).
- Another cause of social injustices was "anxiety over material necessities," as mentioned in a 1913 physician's address to graduates of the El Reno Sanitarium. Such anxiety "precludes living the ideal, full, free and independent effective life" (Young, 1913, p. 266).
- Marion Faber (1927), a registered nurse, noted that it is "effects of the environment that cause deformation of the personality" (p. 1048).
- Joseph Mountin, a physician and then an assistant surgeon general of the United States, stated that the "hospital hierarchy tries to provide social service according to the rules of private competitive enterprise," and this "requires a financial sleight of hand to keep the institution going" (1943, p. 34).
- According to William Kilpatrick, a doctorally prepared educator, these hierarchies resulted in a "factory system that reduces individuals to a non-entity amid the bigness of the organization" (1921–1922, p. 791).
- Concerns about increasing levels of education led two doctorally prepared academic educators to suggest that "vested interest will preclude the development of professionalism (in nursing) as hospitals will not be able to adjust to the loss of student work hours" (Bixler & Bixler, 1945, p. 732).
- Isabel Stewart, a nurse and faculty member at Columbia University, wrote that custom and training are the great authorities and are rigid and static. Stewart further noted that "authority becomes entrenched and does not allow for change in the individual" (1921–1922, p. 908).
- Allen Gregg, a physician and Director of Medical Sciences at the Rockefeller Foundation, attributed injustices to "envy and malice and hate and violence" (1940, p. 738).
- Paul Johnson (1928), in an address to the Massachusetts State League of Nursing Education, stated: "[T]he first and most powerful influence upon human minds is the unconscious operation of social custom ... the question of what to teach is superfluous ... what is taught is the product of long experience of moral custom" (p. 1087). Johnson also suggested that, to address the conditions of social injustice, nurses must "seek by criticism and appreciation to broaden the bypath ... to decrease moral provincialism which makes men blind to good beyond their own ... this [moral provincialism] may be overcome by historical and cultural sympathy with others and understanding and appreciation of values that have appealed to other people" (p. 1087).
- Katherine McClure (1951), a nurse professor, noted the need to "improve the environment and conditions of the persons she nurses without remaking them to suit ourselves" (pp. 221–222).

- Bixler and Bixler (1945) stated that nurses' social attitudes should reflect the conception that "every citizen is entitled to health care" (p. 733).
- Taylor (1934) wrote that nurses must have a "broad sense of justice" (p. 475), should "not know color or creed" (p. 473), and must "be for the poor as well as the rich" (p. 473).
- Kilpatrick (1921–1922) further addressed how to undo social injustices by stating that nurses should "seek the development and expression of each in relation to all, and cause others to grow" (p. 795).
- Stewart (1921–1922) stated that "knowledge, culture, individual development, freedom, health and expertness are used in service of the social group," emphasizing that "education has a social purpose and nursing is no exception" (p. 908).
- Noted anthropologist Margaret Mead (1956), in an address to a convention of the American Nurses Association (ANA), stated that "nursing stands between those who are vulnerable and the community that may forget them, not care for them" (p. 1002).
- Genevieve Noble, a graduate nursing student, understood that nurses must notice injustice when she stated that the "nurse cannot be indifferent to the welfare and happiness of the undernourished child in the street or the maid working in her corridor" (1940, p. 161).
- Esther Lucille Brown, a researcher for the Russell Sage Foundation who was the author of reports about nursing, recognized that "nursing must create alliances with problems outside the privileged home and hospital, and should be concerned with those who have chronic disease, are aged and physically handicapped" (Goostray & Brown, 1954, p. 720).
- Elizabeth Porter, then president of the ANA, summarized many of the social conditions that create social injustices and inequities (i.e., the focus of emancipatory knowing). Porter (1953) noted that "hunger, poverty, injustice and disease are the enemies of peace," and "when man arrogates to himself blessings that he denies others, these blessings begin to slip through his fingers"; "a chain around another's neck means there is a chain about your own"; and "passivity or acquiescence to the chains of others means you enslave yourself" (p. 948). For Porter, necessary actions included "supporting humanitarian programs on a worldwide scale," taking responsibility to change the "conditions in which men live and the conditioning of their mind" (p. 948), and "putting the good of the world and community before the selfish interest of individuals or specialized groups" (p. 949).

To summarize, the early nursing literature addressed the importance of emancipatory knowing by acknowledging that social injustices existed while accounting for the conditions that created them. These nurses recognized the importance of acting in relation to the needs of others while understanding that effective change must come from a grassroots position. This literature is replete with directives for nursing actions required to rectify societal injustices and conditions that privilege one group over another. Injustices were not hidden or mystified. Rather, and perhaps concurrent with the expansion of nursing into community-based practices, the necessity to recognize social inequalities and take strong measures to rectify them was emphasized.

Ethical Knowledge and Knowing

Before the 1950s, ethics was primarily represented as virtues possessed by the nurse. Nurses were expected to be moral individuals, who, it follows, do the right thing. Virtue and responsibility were paramount for nurses. Duty and responsibility included protection, truth telling, and imparting specialized knowledge (Conrad, 1947; De Witt, 1901; Warnshius, 1926).

- An editorial in the *American Journal of Nursing* noted that "the doctor is responsible for the general conduct of the case, but the nurse is responsible for the honest performance of her own duties" (De Witt, 1901, p. 15). Further, "born qualities added to training" were critical for ethical conduct.
- According to Drake, "A good nurse will die before admitting she is even tired [for] loyal service is one of the articles of the profession's religion" (1934, pp. 137–138). Moral fitness for nursing was important, and moral examinations were recommended.
- Nurse Agnes Riddles (1928) stated that "women [nurses] should hold their position only after a moral examination as well as a technical one" (p. 29). Riddles listed a variety of moral infractions attributable to nurses of the time, including a lack of consideration for the patient, the neglecting of aseptic precautions, disrespecting human life, and a lack of proper experience with assembling needed nursing materials.
- Charlotte Aikins (1915), presumably a nurse educator, outlined an entire curriculum for teaching ethics in *Trained Nurse and Hospital Review.* The curriculum included knowledge of "the customs and laws of the hospital world which she (student) must be admonished to accept meekly" and "personal virtues of importance such as reticence, tact, and discretion in order that she may "do no harm" (p. 136). "Health, carriage, voice, manner, habits and general deportment" (p. 136) also were important. During the junior year, ethics would cover "handling of supplies and appliances, avoiding accidents, use of good surgical technique, wise use of recreation and holidays, and the necessity of a good conscience" (p. 137).
- Another early nurse mentioned the need to keep preconceptions and prejudices to a minimum as a part of ethical conduct (Oettinger, 1939).
- Paul Johnson (1928), in an address to a statewide gathering of nurses, asked, "What should ethics teach?" (p. 1084). Ethics, according to Johnson, is the "science of right conduct" (p. 1085). Ethics investigates "boldly" what this is by "questioning moral tradition, examining moral facts, and searching out moral values" (p. 1085). Ethics requires "careful investigation, open-minded judgment, the practice of reasonableness and intelligent doubting" (p. 1085). Ethical sensitivity, rather than the rules approach of "laying down exact rules for conduct" (p. 1084), was important to cultivate.

In summary, the early periodical literature generally reflects a view of ethical behavior and comportment as conforming to individual virtues, although early articles also challenged virtue ethics and its position that a good person will do the right thing. Religious living, self-sacrifice, and a nearly blind duty to others' rules and prescriptions evidenced such virtues. Duty often was expressed in religious admonitions to love, live right, and have faith; duty was seen as a sacred obligation. Moral fitness for nursing was important, and moral examinations were recommended. The establishment of rules as the basis for biomedical ethics was questioned. Although most of what is considered ethical comes from religious traditions and authoritative trust in others, these writers also discussed questioning traditions and making responsible judgments, studying what one doubts, and analyzing and criticizing basic precepts.

These early authors also suggested a variety of goals for ethical knowledge and knowing, including the protection of patients' privacy and rights, advocacy, and the minimization of patients' discomfort and inconvenience. Broader goals also were mentioned, such as increasing tolerance and respect by respecting the worth, autonomy, and dignity of individuals; assisting with the development of the individual; strengthening society and the Self; developing economic security; and promoting peace.

Personal Knowledge and Knowing

The importance of the *person* of the nurse is evident in the prevailing ethics of the time, which called for a virtuous person. However, qualities of a person beyond virtue also are found in the early literature.

- Margaret Conrad (1947), writing about the nature of expert nursing care, recognized the necessity for a well-balanced, integrated personality to contribute to the care of others.
- Allen Gregg (1940), a physician, in an address given at national nurse meetings, asked nurses to "seek honestly and earnestly to find what really matters to us and what beliefs and convictions we hold" (p. 738). Gregg also redefined virtue as "the inner life as well as the outer in consistency of behavior with one's own thoughts and feelings" (p. 740) and further stated that "motives and conduct must harmonize" (p. 740). Motives must be sound, or there is "no virtue in the great sense, no independence, and no self-confidence" (p. 741). The fundamental importance of personal knowledge is acknowledged in that "only when a person is something to herself can she become anything to anybody else" (p. 741). Gregg recognized that science could not provide personal knowledge because "the social wisdom of man does not derive from chemistry and physics and mechanical skill. Decency does not visit our common dwelling place without invitation" (p. 739).
- Genevieve Noble (1940), writing as a student in "The Spirit of Nursing," emphasized the need for an inherent inner self-discipline rather than an imposed discipline for adequate nursing care.
- Katherine Oettinger (1939) gave equal importance to personal knowing and empirics by stating that "the personality of the nurse is quite as important as the distinctive facts she learns," that such a nurse is "free from conscript minds giving conscript thoughts" and is "free to change the status quo" (p. 1224).

In summary, important personal characteristics included an acceptance of the Self that is grounded in self-knowledge and confidence. Personal integrity, honesty, enthusiasm, versatility, courageousness, stability, and emotional diversity were important features of personal knowledge. Such knowledge is created by engagement with life, finding out what really matters, and reflecting on it. Nursing practice requires a depth of personal knowing that acknowledges the validity of feelings, an openness to freely discussing feelings, and an examination of reciprocal emotions in dialogue and relation. A nurse of high personal character displays an inner and outer harmony and commands the respect of his or her Self and of others. Nursing's historical literature suggests that a host of personal attributes that go beyond virtuous behavior, including self-discipline, knowledge of the Self, and an openness to the processes of reflection to create actions with integrity are basic to good nursing care.

Aesthetic Knowledge and Knowing

A sense that nursing has an artistic component is clearly evident in the early periodical literature.

- L. F. Simpson (1914), another physician who was speaking to nurses, stated that "real nursing is an art; and a real nurse is an artist" (p. 133).
- Conrad (1947) stated that the art of nursing included such things as "knowing what the patient wants before she is asked" (p. 162). It arises from "combining instinct, knowledge and experience" (p. 162). According to Conrad, art depends on imagination and resourcefulness and requires "true perspective" (pp. 162–163). Furthermore, art requires practice, and some nurses "never acquire it" (Simpson, 1914, p. 135).
- Austin Drake (1934), a layperson, put it the following way: "circumstances alter cases. . . . the nurse adapts her roles at will according to her patient's physical state and particular mode . . . if he is able and desires . . . she talks, otherwise she is silent, intent upon her duties . . . the severity of the illness does not determine this" (pp. 136–137).
- Lois Mossman (1923), an assistant professor of education, acknowledged that "science cannot explain what happens when we respond to beauty of form or motion but the response is pleasurable and influences what we are doing" (p. 318). Mossman asked novice nurses to "experience beauty, to see it in the commonplace, to learn of books, poems, pictures, and music that interpret beauty and draw from them to fit the needs of those we serve" (p. 319). According to Mossman, "Life is rhythmical and lights must be set off by the shadows" (p. 319).
- Edward Garesche (1927), a Roman Catholic priest, eloquently expressed the elusiveness of assessing our art and the importance of distinguishing it from empirics: "the service of the learned professions does not bear measuring while it is being rendered" (p. 901).

In summary, the early literature represents aesthetics as a combination of knowledge, experience, intuition, and understanding. Aesthetic knowing was creative and intuitive and consisted of exquisite judgments that were made without conscious awareness but rather were sensed intuitively by unexplained insight and hunches. Aesthetic knowledge was gained through appreciation of the arts and by subjective sensitivity to individual differences. Aesthetic knowing was also gained by personal imitation of those who possessed the art. Experience was seen as important to the development of aesthetic knowing. Aesthetic knowing required speculation, imagination, and the superimposition of impressions on facts. The practitioner who had a sincere intentionality and the ability to carry out sophisticated assessment could act artfully. It was through the interpretation of interaction that each succeeding interaction became more meaningful. Art in the more traditional sense was also recognized as important to the art/act of nursing.

Empiric Knowledge and Knowing

Before the "era of science" in the mid-1950s, there was clear recognition of scientific knowledge as a source of power.

- A physician who addressed the annual meeting of the Michigan Nurses Association acknowledged that scientific knowledge had increased and asked nurses to acknowledge its power and value for producing knowledge. The physician cautioned against quackery and portrayed science as a source of legitimate criteria for the selection of information provided to patients (Warnshius, 1926). Despite the value of science, this physician also emphasized the importance of a central focus on the welfare of the patient.

- According to Margaret Conrad (1947), a baccalaureate-prepared professor of nursing, this required an understanding of the laws of nature and the principles of physics, chemistry, physiology, and psychology. In other early articles, the procedural and technical aspects of nursing were emphasized, including bed making; food tray handling and feeding; carrying out personal hygienic measures, such as bed baths and oral hygiene; and managing delegated medical procedures, such as drains, catheterizations, enemas, alcohol baths, vital signs, and medication administration (Brigh, 1944; Mountin, 1943).

- Muriel Burgess (1941), a nursing student, outlined the "facts of care," which included diagnosis; social factors such as heredity, environment, and education; and medical factors such as family history, history of the present illness, symptom onset, physical examination, and laboratory and radiography findings. Burgess further noted that the plan should include the progress of the patient and make use of graphs whenever possible. The treatments prescribed and the continuing plan for care were also important.

- Genevieve and Roy Bixler (1945), two doctorally prepared educators, addressed the development of empirics and wrote "the elements of science should be defined and organized, gathered from every science contributing to nursing and arranged in the most convenient order for thought" (p. 730). Bixler and Bixler stated that scientific compartmentalizations were artificial, arbitrary, and to be avoided by nursing science. Nursing science existed apart from practice, but its use in the service of professional practice represented a "new synthesis" (p. 731). Science, they asserted, needed to be integrated as an art.

- The 1947 editorial "Changes in Nursing Practice" in the *American Journal of Nursing* emphasized the need for nurses to develop keen observation skills because "the lack of descriptions or records of nursing care based on actual experience is appalling" (p. 655). Written observations could form the basis for a complete patient study to provide an interpretive picture of current nursing.

- In a speech at a student nurse convention, Blanche Pfefferkorn (1933), who was identified only as a registered nurse, stated that empiric knowledge came from questionnaires, detached observation, and field studies. According to Pfefferkorn, a scientific attitude was important. Scientific knowledge included "facts that were organized into a form or structure that were not dynamic and reports of field studies" (p. 260). Regardless of the source, scientific knowledge served as a skeleton and answered questions about "what"; good science represented the "what" of nursing very well. Pfefferkorn noted that the nurse needed to know "how"—not just "what"—and stated that field studies could "enliven fact gathering by providing knowledge of how" (p. 260).
- Agnes Meade (1936), a nurse, wrote "Training the Senses in Clinical Observation" and cautioned about the following pitfall of scientific bias: "a distinguishing feature of scientific observation is that the observer knows what is being sought, and to a certain extent what is likely to be found" (p. 540).

In summary, in the early literature, the nature and importance of science for nursing were clearly reflected. Early authors envisioned ways for empiric knowledge to be created and displayed. Although scientific-empiric knowledge could come from disciplines outside of nursing, there was a recognition of the unique nature of nursing science. Empirics was typically represented as the knowledge of the underlying principles and techniques associated with nursing.

Formal observation was also established as a valued technique and a skill that was critical for the development of nursing empirics. Principles, facts gleaned from observation, and procedural guides for action were important forms of empirics that were necessary for completing the routine hygienic care of patients as well as delegated medical tasks. Despite the recognition of the value of empirics, the idea that science alone is an inadequate practice guide appears frequently. A physician addressing a graduating class of diploma nurses stated that "the profession of nursing is an art depending upon science. In nursing the art must always predominate though underlying science is important" (Worcester, 1902, p. 908).

THE EMERGENCE OF NURSING AS A SCIENCE

The shift toward a concept of nursing knowledge as predominantly scientific began in the 1950s and took a strong hold during the 1960s. This shift toward knowledge as science produced significant changes in what was considered important in nursing. Nursing gradually shifted from a perspective that emphasized technical competence, duty, and womanly virtue to a perspective that focused more on effective nursing practice (Hardy, 1978). In many ways, the shift toward science was a welcome change. However, this move was made at the sacrifice of the development of ethics for individual and collective practice, the development of a nurse's character, the artistic and aesthetic dimensions of practice, and critical attention being paid to injustices in health care practices. The development of knowledge in relation to other patterns of knowing, which was so necessary for practice and so evident in nursing's work historically, was largely neglected until the early 1990s.

The shift toward science as the basis for developing nursing knowledge was influenced by the involvement of nursing in the two world wars in the first half of the 20th century. The wars created social circumstances that led to substantial shifts in roles for women and nurses. During the wars, with many men away from their homes, women were freed from constraints and learned to manage their responsibilities in accord with their own priorities and preferences. Many women entered the skilled or unskilled labor force while men were away in battle. Women who were nurses were needed to support the war effort by providing care for the sick and wounded. The U.S. government instituted war-related programs to make nursing preparation available to women who agreed to serve in the war (Kalisch & Kalisch, 2003; Kelly & Joel, 2001).

Partly because of the greater demand for technically skilled nurses to serve the war effort, by the decade of World War II, women had begun to enter institutions of higher learning in greater numbers. The early nursing leaders' vision of nursing education within colleges and universities began to be realized. After the end of World War II, many educational programs were established within institutions of higher learning, and graduate programs for nurses began to appear. Academic institutions required faculty to hold advanced degrees and encouraged them to meet the standards of higher education with regard to providing service to the community, teaching, and performing research. Research standards adhered to the more traditional objectivist criteria of scientific-empiric work, which limited the nature of credible scholarship among academic nurses. Nurse-scientist programs were established to enable nurses to earn doctoral degrees in other disciplines; the research skills that were learned could then be applied in nursing. As academically based nurses gained skills in the methods of science, conceptual frameworks and other types of theoretic writings began to emerge.

In 1950, *Nursing Research* was established, the first research journal for nurses. Books about research methodologies and explicit conceptual frameworks, often called "theories of nursing," began to appear. Early research reports often focused on describing the actions performed by nurses rather than the clinical problems of patients. Although less sophisticated with regard to method than current reports, these writings began to reflect the qualities of serious empiric scholarship and investigative skill. Various schools of thought emerged regarding the nature of nursing practice and nursing's knowledge base, providing a fresh flow of ideas that could be examined by members of the profession. These writings provided a stimulus for early efforts to develop theory and, eventually, to broaden knowledge-development efforts.

By the 1960s, doctoral programs in nursing were being established. By the end of the 1970s, the number of doctorally prepared nurses in the United States had grown to almost 2000. Approximately 20 doctoral programs in nursing had been established, and master's degree programs were maturing in academic stature and quality. Master's programs began focusing on preparing advanced practitioners in nursing rather than educators and administrators, whereas doctoral programs increasingly focused on the development of nursing knowledge. Early doctoral programs were built on the ideal of the academic research degree, which was typically a doctor of philosophy (PhD). With the development of advanced educational programs, nurses could formally consider the processes for developing nursing knowledge.

Nurse scholars began to debate ideas, points of view, and methods in the light of nursing's traditions (Hardy, 1978; Leininger, 1976). These debates are reflected in the literature of the late 1960s and the early 1970s (Dickoff & James, 1968, 1971; Dickoff, James, & Wiedenbach, 1968; Ellis, 1968; Folta, 1971; Walker, 1971; Wooldridge, 1971). Fundamental differences in viewpoints on nursing science provided nurse scholars with the opportunity to learn, sharpen critical-thinking skills, and acquire knowledge about the processes and limitations of science.

As an overt and deliberative focus on knowledge development began to take shape in nursing, a prevailing view emerged of nursing as a service that required a strong base in science. Debates reflected various views of science and metatheory and the preferred methods for producing sound nursing knowledge. Despite the lively debates and substantive issues focused on scientific knowledge, the idea that nursing requires the development of a broad knowledge base that includes all patterns of knowing has never been lost. Even when this broad view was not explicitly mentioned in the debates (as was common during the 1970s), the broad conceptualizations labeled as "theories" implicitly required multiple ways of knowing. The persistent dominance of science can be attributed in part to academic nurses' need to gain legitimacy in their university communities and to nurses' need to achieve political and personal legitimacy within medicine and society in general. Regardless of the societal context, the wholistic focus of nursing has endured.

EARLY TRENDS IN THE DEVELOPMENT OF NURSING SCIENCE

Throughout the second half of the 20th century, three major trends contributed to evolving directions in the development of nursing knowledge. These trends, as would be expected, centered on the empiric pattern. However, there are threads of continuity that reflect ethics, aesthetics, personal knowing, and emancipatory knowing, as we show in the sections that follow. Two important trends are the (1) use of theories that have been borrowed from other disciplines and (2) development of conceptual frameworks that define nursing.

Use of Theories Borrowed from Other Disciplines

As the educational preparation of nurses expanded, theories developed in other disciplines were recognized as also being important for nursing. Problems in nursing practice with no apparent ready solution began to be viewed as resolvable if theories, and approaches to theory development from other disciplines were applied. For example nurses recognized that young children needed the continuing love and support of their parents and families during hospitalization. The strict rules of hospitals that severely restricted visitation interrupted these primary family ties. As psychologic theories of attachment and separation developed, nurses found an explanation for the problems experienced by hospitalized children and were able to change visitation practices to provide for sustained contact between parents and children.

Although theories from other disciplines have been useful, nurses also have exercised caution rather than arbitrarily applying these theories. In some cases, the theories of other disciplines do not take into consideration significant factors that influence a nursing situation. For example, some theories of learning that are applicable to classroom learning do not adequately reflect the process of learning when an individual is faced with illness, nor do they address the ethical issues a nurse might face when disclosing sensitive information to a patient. Although borrowed theories may be useful, their usefulness cannot be assumed until they are examined from the perspective of nursing in nursing situations (Barnum, 1998; Walker & Avant, 2004). The trend of using theories from related disciplines may have been an outgrowth of predoctoral and postdoctoral fellowship funding for nurses that began in the mid-1950s. This funding nurtured a cadre of nurse scientists who studied research approaches in fields related to but outside of nursing. After these nurses were educated, they would return to nursing and conduct research, thereby contributing to nursing's knowledge base.

Development of Philosophies and Conceptual Frameworks That Define Nursing

As nurses began to reconsider the nature of nursing and the purposes for which nursing exists in the light of science, they began to question many ideas that were taken for granted in nursing and the traditional basis on which nursing was practiced. They wrote and published idealized views of nursing and of the type of knowledge, skills, and background needed for practice. As an ideal view of nursing, these frameworks and philosophies did not arise from practice per se but did reflect a reasonably attainable vision of what nursing could be. Writings of the 1960s and 1970s made significant contributions to the development of theoretic thinking in nursing. Many have been used as a basis for curricula and as guides for practice and research.

Many early nursing conceptual frameworks and philosophies include a description of the *nursing process.* This process, which is similar to both scientific methods of problem solving and research processes, is a framework for viewing nursing as a deliberate, reflective, critical, and self-correcting system. The nursing process replaced the rule-oriented and principle-oriented approaches that were grounded in a medical model in which the nurse functions as a physician's assistant. The nursing process relied heavily on what could be assessed through observation. Before there was a focus on the nursing process, unexamined rules and principles were used to guide the nurse in routine hygienic care, the performance of treatment procedures, and the administration of medications to treat disease. Because a rule-oriented approach did not encourage reflective problem solving and was not consistent with education in institutions of higher education, the shift to the nursing process as a way to approach care encouraged nurses to cultivate basic inquiry skills. *Nursing diagnosis,* which evolved from the nursing process and began to move nursing away from theoretic dependence on a medical model, was one method for organizing the domain of nursing practice. The early literature regarding nursing diagnosis included both practical and theoretic ideas about developing a taxonomy of nursing diagnoses and testing their validity.

Conceptual frameworks for nursing education and practice proliferated during the 1960s and 1970s. The then-current emphasis on systems theories is evident in the work of Callista Roy, Imogene King, Dorothy Johnson, and Betty Neuman. The movement of psychiatric care into community-based settings after the development of new drugs for the management of psychiatric illness contributed to a theoretic focus on the importance of interpersonal communication; this focus is notable in the work of Hildegard Peplau, Joyce Travelbee, and Ida Jean Orlando. The emergence of chronic disease with the control of communicable disease and a focus on wholism is reflected in Myra Levine's conservation principles framework as well as in Dorothea Orem's theoretic writings on self-care. Many nurse scientists who benefited from early funding for doctoral education received training in fields such as sociology and anthropology, in which a focus on the development of broad, grand theories was prominent; this influence is notable in the work of Madeleine Leininger. The conceptual frameworks of Martha Rogers, Rosemarie Parse, and Margaret Newman reflect theoretic perspectives linked to developments in modern physics that moved beyond earlier system concepts of equilibrium.

There was considerable debate about whether the writings of leaders such as Callista Roy, Betty Neuman, Imogene King, and Dorothea Orem and others should be called "models," "theories," or "philosophies." This debate reflected an underlying acknowledgment that empiric knowledge alone was an inadequate metatheory for practice. How to name these theory-like constructions: theories, conceptual models, theoretic frameworks, conceptual frameworks? This remains a debatable subject, and various terminologies can be found in the contemporary theoretic literature. We have chosen to refer to these broad theory-like structures as *conceptual frameworks* or *theoretic frameworks,* and their authors we call *theorists.* Regardless of labels, nursing practice consistent with these (and other) conceptual frameworks was taught in educational institutions, integrated into practice, and used to guide research. The use of conceptual frameworks cultivated a tacit recognition of the significance of multiple patterns of nursing knowledge. As nurses began to integrate these ideas into practice settings, the actual and potential relationships between nursing's conceptual frameworks and nursing practice became clearer. Practicing nurses found a new sense of purpose and direction that was consistent with the basic values of nursing, and they also achieved a sense of the increasing effectiveness as a result of systematic and thoughtful forms of nursing practice. Transferring these ideals of practice into the health care setting also served to illuminate the difficulties of finding nursing opportunities in the increasingly competitive health care system. Table 2-1 is a historical chronology of nurse theorists' work during the latter half of the 20th century.

Many of these theorists are no longer alive, but nurses who use and continue to develop their models keep their work alive. Appendix A on Elsevier's *Evolve* website (http://evolve.elsevier.com) summarizes our perspectives of the essential features of the early work of the theorists listed in Table 2-1. Some of these theorists continue to develop their ideas and change their perspectives, but their work remains significant because their ideas have stood the test of time with regard to forming fundamental values and perspectives of the discipline. Because conceptual frameworks change as they are linked to research findings, used in education and practice, and critiqued and expanded, users of Appendix A are cautioned that these summaries are historical in nature. There is a wealth of information about many of the nurse theorists listed in Table 2-1 available on the Internet that can provide perspectives about more current work related to those theoretic frameworks. Even for those theorists who continue to develop their ideas, their

TABLE 2-1 **Chronology and Key Emphases of Early Conceptual Frameworks in Nursing: 1952–1989**

Year*	Theorist(s)	Key Emphasis
1952	Hildegard E. Peplau	The interpersonal process is a maturing force for the personality
1960	Faye G. Abdellah, Irene L. Beland, Almeda Martin, and Ruth V. Matheney	The patient's problems determine the appropriate nursing care
1961	Ida Jean Orlando	The interpersonal process alleviates distress
1964	Ernestine Wiedenbach	The helping process meets the patient's needs through the art of individualizing care
1966	Lydia E. Hall	Nursing care involves directing the patient toward self-love
	Virginia Henderson	Empathic understanding and the knowledge of the nurse help patients move toward independence
	Joyce Travelbee	The meaning found in an illness determines how people respond
1967	Myra E. Levine	Wholism is maintained by conserving integrity
1970	Martha E. Rogers	The person and the environment are energy fields that evolve negentropically
1971	Dorothea E. Orem	Self-care maintains wholeness
	Imogene M. King	Transactions provide a frame of reference for goal setting
1976	Callista Roy	Stimuli disrupt an adaptive system
	Josephine G. Paterson and Loretta T. Zderad	Nursing is an existential experience of nurturing
1978	Madeleine M. Leininger	Caring is universal and varies transculturally
1979	Jean Watson	Caring is a moral ideal that involves mind, body, and soul engagement with another
	Margaret A. Newman	Disease is a clue to preexisting life patterns
1980	Dorothy E. Johnson	Subsystems exist in dynamic stability
	Betty Neuman	Individuals, as wholistic systems, interact with environmental stressors and resist disintegration by maintaining a normal line of defense
1981	Rosemarie Rizzo Parse	Indivisible beings and the environment co-create health
1982	Nola Pender	Health-promoting behavior is determined by individual characteristics and experiences as modulated by perceptions as well as interpersonal and situational factors
1989	Patricia Benner and Judith Wrubel	Caring is central to the essence of nursing; it sets up what matters, thus enabling connection and concern, and it creates the possibility for mutual helpfulness

*Date of first major publication.

work remains true to the essential core of the conceptual model as originally proposed. Website resources and information can be accessed with the use of key search terms or theorists' names. Applying the processes of description and critical reflection of theory as described in Chapter 8 will help to ensure your ability to evaluate appropriately the information available on theorist-related websites.

The conceptual frameworks developed during the 1960s and 1970s were important for broadly defining nursing and naming the phenomena central to nursing's domain of concern. These ideas were extremely valuable because they shifted nursing away from a medical model of practice that was characterized by the correct performance of routine nursing and medical procedures and the administration of medication. They broadened nursing's role in society by describing how nursing functions to achieve a socially relevant purpose and by delineating the contextual variables that were important to the practice of nursing. The philosophic values embedded in early nursing frameworks reflect central assumptions and value positions on which nursing rests. At the same time, these conceptual frameworks were characterized by a relatively functional view of nursing and health. They defined what nursing is, described the social purposes that nursing serves, detailed how nurses should function to realize these purposes, and defined the parameters and variables that influence illness and health processes.

For example, Callista Roy, Dorothea Orem, Virginia Henderson, and Hildegard Peplau focused on descriptions of illness and health: what nurses do to assist a person with moving toward health. These frameworks present explanations of how nursing actions function in practice to enhance health and well-being. The functions described are theoretic in nature in that they are conceptualized at a relatively abstract level. Nursing is viewed as a set of roles or functions rather than as concrete technical procedures. These abstract ideas about nursing functions are woven into explanations of relationships between the nurse's roles and functions and the theorist's idea of a desired nursing outcome related to health and well-being.

During the later 1970s and the 1980s, there was a noticeable qualitative shift in theoretic ideas developed for the purpose of broadly defining nursing practice. Rather than reflecting a functional perspective of the role of nursing in society, later conceptual frameworks tended to move to qualitative dimensions that characterized nursing's role not as what nurses do but as the essence of what nursing is. This shift offered the potential to move nursing from a context-dependent reactive position to a context-interactive proactive stance. These approaches combined direct observations of nurses and their practice with systematized insights that were guided by existing conceptual and theoretic frameworks and philosophies of nursing as well as other literature sources. For example, both Jean Watson (1979) and Patricia Benner and Judith Wrubel (1989) grounded the essence of nursing in caring. They used theoretic reasoning derived from a deliberate philosophic stance that is explicit in their writings and from the experience of the practice of nursing in many different contexts. The themes or patterns that characterize the essence of caring are those reflected in the actions, thoughts, values, and priorities of the practicing nurse.

Another early formal movement defined the discipline by locating the source of nursing theory in nursing practice and calling for the systematization of practice knowledge into theory. This approach was particularly influenced by the writings of Dickoff and

James and their colleagues, who were well known for theorizing about the nature of theory for a practice discipline (Dickoff & James, 1968; Dickoff et al., 1968). They proposed a radically different view for developing theory that challenged the scientific metatheory that prevailed during the 1960s. Dickoff and James described how theory is developed from the systematization of practice-based rules, guidelines, and nursing activities that are known to work. Theory was in part the systematization of practice-based variables, and it could exist at one of four levels: (1) factor isolating, (2) factor relating, (3) situation relating, or (4) situation producing.

Dickoff, James, and colleagues also recognized the value-laden nature of theory in nursing and called for an explicit recognition and naming of the values toward which theory development was proceeding; this aspect of theory they called *goal-content.* Their theory of theories proposed the formulation of prescriptions that would be used, in combination with a survey list, to reach the goal. The survey list was organized around six categories: (1) agency, (2) patiency, (3) dynamics, (4) structure, (5) terminus, and (6) procedure. The list was basically an enumeration of factors that did not qualify as prescriptions that were recognized as affecting movement toward the goal (Dickoff & James, 1968). The inclusion of values within the structure of theory and the recognition that theory was more like a flexible guide to practice (rather than a global framework to be systematically tested) provided a revolutionary view of empiric knowledge. The Dickoff and James approach to nursing metatheory, which was intensely discussed in the literature and at conferences, reflected a growing recognition that the nature and value of scientific-empiric theory for nursing was unclear. Dickoff and James asked the discipline to question the nature of theory and the value of objectivist prescriptions for practice theory and to attempt to articulate a clearer concept of nursing practice.

METALANGUAGE OF NURSING CONCEPTUAL FRAMEWORKS

Central concepts or shared images can be described when the conceptual frameworks listed in Table 2-1 are grouped around common themes. Four concepts have been widely recognized as common to nursing's conceptual frameworks: (1) nursing, (2) the person, (3) the society and environment, and (4) health. We have chosen the term *metalanguage* rather than *metaparadigm* to refer to these concepts. Although these four elements have elsewhere been considered nursing's metaparadigm (Fawcett & DeSanto-Madeya, 2012), our definition and use of the term *paradigm* is inconsistent with this terminology. The prefix *meta* means that which is encompassing or transcending. Thus, metalanguage is language that is used to describe or analyze (include or encompass) another language or system of symbols (*Encarta World English Dictionary,* 1999). The following sections provide a view of these four metalanguage concepts in early conceptual frameworks. We draw on the first major publication of each of the nurse scholars in this analysis.

Nursing

In nursing's theoretic writings, nursing is generally represented as a helping process with a primary focus on interpersonal interactions between a nurse and another individual.

This general idea does not clearly distinguish nursing from other helping disciplines, but it provides an important focus for deciding what type of knowledge is needed for nursing practice. The interpersonal nature of nursing practice distinguishes nursing from medicine in that medicine focuses on surgical and pharmacologic interventions, with interpersonal interactions being secondary to these interventions. Within a medical model of nursing, the nurse's primary functions relate to medical assessment, diagnosis, treatment, and medication administration as delegated medical tasks. Within a nursing framework, when interpersonal interactions are primary, technical and medical functions support the primary interpersonal interactions.

Although different nurse authors present conceptualizations of the nature of nursing consistent with the idea of interpersonal interactions as a primary focus, important differences exist with regard to their definitions and conceptualizations. For some, the person with whom the nurse interacts largely defines the direction of the interaction and the specific actions that are taken to achieve the goals of the interaction. The nurse's role in the interaction is primarily one of facilitating. When this view of the nature of nursing is incorporated into a framework or model, nursing is viewed as enabling the will and behavior of the person who is receiving care.

Other theoretic models present a view of the interpersonal process as either shared or initiated by the nurse. In this view, nursing processes and actions rest primarily on the nurse's initiative, knowledge, and approaches. The theoretic ideas that emerge from this view focus on nursing actions to reach the goal of the interaction.

Each of these perspectives is consistent with the practice of nursing in that nurses encounter some situations in which the patient primarily directs the interaction and other situations in which the nurse is the initiator; some conceptual frameworks account for this diversity. The common significant thread is the primacy of human interaction for creating human health and wholeness.

The Person

All conceptual frameworks include ideas about the general nature of humans. The most consistent philosophic component of the idea of the person is the dimension of wholeness or wholism. Although various conceptual frameworks may view the ill or diseased person as having problems with need fulfillment, integration, adaptation, role fulfillment, and so forth, the central impediment to health or healing is dealt with holistically in various senses of the word.

The nature of wholism as a concept is difficult to address from the perspective of traditional Western philosophies that are grounded in reductionism. In the reductionist view of wholism, the whole is equal to the sum of the parts; interrelationships among the parts are emphasized, and generalizations can be made about the whole from understanding how the parts of the whole interrelate (Newman, 1979, 1999). Western culture embraces this view, and nurses, as with others in this culture, have learned to think about parts of lives, parts of bodies, and parts of human experiences.

In a purer sense that is more consistent with Eastern traditions, wholism means that the whole is greater than the sum of the parts: the whole cannot be reduced to its parts without losing something in the process. Martha Rogers, Margaret Newman, Joyce Travelbee, and Patricia Benner are among the nurse scholars whose work reflects a view that the individual is different from and greater than the sum of his or her parts. Other nursing theorists explicitly or implicitly hold to the idea that the whole is equal to the sum of the parts, assuming that the individual is a system with biologic, sociologic, and psychologic components. Although this is not consistent with wholism in its purest sense, there still is a strong commitment to the idea that all components of the individual need to be considered.

Society and Environment

The concepts of society and environment are central to the discipline of nursing and reflected across conceptual frameworks, although these concepts are not addressed as explicitly in some writings as in others. Several nursing frameworks include a concept of society or culture and present it as a critical interacting force that shapes the individual environment. Environment was central for Nightingale when she formulated her concept of nursing. Nightingale believed the primary focus for nursing was to alter the physical environment to place the human body in the best possible condition for the reparative processes of nature to occur. More recent conceptual frameworks deemphasize environment or view it as being encompassed within a concept of society; sometimes the word *society* is used to include the environment. However, the concept of environment remains a significant one (Jarrin, 2012). Martha Rogers and theorists who build on her ideas focus on a concept of environment as indistinguishable (except conceptually) from the concept of person. Most other conceptual frameworks separate the person from the environment, thus implying that boundaries separate the two. As with the concept of person, environmental concepts vary, but they appear across conceptual frameworks.

Health

The concept of health is typically identified as the goal of nursing. Nightingale (Newman, 1999; Nightingale, 1852/1979) stated that "the same laws of health or of nursing, for in reality they are the same, obtain among the well as among the sick" (p. 9), implying that health is a state of order within natural laws. Contemporary nursing models are remarkably congruent with this early conceptualization. Some frameworks are based on a conceptualization of a health-illness continuum, with the purpose of nursing being to assist the ill person with achieving the greatest possible degree of health. Other nurse authors view the concept of health as something more than or different from the absence of disease. For them, health exists independently from illness or disease. In these views, health is a dynamic process that changes with time and that varies with life circumstances. Some authors view the health process as interdependent with circumstances of the environment, whereas others view the health process as originating with the individual.

In an attempt to deal more specifically with ideas related to health, several nurse authors avoid using the terms *health* and *illness*. An example is the use of the term *conserving wholism* by Myra Levine (1967). This concept directs nurses to focus on the totality of a person's situation rather than on the typical parameters that have come to be commonly known as health. Avoiding the use of health and illness allows for the use of terms related to health that more specifically reflect nursing's concerns and that deemphasize the focus on disease or illness.

DEVELOPMENT OF MIDDLE-RANGE PRACTICE-LINKED THEORY

During the 1980s, Meleis (1987) brought into clear focus the need for nurses to develop substantive theory that provides a meaningful foundation for the development of nursing practice in relation to specific practice concepts. In accord with the observation of many practicing nurses, Meleis acknowledged the value of theories broad in scope for defining the general parameters on which nursing function is based. However, Meleis emphasized that theory of a different type was required to give more specific guidance to nursing practice; this form of theory would prove to align more closely with the empiric pattern of knowing and knowledge. Meleis' plea also reflected the need for nursing to move away from its long-term discussions and debates about the nature of theory, knowledge, and the proper functions of nursing. She called on nurses to focus on developing substance in theory and substantive, more readily observable and accessible nursing concepts grounded in a practice context.

Nursing theory of this type is developed in concert with research questions that are directly or indirectly linked to important practice issues. It avoids a focus on methodology for methodology's sake and shifts the focus to understanding nursing-related phenomena. Substantive middle-range theory can inform practice and lead to new practice approaches as well as investigate factors that influence the outcomes desired in nursing practice.

Im and Meleis (1999) introduced the idea of *situation-specific theory*, a variant of middle-range theory that underscores the importance of considering the context in which a theory will be used. Whereas middle-range theory narrows the conceptual focus of a theory and substantive middle-range theory further defines the focus as being clinically relevant concepts, situation-specific theory emphasizes the need to consider the unique context for which the theory is developed. Situation specificity is important because of variability within particular populations, fields of practice, and subsequent approaches to clinical phenomena. Unlike substantive middle-range theory, which is presumed to be more broadly generalizable across different populations, situation-specific theory addresses the particular and unique needs of a group of people in a specific context. Situation specificity is particularly important for evidence-based practice in that best research evidence should be appropriate to the population within which the research will be used, especially when variables of importance to care have been part of the situational considerations. Substantive middle-range theory in nursing tends to cluster around a concept of interest, such as social support, uncertainty, grief, fatigue, or life transitions.

TRENDS IN KNOWLEDGE DEVELOPMENT

What counts as knowledge does not remain static. Knowledge historically reflects the social, political, and professional climate in which knowledge development occurs. The context within which knowledge is developed determines and influences what counts as knowledge and how knowledge structures are valued and evaluated. For several years after Carper (1978) published her work regarding the knowing patterns, knowledge forms and development processes other than those associated with empirics were seen as important to nursing and became more generally accepted. The adherence to a specific methodology or template for knowledge development was being replaced with a requirement for rigor and disclosure of methodology rather than following a strict formula. Although many knowledge developers in nursing remain firmly rooted in the assumptions and methodologies of empirics, knowledge structures are emerging that are not empiric in the sense that a strict interpretation of the pattern of empirics assumes. Although communicated and developed in language, these structures are not grounded in objectivist assumptions and scientific notions of reliability and validity. It is possible to conceptualize empiric knowledge broadly to include forms of interpretive work that culminate in the identification of themes (phenomenology) or detailed descriptions (ethnographies) as falling within the empiric pattern. However, some emerging knowledge forms and methods rest on different assumptions and methodologies and fall outside the realm of empirics. Several important trends in theory development and use are described in the following sections.

The Move Away from Methodolotry

There is currently a trend to blend and use a variety of knowledge development processes to achieve a given research aim rather than to adhere to strict methodologic imperatives. Many scholars are moving from a focus on method and technique to a focus on problem solving or the achievement of study goals. Because the methodologic process is tailored to accomplish research objectives, various approaches to inquiry are modified and blended. The qualitative/quantitative dichotomy is being questioned as a way of categorizing methodologic approaches. There is growing recognition that qualitative data may be important to obtain in primarily experimental designs and, conversely, that quantitative data may be useful in naturalistic inquiry. Rather than combining approaches (i.e., performing both a quantitative and a qualitative study), the purpose of the research determines how findings are blended. *Critical multiplism* (Letourneau & Allen, 1999), *multivocality* (Savage, 2000), and *intersectionality* (Kelly, 2009, 2011) are examples of terms used to denote these types of methods. This trend signals maturity in nursing scholarship wherein professional research purposes take precedence over methodologic loyalties.

Interpretive and Critical Approaches

In a classic article, Allen, Benner, and Diekelman (1986) suggested three categories for the classification of research: empiric-analytic, interpretive-hermeneutic, and critical-social. Empiric-analytic work conforms to the traditions of empirics as conceptualized by Carper, which means that the work relies on perceptually grounded and objective replication and validation research methods. Some forms of interpretive work remain faithful to this traditional objectivist assumption, but some forms of interpretive work fall outside the realm of traditional objectivist empirics. Interpretive approaches, such as grounded theory, phenomenology, analyses of language, and hermeneutic inquiry, assess truth value (reliability and validity) by consensus between the researcher and the participants.

The assumption of an objective reality with meaning that is independent of the observer is not taken as a given. Grounded-theory approaches, which are now applied in a variety of forms, are constructed out of shared understandings between the researcher and the participants (Crotty, 1998). Methodologies grounded in the philosophy of phenomenology seek to account for the nature of the experience from the experiencer's point of view. Although these accounts may be judged as "good" or "less than good," they clearly do not rest on objectivist assumptions about the existence and nature of a reality independent from the observer. As with empirics, however, their conclusions are drawn from interpretations that are fundamentally grounded in sensory perceptions, whereas truth value (i.e., reliability and validity) relies on a consensus of meaning that is particular and situated. Noncritical forms of hermeneutic inquiry recognize context to be important to the shaping of knowledge. The researcher moves back and forth between what is being interpreted and an ever-enlarging context that accounts for the researcher's unique perspective within the situation to create a reasonable (loosely valid) understanding.

Critical approaches seek to illuminate structures of domination and in nursing are addressing health care structures that compromise the quality of care for people on the basis of factors such as class, economics, race, age, gender, disability, or sexual orientation (Cowling & Chinn, 2001; Fontana, 2004; Im, 2013; Kagan, Smith, & Chinn, 2014; Kramer, 2002; Pitre, Kushner, Raine, & Hegadoren, 2013). Critical social theory is not theory in the sense of empiric theory, which focuses on an objectivity of observation that allows for a degree of generalizable description, explanation, and prediction. The primary purpose of critical theory is to create social and political change. Critical theory takes the form of narrative analyses that illuminate how social practices that are institutionalized (e.g., in political or educational institutions) enable unjust practices for the benefit of a dominant group. Critical theory may have several foci. Critical feminist theory centers on issues of gender discrimination; critical social theory focuses on class issues as they perpetuate unfair educational, political, and other social practices. The "critical" focus points to a need to undo and remake oppressive social structures.

Intersectionality is a form of critical scholarship based on the premise that health disparities and social disadvantage occur in a context of many intersecting factors that have a multiplicative effect. These intersecting factors include social identities such as gender, race, class, ability/disability, sexual orientation, and religion. Every social group is seen as having unique qualities, and each individual within the group is situated within the social structure in ways that intersect with the person's unique social identities to create social inequities. An intersectional approach yields a more comprehensive understanding of the interrelated nature of health disparities. Intersectional approaches address two levels of analysis: the nature of structural oppression creating the disparity and the nature of the individual's intersecting identities that shape the person's experience of the situation (Kelly, 2009, 2011).

Poststructuralist Approaches

Research consistent with the analytic methodology of poststructuralism appears frequently in the nursing literature (Allen & Hardin, 2001; Arslanian-Engoren, 2002; Cloyes, 2006; Francis, 2000; Thompson, 2007; Tinley & Kinney, 2007). Poststructuralism is an outgrowth of structuralism. In linguistics, *structuralism* is the view that the meaning of words is given by context or by the linguistic frame that surrounds a word. The single word "duck," for example, has no stable referent, and whether this utterance is referring to a type of bird or is a directive to avoid hitting a low-hanging tree branch cannot be known without encountering the word in context. The poststructuralist movement moves language away from a representational view. This means that words do not stand for something that is either given objectively (as traditional forms of empirics assume) or known from a context of usage. Rather, language—or, more broadly, discourse—creates and determines possibilities. Discourses are whole systems of representations that include text, visuals, and behavioral actions that surround, are associated with, reference, or create experiences and understandings. Critical analyses that use language and systems of discourse, as data uncover how language functions to perpetuate networks of oppression and domination, add important new dimensions to nursing knowledge.

Deconstruction and Postmodernism

Deconstruction is an elusive term to define but generally refers to processes that take apart assumptions, ideologies, and frames of reference that are buried and unnoticed in text. *Text* refers to what is written as well as to other visual representations of situations and events, such as advertisements, cartoons, and film (Kress, Leite-Garcia, & van Leeuwen, 1996; van Dijk, 1997). Deconstructive work often focuses on text that is problematic in relation to sustaining inequities that create disadvantage for one group for the benefit of another. However, deconstruction is much more than even critical analysis. Deconstruction involves making explicit and coming to understand that certain features of text (e.g., implicit assumptions, ideologies, frames of reference) cannot be warranted as a basis for truths. In this way, deconstruction is useful for undermining language and social contexts that promote inequities and injustices.

Alternatively, *postmodernism* is a term with broader meaning, but as with deconstruction, it has a variety of unclear meanings and uses. In a general sense, the postmodern era is the one that followed the modern era. *Modernism,* as it relates to science, began with a move to account for natural phenomena by using scientific approaches rather than appealing to religious and metaphysical explanations. Thus, modernism signaled the end of religious authority as the basis for understanding the world. Modernism has become associated with the age of science and scientific inquiry. As discoveries in modern physics began to uncover the fallibility of scientific explanation, and the social agenda of science failed, this enabled the move toward postmodernism. Postmodernism in relation to methods of inquiry is reflected in the increasing use of nonscientific methodologies as well as the combining of multiple methods within a single research project. The reference to "anything goes" often is coupled with references to postmodernism. Although "anything goes" is reasonable in one sense, any notion of arbitrariness or relativism is unwarranted. The postmodern era has loosened the idea of what counts as legitimate knowledge, but it should not signal that sloppy approaches to knowledge development are acceptable. Although various methods may be legitimate, they must be carried out carefully and rigorously to be useful.

Clinical Application and Production of Knowledge

Growing concern about the need to link practice and knowledge has resulted in significant trends in practice, research, and development of knowledge in nursing. These trends reflect a concern for the increased clinical relevance of theory and research, transdisciplinary relevance, and improvement in the quality of care while achieving a realistic economy in health care (Bach, Ploeg, & Black, 2009; Moch et al., 2008; Ploeg, Davies, Edwards, Gifford, & Miller, 2007; Richardson-Tench, 2012; Rolfe, 2006).

Evidence-Based Practice

During the 1990s, evidence-based nursing practice began to receive attention in the nursing literature. The idea of evidence-based practice originated in the medical literature as a way to help ensure that high-quality research was deliberately used in clinical decision making. Evidence-based medicine incorporated a variety of empiric and nonempiric knowledge forms, arranged in a hierarchy, as evidence (Mazurek-Melnyk, Stone, Fincout-Overholt, & Ackerman, 2000).

Evidence-based nursing practice also focuses on the necessity of integrating quality research into practice decisions in order to provide high-level nursing care. It is important to note that evidence-based nursing practice is not simply the application of single studies or using the results of meta-analyses in client care. Rather, evidence-based nursing practice requires the integration of best research evidence with such things as clinical expertise, expert opinion, health care resources, clinical state and setting, circumstances, and patient preferences (Melnyk & Fineout-Overholt, 2011; DiCenso, Guyatt, & Ciliska, 2005).

Models of research evidence generally assign the highest truth value to knowledge generated using more traditional empirics. Although case analyses and qualitative studies count as evidence, these have less credibility (Phillips et al., 1998/2009; Schunemann, Best, Vist, & Oxman, 2003). Characterizing best research evidence as a highly empiric form of knowledge that evolves from data-based, experimental, and quasi-experimental research methodologies has received criticism that challenges the persistent predominance of empirics as a way of knowing in nursing (Fullbrook, 2003; Holmes, Perron, &

O'Byrne, 2006; Mowinski-Jennings & Loan, 2001; Satterfield et al., 2009). A strictly empiric view of research evidence seems to be changing and many models of evidence-based practice acknowledge the value of such things as peer-reviewed standards and evidence-based theories although a bias for traditional research seems to prevail (Armola et al., 2009; Fineout-Overholt, Mazurek-Melnyk, & Schultz, 2005; Melnyk & Fineout-Overholt, 2011).

The nature of evidence-based nursing practice will likely continue to evolve. We favor an approach that views evidence-based practice as the integration of best research evidence (including less traditional knowledge development approaches) with clinical factors, expert opinion, and patient preferences and values (DiCenso et al., 2005; Melnyk & Fineout-Overholt, 2011; Salmond, 2013; Thorne & Sawatzky, 2014). The shift in terminology to *evidence-informed practice* now widely found in the literature acknowledges that although clinical decision making should consider a wide variety of credible evidence, the process must also integrate client/patient and circumstantial factors. We applaud and favor this shift in terminology and believe it more clearly represents the nature of clinical decision making. Evidence-informed nursing practice and models of evidence-based clinical decision making that acknowledge the importance of factors other than empiric research require all patterns of knowing. For example, the interpretation of patient preferences and clinical circumstances requires attending to aesthetic, ethical, and personal knowing. Understanding the politics of how health care resources affect the circumstances of care is grounded in emancipatory knowing. In short, clinical expertise requires broad knowing within all patterns.

Practice-Based Evidence and Translational Research

All health care disciplines have increasing concern for creating a closer link between what is effective in practice and evidence that is based on effective practice (Moch et al., 2008; Satterfield et al., 2009; Wallin, 2009). This trend is labeled by various terms, including *practice-based evidence* and *translational research.* References to practice-based evidence in the health care literature refer to the validation in practice of clinically used approaches and techniques that are known to be effective for promoting health-related goals. The call for practice-based evidence emphasizes a focus on investigating and validating what seems to be effective in practice as a way of generating research evidence for integration into evidence-based decision making (Fox, 2003; Girard, 2008; Simons, Kushner, Jones, & James, 2003). Proponents of practice-based evidence suggest that the top-down approach (i.e., research to practice) currently valued in hierarchies of research evidence uses methodologies to generate outcomes that may not be workable in the practice arena. For example, randomized controlled clinical trials, which are taken to be highly valuable sources of empiric evidence, control for variables that are at work in the clinical environment. Proponents of practice-based evidence suggest that the stripping away of situational variables and the control necessary for many experimental studies produce a knowledge structure that is too decontextualized to be useful and thus should not be used to guide practice. Rather, evidence must be generated out of or situated within the context from which it is generated to be useful to practitioners (Simons et al., 2003).

Translational research reflects a type of "research-to-practice" approach. Simply stated, translational research is designed to take evidence a step further by validating it in the practice setting. Translational research initiatives are now part of the U.S. National Institutes of Health (2009) roadmap. Interest in promoting translational research has been prominent in clinical practices where an interest in moving basic research studies into practice as quickly as possible (Bakken & Jones, 2006; Titler, 2004; Wallin, 2009). Thus, translational research promotes the use of research discoveries in clinical settings.

Emergence of the Practice Doctorate

Although its effect on knowledge development remains to be seen, the emergence of the doctorate of nursing science (DNS) has the potential to influence how knowledge in nursing is created and used in clinical practice and in nursing in general. The DNS, also referred to as the *practice doctorate,* was originally developed in the 1960s. However, the expansion of these early programs to prepare nurses with a practice doctorate was eclipsed by the growth of research-oriented PhD programs (Fitzpatrick & Wallace, 2009).

Recently, the DNS has begun to reemerge as a viable educational option in nursing. The American Association of Colleges of Nursing (AACN) (2006) began serious discussions about the DNP in 2001 and released "The Essentials of Doctoral Education for Advanced Nursing Practice" in 2006. Currently, the AACN website lists nearly 300 schools that offer DNP programs.

In general, the DNP focuses on advanced clinical care and the application and generation of evidence that supports improved care (Acorn, Lamarche, & Edwards, 2009; Mundinger, Starck, Hathaway, Shaver, & Woods, 2009). According to AACN, practice-focused doctoral programs deemphasize theory, metatheory, research methodology, and statistics that are part of research-focused programs. Foundational competencies that must be addressed by curricula in DNP programs for accreditation by the Council for Collegiate Nursing Education have been proposed. Multiple competencies within eight foundational areas are enumerated in the AACN essentials article (2006). Examples of competencies listed in the document include the following:

- Evaluate new practice approaches on the basis of nursing theories and theories from other disciplines.
- Use analytic methods to critically appraise literature and other evidence to determine and implement the best evidence for practice.
- Design and implement processes to evaluate outcomes of practice, practice patterns, and systems of care within a practice setting, health care organization, or community to determine variances in practice outcomes and population trends.
- Use research methods to collect data to generate evidence for nursing practice.
- Analyze data from practice, design evidence-based interventions, predict and analyze outcomes, and identify gaps in evidence for practice.
- Disseminate findings from evidence-based practice and research.
- Analyze epidemiologic, biostatistical, environmental, and other appropriate scientific data related to individual, aggregate, and population health.
- Evaluate evidence-based care to improve patient outcomes.

In our view, these competencies can have a significant impact on the way knowledge is developed and used in nursing. The practice focus of these competencies and their basis in research and analytic clinical investigation strategies mandates that research and practice complement one another. Competencies such as these reflect the need for translational research as well as practice-based evidence. It is reasonable to assume that such competencies will require communication between academic nurses and clinical nurse researchers to achieve the goals of high-quality nursing care.

In summary, the grip of traditional empirics in nursing seems to be moderating, perhaps signaling a return to our history of wholism with regard to knowing and knowledge development. During the 1960s, a scientific metatheory dominated the literature but never really took hold. Gradually, nursing moved away from a metatheoretic focus on empirics, as expressed in objectivist research approaches that are descriptive, correlational, quasi-experimental, or experimental. Naturalistic and qualitative approaches to practice began to appear with greater frequency during the 1980s. More recently, the importance of language for determining what counts as knowledge is being recognized, and critical research that undermines unjust and inequitable social conditions is being conducted. Ongoing emphases on evidence-based nursing practice that requires the integration of broad forms of knowledge formally acknowledges that empiric evidence is only part of what is needed for the making of good clinical decisions. A focus on practice evidence and translational research reemphasizes moving evidence into practice in a way that benefits the patient. The foundational competencies for the practice doctorate hold the promise of creating a research agenda that more fully serves the needs and interests of people who receive nursing care.

CONTEXTS OF KNOWLEDGE DEVELOPMENT

As illustrated in this chapter, specific circumstances and contexts affect the development of knowledge. What defines knowledge, what sources identify the best knowledge, and how nurses use and construct knowledge are greatly influenced by—if not determined by—the interrelationship between values and resources at multiple levels. These levels can be categorized as individual, professional, and societal.

Values

Individual values include a specific nurse's commitment, personal philosophy, motives, beliefs, and priorities. Think about what sorts of research approaches you might find more valuable than others and whether you even believe that research is an important area to study. If you value research, what is your motive for learning about it? Employment in an academic setting? Making a difference in people's lives? Both? Is uncovering research evidence something you attend to because you have to or because you want to? Is it something you do after you have practiced technical skills?

Professional values are beliefs and attitudes about what is good and right that generally are held in common by members of a profession and that are used to guide professional action. These values are expressed in formal statements issued by professional groups in the form of codes, standards of practice, and ethical principles and are also reflected in themes repeated in the literature and in the collective actions taken by professional organizations. The current emphasis on the practice doctorate and the move toward evidence-based nursing practice reflect professional values that are being expressed today. How has the professional valuing of evidence-based practice influenced your learning? How has it affected the practices of nurses with whom you have come in contact? Will the profession's valuing of the professional doctorate change its research productivity for the better?

Societal values are expressed through societal choices, sanctions, and moral behavior during a given period in history. The focus on national and international security in the wake of terrorist activities and the use of monetary resources to promote security reflect its value for society. Has the valuing of national security affected the financial resources available to you as a student? How have societal values affected grant funding within academic institutions? How have they affected the topic on which you focus a research proposal for funding? Has the valuing of capitalism and corporate structures as well as the consolidation of hospital services into large entities changed your ability and others' abilities to enact evidence-informed clinical decision making?

Resources

Resources also can also be viewed as individual, professional, or societal. *Individual resources* include the natural and acquired talents that are shared among members of a discipline, including cognitive style, intellectual abilities, life circumstances, and educational preparation. The nature of your educational preparation (i.e., what you are exposed to and learn as a student) is a resource that you will bring to nursing. Will an ability to think in a linear fashion mean that you will bring expertise in quantitative methods to the profession? Might the gift of a nonlinear cognitive style signal your contribution to aesthetic knowing and practice? What talents will you share that evolve from those life experiences and interests that are unique to you? Did you grow up in another country and thus can contribute a unique understanding of how to study effectively the health care needs of your country's citizens? How might the financial and other resources that you have to support additional education determine the resources that you bring to nursing?

Professional resources reflect the collective resources of the discipline for knowledge development. Examples of professional resources include a growing body of literature and practice traditions, the ability to communicate these traditions among members of the profession, the educational attainments of members of the profession, the nature of the education of the profession's members, and the methodologies and instrumentation available for knowledge development. In other words, what you bring to nursing and develop as a practitioner, in addition to the contributions of a host of other nurses, will constitute nursing's professional resources. As practitioners and students are exposed to the techniques and meanings of evidence-based practice, will knowledge resources of the discipline change? Will nurses who hold the practice doctorate change nursing's knowledge resources? Might you and others embrace critical theory or the tenets of practice-based evidence as a way to better integrate research into clinical decision making? If you are interested in knowledge development related to aesthetic knowing, are there professional resources to assist you with learning how to do this? Do available information systems ease or deter the retrieval of evidence to be integrated into clinical decision making? Has nursing made use of the Internet in such a way that it is a valuable resource for care? Are there professional practice traditions you must obey that you think are counterproductive? Will nursing pay enough for you to sustain a reasonably comfortable lifestyle? Will nursing services where you work have the political clout to advocate for improved client and patient care?

Societal resources affect the nature of the material and nonmaterial resources that are available to support knowledge development in nursing. The acquisition of societal resources depends on features of both society and the profession. For example, political influence is required to obtain funds, materials, and space to carry out the activities of the discipline. If the political system of society reflects priorities other than those that involve nursing, societal resources are less available to nursing than to other groups who reflect those priorities. For example, how has the societal interest in national and international security affected resource allocation for nursing in your practice area? If you are a student, what trends are affecting your financial aid possibilities? Have you (or someone you know) been relocated out of your space or lost your job because of special funding initiatives? How successful will nursing be in the securing of resources to develop a broad conceptualization of knowing if scientific knowledge is still largely held to be the most valuable? Has the tax base available for health care been deflected into other arenas, thereby changing the way that you counsel an elderly person about how to obtain prescription medications?

The relationships between and among values and resources are intertwined, and, in some cases, it is difficult to determine how a given factor that affects knowledge development should be categorized. Categorization is never the goal; rather, it is important to understand how factors in a broad array of contexts interrelate to determine health care needs, how those needs are approached, and who provides care.

In addition, when individual, professional, and societal values are basically congruent, there is relative stability, and new insights tend to build on what is already established as the knowledge of the discipline. When individual, professional, or societal values change, the potential exists for creating fundamental changes in knowledge and practice. For example, political decisions that are made by government entities require value decisions about who deserves and who does not deserve to receive the resources of a society. As history shows, if female scientists are consistently provided with limited or no societal resources, this impedes the ability of women to influence value decisions about how money should be allocated. Nursing represents a group of mostly women (a professional resource) within a societal context that devalues female scientists, which influences the profession's ability to exert influence on society to gain access to resources. The contemporary women's movement has created a stimulus for recognizing societal restrictions on nursing as a gender-segregated occupation and the effects of the systematic oppression of nurses and nursing (Group & Roberts, 2001; Malka, 2007; Roberts, 1983). Feminist theory, which shares many of the traits of nursing theory, provides a perspective for changing social values and shifting social resources. Feminism places an urgent demand on society for a values transformation that is consistent with nursing's vision of health, the health care system, and nursing (Chinn & Wheeler, 1985; Roberts & Group, 1995). As women's experience becomes increasingly valued as a resource for developing knowledge, the resulting values will conflict with traditional views, and the new values will open avenues for change.

Think About It

1. How have some of the events, trends, and issues in nursing today been grounded in or how do they depend on past events?
2. What mistakes are we making today with regard to knowledge development, and how will they affect future nursing care? What current events and trends are definitely not mistakes with regard to knowledge development, and why?
3. How would you change nursing's values and resources to promote knowledge development?

REFLECTION AND DISCUSSION – SUPPLEMENT ⊖

References

Abdellah, F. G. (1969). The nature of nursing science. *Nursing Research, 18,* 390–393.

Achterberg, J. (1991). *Woman as healer.* Boston, MA: Shambhala.

Acorn, S., Lamarche, K., & Edwards, M. (2009). Practice doctorates in nursing: Developing nursing leaders. *Canadian Journal of Nursing Leadership, 22,* 85–91.

Aikins, C. A. (1915). Teaching ethics in hospital schools. *Trained Nurse and Hospital Review, 54,* 135–137.

Allen, D., Benner, P., & Diekelman, N. (1986). Three paradigms for nursing research: Methodological implications. In P. L. Chinn (Ed.), *Nursing research methodology: Issues and implementation* (pp. 23–38). Rockville, MD: Aspen.

Allen, D., & Hardin, P. K. (2001). Discourse analysis and the epidemiology of meaning. *Nursing Philosophy, 2,* 163–176.

American Association of Colleges of Nursing. (2006). *The essentials of doctoral education for advanced nursing practice.* Retrieved from http://www.aacn.nche.edu/DNP/pdf/Essentials.pdf.

American Nurses Association. (2008). *Adah Belle Samuel Thoms (1870–1943) 1976 inductee.* Retrieved from http://nursingworld.org/FunctionalMenuCategories/AboutANA/WhereWeComeFrom/HallofFame/Inductees ListedAlphabetically/thomab5590.aspx.

American Nurses Association. (2009a). *Mabel Keaton Staupers (1890–1989) 1996 inductee.* Retrieved from http://www.nursingworld.org/AdahBelleSamuelThoms.

American Nurses Association. (2009b). *Susie Walking Bear Yellowtail (1903–1981) 2002 inductee.* Retrieved from http://nursingworld.org/FunctionalMenuCategories/AboutANA/WhereWeComeFrom/HallofFame/ InducteesListedAlphabetically/SusieWalkingBearYellowtail.aspx.

Armola, R. R., Bourgault, A. M., Halm, M. A., Board, R. M., Bucher, L., Harrington, L., et al. (2009). AACN levels of evidence: What's new? *Critical Care Nurse, 29*(4), 70–73.

Arslanian-Engoren, C. (2002). Feminist poststructuralism: A methodological paradigm for examining clinical decision-making. *Journal of Advanced Nursing, 37,* 512–517.

Ashley, J. (1976). *Hospitals, paternalism, and the role of the nurse.* New York, NY: Teachers College Press.

Bach, V., Ploeg, J., & Black, M. (2009). Nursing roles in end-of-life decision making in critical care settings. *Western Journal of Nursing Research, 31,* 496–512.

Bakken, S., & Jones, D. A. (2006). Contributions to translational research for quality health outcomes. *Nursing Research, 55*(2S), S1–S2.

Barnum, B. J. S. (1998). *Nursing theory* (5th ed.). Boston, MA: Lippincott-Raven.

Benner, P. A., & Wrubel, J. (1989). *The primacy of caring: Stress and coping in health and illness.* Menlo Park, CA: Addison-Wesley.

Bixler, G. K., & Bixler, R. W. (1945). The professional status of nursing. *American Journal of Nursing, 45,* 730–735.

Brigh, S. M. (1944). We cannot afford to hurry: Training within industry applied to nursing. *American Journal of Nursing, 44,* 223–226.

Burgess, M. E. (1941). A plan for nursing care. *American Journal of Nursing, 41,* 215–218.

Carper, B. A. (1978). Fundamental patterns of knowing in nursing. *ANS Advances in Nursing Science, 1*(1), 13–23.

Changes in nursing practice. (1947). *American Journal of Nursing, 47,* 665.

Chinn, P. L., & Wheeler, C. E. (1985). Feminism and nursing. *Nursing Outlook, 33,* 74–77.

Christy, T. E. (1969). Portrait of a leader. *Nursing Outlook, 6,* 72–75.

Cloyes, K. G. (2006). An ethic of analysis: An argument for critical analysis of research interviews as an ethical practice. *ANS Advances in Nursing Science, 29*(2), 84–97.

Cohen, I. B. (1984). Florence Nightingale. *Scientific American, 250,* 128–137.

Conrad, M. E. (1947). What is expert nursing care? *American Journal of Nursing, 47,* 162–163.

Cowling, W. R., & Chinn, P. L. (2001). Conversation across paradigms: Unitary-transformative and critical feminist perspectives. *Scholarly Inquiry for Nursing Practice, 15,* 347–365.

Crotty, M. (1998). *The foundations of social research: Meaning and perspective in the research process.* London, England: Sage.

De Witt, K. (1901). Specialities in nursing. *American Journal of Nursing, 1,* 14–15.

Dennis, K. E., & Prescott, P. A. (1985). Florence Nightingale: Yesterday, today, and tomorrow. *ANS Advances in Nursing Science, 7*(2), 66–81.

DiCenso, A., Guyatt, G., & Ciliska, D. (2005). *Evidence based nursing: A guide to clinical practice.* St. Louis, MO: Mosby.

Dickoff, J., & James, P. (1968). A theory of theories: A position paper. *Nursing Research, 17,* 197–203.

Dickoff, J., & James, P. (1971). Clarity to what end? *Nursing Research, 20,* 499–502.

Dickoff, J., James, P., & Wiedenbach, E. (1968). Theory in a practice discipline. Part 1: Practice-oriented theory. *Nursing Research, 17,* 415–435.

Dock, L. L. (1902–1903). Sanitary inspection: A new field for nurses. *American Journal of Nursing, 3,* 529–532.

Donahue, M. P. (2011). *Nursing, the finest art: An illustrated history* (3rd ed.). St. Louis, MO: Mosby.

Dossey, B. M. (2010). *Florence Nightingale: Mystic, visionary, healer.* Philadelphia, PA: Davis.

Drake, A. (1934). How the patient judges nursing. *Trained Nurse and Hospital Review, 93,* 135–138.

Ehrenreich, B., & English, D. (1993). *Witches, midwives and nurses: A history of women healers.* New York, NY: The Feminist Press.

Ellis, R. (1968). Characteristics of significant theories. *Nursing Research, 17,* 217–222.

Encarta World English Dictionary. (1999). Retrieved from http://encarta.msn.com/encnet/features/dictionary/DictionaryResults.aspx?lextype=3&search=metalanguage.

Evans, A. M., Pereira, D. A., & Parker, J. M. (2009). Discourses of anxiety and transference in nursing practice: The subject of knowledge. *Nursing Inquiry, 16,* 251–260.

Faber, M. J. (1927). The education of the self. *American Journal of Nursing, 27,* 1047–1050.

Fawcett, J., & DeSanto-Madeya, S. (2012). *Contemporary nursing knowledge: Analysis and evaluation of nursing models and theories.* Philadelphia, PA: Davis.

Fineout-Overholt, E., Mazurek-Melnyk, B., & Schultz, A. (2005). Transforming health care from the inside out: Advancing evidence-based practice in the 21st century. *Journal of Professional Nursing, 21*(6), 335–344.

Fitzpatrick, J. J., & Wallace, M. (2009). *The Doctor of Nursing Practice and Clinical Nurse Leader: Essentials of program development and implementation for clinical practice.* New York, NY: Springer.

Folta, J. R. (1971). Obfuscation or clarification: A reaction to Walker's concept of nursing theory. *Nursing Research, 20*(6), 496–499.

Fontana, J. S. (2004). A methodology for critical science in nursing. *ANS Advances in Nursing Science, 27*(2), 93–101.

Fox, N. J. (2003). Practice-based evidence: Toward collaborative and transgressive research. *Sociology, 37*(1), 81–102.

Francis, B. (2000). Poststructuralism and nursing: Uncomfortable bedfellows? *Nursing Inquiry, 7,* 20–28.

Fullbrook, P. (2003). Developing best practice in critical care nursing: Knowledge, evidence and practice. *Nursing in Critical Care, 8*(3), 96–102.

Garesche, E. F. (1927). Professional honor. *American Journal of Nursing, 27,* 901–904.

Girard, N. J. (2008). Practice-based evidence. *AORN Journal, 87*(1), 15–16.

Goostray, S., & Brown, E. L. (1954). American nursing: History and interpretation. *American Journal of Nursing, 54,* 719–721.

Gregg, A. (1940). An independent estimate of nursing in our times. *American Journal of Nursing, 40,* 737–745.

Group, T. M., & Roberts, J. I. (2001). *Nursing, physician control and the medical monopoly.* Westport, CT: Praeger.

Hall, L. E. (1964). Nursing: What is it? *The Canadian Nurse, 60,* 150–154.

Hardy, M. E. (1978). Perspectives on nursing theory. *ANS Advances in Nursing Science, 1*(1), 37–48.

Henderson, V. (1964). The nature of nursing. *American Journal of Nursing, 64*(8), 62–68.

Henderson, V. (1966). *The nature of nursing.* New York, NY: Macmillan.

Holmes, D., Perron, A., & O'Byrne, P. (2006). Evidence, virulence, and the disappearance of nursing knowledge: A critique of the evidence based dogma. *Worldviews on Evidence-Based Nursing, 3,* 95–102.

Hughes, L. (1980). The public image of the nurse. *ANS Advances in Nursing Science, 2,* 55–72.

Hughes, L. (1990). Professionalizing domesticity: A synthesis of selected nursing historiography. *ANS Advances in Nursing Science, 12,* 25–31.

Im, E. O. (2013). Practical guidelines for feminist research in nursing. *ANS Advances in Nursing Science, 36*(2), 133–145.

Im, E. O., & Meleis, A. I. (1999). Situation-specific theories: Philosophical roots, properties, and approach. *ANS Advances in Nursing Science, 22*(2), 11–24.

Jarrin, Olga F. (2012). The integrality of situated caring in nursing and the environment. *ANS Advances in Nursing Science, 35*(1), 14–24.

Johnson, P. E. (1928). What should ethics teach? *American Journal of Nursing, 28,* 1084–1090.

Kagan, P. N., Smith, M. C., & Chinn, P. L. (Eds.). (2014). *Philosophies and practices of emancipatory nursing: Social justice as praxis.* New York, NY: Routledge.

Kalisch, B. J., & Kalisch, P. A. (2003). *American nursing: A history* (4th ed.). Philadelphia, PA: Lippincott, Williams & Wilkins.

Kelly, L. Y., & Joel, L. A. (2001). *The nursing experience: Trends, challenges and transitions* (4th ed.). New York, NY: McGraw-Hill.

Kelly, Ursula A. (2009). Integrating intersectionality and biomedicine in health disparities research. *ANS Advances in Nursing Science, 32*(2), E42–E56.

Kelly, Ursula A. (2011). Theories of intimate partner violence: From blaming the victim to acting against injustice intersectionality as an analytic framework. *ANS Advances in Nursing Science, 34*(3), E29–E51.

Kilpatrick, W. H. (1921–1922). The basis of professional ethics in nursing. *American Journal of Nursing, 22,* 790–798.

Kramer, M. (2002). Academic talk about dementia caregiving: A critical comment on language. *Research and Theory for Nursing Practice, 16*(4), 263–280.

Kress, G., Leite-Garcia, R., & van Leeuwen, T. (1996). Discourse semiotic. In G. Kress & T. van Leeuwen (Eds.), *Reading images: The grammar of visual design* (pp. 257–291). London, England: Routledge.

Leininger, M. M. (1976). Doctoral programs for nurses: Trends, questions, and projected plans. *Nursing Research, 25,* 201–210.

Letourneau, N., & Allen, M. (1999). Post-positivistic critical multiplism: A beginning dialogue. *Journal of Advanced Nursing, 20,* 623–630.

Levine, M. E. (1967). The four conservation principles of nursing. *Nursing Forum, 6*(1), 93–98.

Levine, M. E. (1999). On the humanities in nursing. *Canadian Journal of Nursing Research, 30*(4), 213–217.

Lovell, M. C. (1980). The politics of medical deception: Challenging the trajectory of history. *ANS Advances in Nursing Science, 2*(3), 73–86.

Malka, S. G. (2007). *Daring to care: American nursing and second-wave feminism.* Chicago, IL: University of Chicago Press.

Mazurek-Melnyk, B., Stone, P., Fincout-Overholt, E., & Ackerman, M. (2000). Evidence-based practice: The past, the present and recommendations for the millennium. *Pediatric Nursing, 26*(1), 77–80.

McClure, K. (1951). Ingredients of gracious nursing. *Nursing World, 125,* 221–224.

Mead, M. (1956). Nursing—primitive and civilized. *American Journal of Nursing, 56,* 1001–1004.

Meade, A. B. (1936). Training the senses in clinical observation. *Trained Nurse and Hospital Review, 97,* 540–544.

Meleis, A. I. (1987). ReVisions in knowledge development: A passion for substance. *Scholarly Inquiry for Nursing Practice, 1,* 5–19.

Melnyk, B. M., & Fineout-Overholt, E. (2011). *Evidence-based practice in nursing and healthcare: A guide to best practice.* Philadelphia, PA: Lippincott, Williams & Wilkins.

Melosh, B. (1982). *The physician's hand: Work culture and conflict in American nursing.* Philadelphia, PA: Temple University Press.

Moch, S. D., Williams, C., Schmitz, S., Slaughter, J., Anderson, S. L., Branson, J., et al. (2008). EBP through student-staff collaboration. *Nursing Management, 39*(8), 12.

Mossman, L. C. (1923). The place of beauty in life. *Trained Nurse and Hospital Review, 81,* 318–319.

Mountin, J. W. (1943). Nursing: A critical analysis. *American Journal of Nursing, 43,* 29–34.

Mowinski-Jennings, B., & Loan, L. A. (2001). Misconceptions among nurses about evidence based practice. *Journal of Nursing Scholarship, 33,* 121–127.

Mundinger, M. O., Starck, P., Hathaway, D., Shaver, J., & Woods, N. F. (2009). The ABCs of the doctor of nursing practice: Assessing resources, building a culture of clinical scholarship, curricular models. *Journal of Professional Nursing, 25*(2), 69–74.

Newman, M. A. (1979). *Theory development in nursing.* Philadelphia, PA: Davis.

Newman, M. A. (1999). *Health as expanding consciousness* (2nd ed.). Sudbury, MA: Jones & Bartlett.

Nightingale, F. (1969). *Notes on nursing: What it is and what it is not.* New York, NY: Dover (Original work published 1860).

Nightingale, F. (1979). *Cassandra.* New York, NY: The Feminist Press (Original work published 1852).

Noble, G. E. (1940). The spirit of nursing. *American Journal of Nursing, 40,* 161–162.

Oettinger, K. B. (1939). Toward inner freedom. *American Journal of Nursing, 39,* 1224–1229.

Pfefferkorn, F. (1933). What of nursing field studies? *American Journal of Nursing, 33,* 258–261.

Phillips, B., Ball, C., Sackett, D., Badenoch, D., Straus, Haynes, B., et al. (2009). Oxford Centre for Evidence-based Medicine—Levels of evidence (March 2009). Retrieved from http://www.cebm.net/index.aspx?o=1025 (Original work published 1998).

Pitre, N. Y., Kushner, K. E., Raine, K. D., & Hegadoren, K. M. (2013). Critical feminist narrative inquiry: Advancing knowledge through double-hermeneutic narrative analysis. *ANS Advances in Nursing Science, 36*(2), 118–132.

Ploeg, J., Davies, B., Edwards, N., Gifford, W., & Miller, P. E. (2007). Factors influencing best-practice guideline implementation: Lessons learned from administrators, nursing staff, and project leaders. *Worldviews on Evidence-Based Nursing, 4*(4), 210–219.

Porter, E. K. (1953). What it means to be a nurse. *American Journal of Nursing, 53,* 948–950.

Reverby, S. M. (1987a). A caring dilemma: Womanhood and nursing in historical perspective. *Nursing Research, 36*(1), 5–11.

Reverby, S. M. (1987b). *Ordered to care: The dilemma of American nursing, 1850–1945*. Cambridge, United Kingdom: Cambridge University Press.

Richardson-Tench, M. (2012). Power, discourse, subjectivity: A Foucauldian application to operating room nursing practice. *ACORN Journal of Perioperative Nursing in Australia, 25*(3), 36–37.

Riddles, A. R. (1928). The force of example. *Trained Nurse and Hospital Review, 80*(1), 27–30.

Roberts, J. I., & Group, T. M. (1995). *Feminism and nursing: An historical perspective on power, status, and political activism in the nursing profession*. Westport, CT: Praeger.

Roberts, S. J. (1983). Oppressed group behavior: Implications for nursing. *Advances in Nursing Science, 5*(4), 21–30.

Rogers, M. E. (1970). *An introduction to the theoretical basis of nursing*. Philadelphia, PA: Davis.

Rolfe, G. (2006). Judgements without rules: Towards a postmodern ironist concept of research validity. *Nursing Inquiry, 13*, 7–15.

Salmond, S. (2013). Finding the evidence to support evidence-based practice. *Orthopaedic Nursing, 32*(1), 16–22.

Sanger, M. (1971). *Margaret Sanger, an autobiography*. New York, NY: Dover.

Satterfield, J. M., Spring, B., Brownson, R. C., Mullen, E. J., Newhouse, R. P., Walker, B. B., et al. (2009). Toward a transdisciplinary model of evidence-based practice. *Milbank Quarterly, 87*, 368–390.

Savage, J. (2000). One voice, different tunes: Issues raised by dual analysis of a segment of qualitative data. *Journal of Advanced Nursing, 31*, 1493–1500.

Schunemann, H. J., Best, D., Vist, G., & Oxman, A. D. (2003). Letters, numbers, symbols and words: How to communicate grades of evidence and recommendations. *Canadian Medical Association Journal, 169*, 677–680.

Scozzari, T. E. (2008). The journey of America's first native nurse. Retrieved from http://yellowstonevalleyw oman.com/view_article?id=202.

Silverstein, N. G. (1985). Lillian Wald at Henry Street, 1893-1895. *Advances in Nursing Science, 7*(2), 1–12.

Simons, H., Kushner, S., Jones, K. D., & James, D. (2003). From evidence-based practice to practice-based evidence: The idea of situated generalization. *Research Papers in Education, 18*, 347–364.

Simpson, L. F. (1914). The psychology of nursing. *Trained Nurse and Hospital Review, 52–53*, 133–137.

Stewart, I. M. (1921–1922). Some fundamental principles in the teaching of ethics. *American Journal of Nursing, 21*, 906–913.

Taylor, E. J. (1934). Of what is the nature of nursing? *American Journal of Nursing, 34*, 473–476.

Thompson, J. L. (2007). Poststructuralist feminist analysis in nursing. In C. Roy & D. A. Jones (Eds.), *Nursing knowledge development and clinical practice* (pp. 129–143). New York, NY: Springer.

Thoms, A. B. S. (1985). *Pathfinders, a history of the progress of colored graduate nurses*. New York, NY: Garland (Original work published 1929).

Thorne, S. E., & Sawatzky, R. (2014). Particularizing the general: Sustaining theoretical integrity in the context of an evidence-based practice agenda. *ANS Advances in Nursing Science, 37*(1), 5–18.

Tinley, S. T., & Kinney, A. Y. (2007). Three philosophical approaches to the study of spirituality. *ANS Advances in Nursing Science, 30*, 71–80.

Titler, M. G. (2004). Methods in translation science. *Worldviews on Evidence-Based Nursing, 1*(1), 38–48.

Tooley, S. A. (1905). *The life of Florence Nightingale*. New York, NY: Macmillan.

U.S. National Institutes of Health. (2009). Re-engineering the clinical research enterprise: Translational research. Retrieved from http://nihroadmap.nih.gov/clinicalresearch/overview-translational.asp.

Van Dijk, T. A. (1997). The study of discourse. In T. A. van Dijk (Ed.), *Discourse as structure and process: Discourse studies: A multidisciplinary introduction* (Vol. 1) (pp. 1–34). London, England: Sage.

Wald, L. (1971). *The house on Henry Street*. New York, NY: Dover.

Walker, L. O. (1971). Toward a clearer understanding of the concept of nursing theory. *Nursing Research, 20*, 428–435.

Walker, L. O., & Avant, K. C. (2004). *Strategies for theory construction in nursing* (4th ed.). Norwalk, CT: Appleton & Lange.

Wallin, L. (2009). Knowledge translation and implementation research in nursing. *International Journal of Nursing Studies, 46*, 576–587.

Warnshius, F. C. (1926). The future of medicine and nursing: The ideal to be sought. *American Journal of Nursing, 26*, 123–126.

Watson, J. (1979). *Nursing: The philosophy and science of caring.* Boston, MA: Little, Brown.

Wheeler, C. E. (1985). The *American Journal of Nursing* and the socialization of a profession. *ANS Advances in Nursing Science, 7*(2), 20–33.

Woodham-Smith, C. (1983). *Florence Nightingale: 1820–1910.* New York, NY: Atheneum.

Wooldridge, P. J. (1971). Meta-theories of nursing: A commentary on Dr. Walker's article. *Nursing Research, 20*, 494–495.

Worcester, A. (1902). Is nursing really a profession? *American Journal of Nursing, 2*, 908–917.

Young, A. D. (1913). The nurse's duty to herself. *Trained Nurse and Hospital Review, 51*, 265–270.

⊖ http://evolve.elsevier.com/Chinn/knowledge/

Why have women passion, intellect, moral activity—these three—and a place in society where no one of the three can be exercised?

Florence Nightingale (1852/1979, p. 25)

Specifically, there is a need to further explore the political, economic, and social forces in communities around the country that influenced the growth of both nursing and medicine during this century. The rigidities and inflexibilities of mythical conceptions about the roles of men and women in health care and the resulting responses of community members need examination also.

J. Ashley (1976, p. x)

After one has worked for a time in healing wounds which should never have been inflicted, tending ailments which should never have developed, sending patients to hospitals who need not have gone if their homes were habitable, bringing charitable aid to persons who would not have needed charity if health had not been ruined by unwholesome conditions, one loses heart and longs for preventive work, constructive work... something that will make it less easy for so many illnesses and accidents to occur; that will help to bring better homes and workshops, better conditions of life.

L. L. Dock (1902–1903, p. 531)

The women who wrote these opening quotes represent a long tradition of emancipatory knowing in nursing. Nightingale's quote makes explicit the challenges that women of her time faced if they wanted to step outside the role that Victorian society had prescribed for them. The Ashley quote highlights the importance of examining the social processes that formed nursing and how those processes contribute to nursing's ability to deliver health care. The quote by Dock goes deeper and suggests the need to shape social processes so that they eliminate social inequities in the first place, thereby making changes that would abolish the need for emancipatory knowing and knowledge.

Nightingale stresses the importance of being aware of inequities that are created by social conditions. Ashley suggests the need to critique, to imagine a different future, and to create formal expressions that can be shared. Dock highlights a defining dimension of praxis by suggesting the need to bring about change that creates situations of empowerment and social equity. It is the Dock quote that addresses the core reason for developing emancipatory knowledge.

Think About It

Consider the issue of environmental pollution. What options do individuals have to protect themselves, and should they pay the price for the health problems that result from exposure to pollution in the environment? Who do you think should be held accountable for the health problems that come from pollution?

This chapter describes the concept of emancipatory knowing and provides an overview of the foundations from which emancipatory knowing in nursing has developed. We detail the dimensions of emancipatory knowing introduced in Chapter 1.

As represented in Figure 3-1, the dimensions of emancipatory knowing surround and connect with the four fundamental patterns of knowing that are represented by the lighter center oval. In this way, emancipatory knowing places a critical lens on both nursing's knowledge development activities and on the practice of nursing. The hazy indistinct outer circle that the double arrows extend beyond underscores the need for nursing to also have a critical lens that addresses the social and political contexts within which nursing functions. This chapter includes examples of approaches that can be used to address the critical questions posed from an emancipatory perspective: "What are the barriers to freedom?" "What changes are needed?" "Who benefits?" and "What is wrong with this picture?" The creative development processes of critiquing and imagining are further explained, and we describe ways in which the formal expressions of emancipatory knowledge are presented and authenticated. Praxis—the process of critical reflection and action used to achieve emancipatory change—is positioned at the center of the model as well as at its outer edges. This signifies the need for an emancipatory knowing focus in the moment of practice as well as in relation to the social context in which the discipline is located.

THE CONCEPT OF EMANCIPATORY KNOWING

In 1995, Jill White proposed the addition of the knowing pattern "socio-political knowing." The concept of emancipatory knowing is closely related to the idea of sociopolitical knowing in that both concepts address working within a social and political system to make change (White, 2014). Both terms refer to making changes that improve patient care. We use the term *emancipatory knowing* in part because it points to the intent and hoped-for outcome of action, and because of the roots of the concept of emancipatory knowing in philosophy (Habermas, 1973, 1979).

Emancipatory knowing emphasizes action that arises from an awareness of social injustices embedded in a social and political system. Emancipatory knowing requires ongoing understanding of the network of social processes that create unjust conditions and changing them so that action to rectify injustices is no longer required. This goes beyond acting on recognized injustices and requires praxis—reflection and action in a continuous circle, where actions are constantly examined to ensure these are moving in the direction of social justice for all.

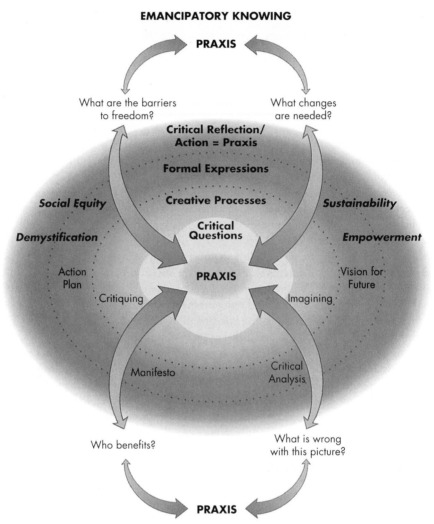

FIGURE 3-1: Emancipatory knowing and knowledge.

Emancipatory knowing is the human ability to recognize social and political problems of injustice or inequity, to realize that things could be different, and to piece together complex elements of experience and context to change a situation as it is to a situation that improves people's lives. Emancipatory knowing cultivates awareness of how problematic conditions converge, reproduce, and remain in place to sustain a status quo that is unfair for some groups within society. Awareness of social injustices and inequities leads to processes that culminate in praxis, which is the integrated expression of emancipatory knowing.

Emancipatory knowing requires critical examination that aims to uncover why injustices seem to remain invisible and to identify specific social and structural changes that are required to right social and institutional wrongs. Emancipatory knowing seeks freedom from institutional and institutionalized social and political contexts that sustain injustices and that perpetuate advantages for some and disadvantages for others.

Emancipatory knowing in nursing means questioning the nature of knowledge and the ways in which knowledge itself—or what is taken to be knowledge—contributes to larger social problems. Emancipatory knowing takes into account the power dynamics that create knowledge as well as the social and political contexts that shape and influence knowledge and knowing. From an emancipatory perspective, knowledge and knowing are constructed in ways that reflect prevailing hegemony or problematic assumptions about "the way things are." *Hegemony* is the dominance of certain ideologies, beliefs, values, or views of the world over other possible viewpoints. These dominant perspectives privilege certain groups over others. Hegemonic views are often hidden and are taken for granted as fact or as the only possibility. Moreover, hegemony tends to recreate itself in ways that make it difficult to change.

Think About It

A dominant assumption or hegemonic view in nursing is that nurses practice as employees of an agency or a corporation rather than as independent practitioners. Institutionalized reimbursement practices of insurance companies and licensure laws are powerful sociopolitical structures that keep this view of how nurses can and should practice in place. Policies that govern how nurses are paid for their services make it difficult to secure reimbursement for independent nursing services. Even when reimbursement is possible, it is more difficult for nurses to receive reimbursement than it is for other health care workers, or they must be reimbursed indirectly. A few nurses have refused to accept the hegemonic assumption that they cannot or should not practice independently, and most nurses are aware that being self-employed or practicing independently is an option for others. However, the prevailing hegemonic view is that the norm is to be an employee and to work within the structures of an agency or corporation, and that it would not be feasible to practice any other way. What do you think?

Hegemonic ideologies and patterns of thinking tend to recreate themselves; in this way, they continue to seem natural and normal across time and generations. This perpetuation of hegemony happens in part when leaders and spokespersons in power speak and act in a way that is consistent with hegemony, thus reinforcing in public their ideas of how the world is and how it should function. This sort of public understanding becomes pervasive and effectively inhibits public awareness of other possibilities.

Without awareness of how things could be different, people conform to hegemonic practices and values. People are often not aware that they are trapped within a hegemonic pattern that creates disadvantages for them, and they remain unaware of alternatives. Alternatively, if they are aware, they may see the alternatives as not truly being possible.

Emancipatory knowing gives rise to the realization that there is something wrong with the way things are and that it is possible to change what is for the better. This awareness can arise when conditions become intolerable or when someone challenges or questions the hegemonic status quo. As people come to understand situations as being unjust, they can mobilize to challenge the way that things are. In so doing, these individuals exercise what may be considered *emancipatory human interest:* they clarify and define what is problematic about their situation from their point of view, and they take action to change it. They also begin to recognize that others share their experience of the situation. Together, they begin to develop actions, insights, and knowledge about the problem and about what is required to correct it or to change the situation for the better.

Consider This Example

The emergence of the women's movement during the latter half of the 20th century is an example of an emancipatory process. Through the mid-1900s, the hegemonic view of women was of the ideal wife and mother who remained a subservient homemaker devoted to her family. These views of womanhood were reflected in the media, government policies, business practices, religious beliefs, and virtually every aspect of public life, as can be seen by browsing through magazines and professional journals of that time.

As women realized that this hegemonic construct of women dominated their experience, small groups of women in the United States and other countries began to examine the circumstances of their lives in consciousness-raising groups—a type of grassroots movement. Women shared experiences and feelings about their lives and formed ideas about how their lives could and should be. Many of their ideas became formalized as feminist theory. Those who spoke publicly were often derided by men and women who felt threatened by the sociocultural changes that were suggested. However, despite widespread resistance, feminist ideas began to make sense to more and more people, and many significant social and cultural changes were initiated.

One of the first changes that feminist leaders called for was a shift to gender-neutral language, and widespread changes began to occur. For example, newspapers stopped publishing their classified ads in separate "Help Wanted—Male" and "Help Wanted—Female" columns; these ads were changed to fall under a heading that simply read "Help Wanted." In this example, emancipatory knowing for women involved their shared awareness of the distress that they experienced with the restrictions that hegemonic ideals of womanhood imposed on their lives. As the outcomes of their shared awareness evolved, emancipatory knowing grew as others began to hear about and comprehend the alternatives that feminist perspectives offered.

Emancipatory Knowing and Problem Solving

Emancipatory knowing is different from but related to problem solving. It is much more than problem solving, however, because emancipatory knowing requires a deep awareness of often hidden injustices and the problematic social practices that create them. Unlike problem solving, which usually focuses on a single discrete case, emancipatory knowing requires seeing the larger picture and correcting social processes, patterns, and structures that create social inequities and injustices.

Before the social changes arising from the women's movement in Western societies, some women who wanted to perform a "man's job," such as medicine or the operation of heavy machinery, solved the problem by dressing and posing as a man. These women may have been aware that the policies and practices of their culture were unjust. Despite potential awareness of the unfairness of the practice, rather than pursuing a critical or emancipatory approach to changing societal rules and policies, they simply solved the problem by accommodating for a fundamentally unfair practice. In this example, accommodating rather than changing can be seen as a discrete, individual, and temporary solution rather than a long-term one. Asking the critical questions associated with emancipatory knowing, when you meet challenges that require this form of problem solving, is one way to initiate the corrective processes of emancipatory knowing.

Emancipatory Knowing and Critical Thinking

Emancipatory knowing differs from critical thinking in that it does not simply seek to improve one's thinking ability, judgment, and problem-solving skills. Once again, the emphasis is on seeing what lies beneath issues and problems and redefining those issues and problems to reveal linkages among complex social and political contexts that create injustices. For example, a critical-thinking approach to hiring practices that are based on gender would focus on gathering the evidence and examining the rationale for restricting hiring in some jobs to women only and in others to men only. The soundness and logic of each explanation for the practice would be examined, and conclusions would be drawn about the practice. Critical-thinking approaches could reveal injustices and inequities and might result in an attempt to reduce gender-specific hiring. However, critical thinking alone would not fully examine the underlying network of social practices that keep the injustice of gender-specific hiring in place or challenge the status quo in a way that would demand long-term change.

Emancipatory Knowing and Reflective Practice

Emancipatory knowing is akin to reflective practice in that emancipatory knowing involves a constant interaction between action and reflection. This process is praxis: the integrated expression of emancipatory knowing, described in more detail later in this chapter. *Reflective practice* is a significant personal process that leads to insight about one's actions and the rationales for actions that have the potential to improve one's practice. Unlike reflective practice, however, praxis requires going beyond personal reflection to uncover deliberately what is unfair and unjust in a situation, to envision how it could be different, and to form alternate explanations and possibilities for change that come from a range of perspectives much broader than that of the individual alone (Schön, 1983).

Many women find great satisfaction and personal joy in their roles as mothers and homemakers. From a reflective practice perspective, they might recognize that their experience fits a hegemonic view of ideal womanhood that could be restrictive in certain ways, but their personal experience is satisfying and rewarding and therefore requires no change.

Alternatively, the emancipatory knowing process of praxis would call for looking beyond personal experience alone to reflect on the broader sociocultural implications of such role prescriptions and for considering the political as well as personal implications of the situation. The personal satisfactions and rewards of homemaking for some women are not negated, but the focus shifts to broader issues and to the outcomes for women and society in general when homemaking and motherhood are prescribed as being primarily women's roles.

To summarize, emancipatory knowing does not allow us to undo hegemonic social structures by just thinking critically about injustices, solving individual or discrete problems, or reflecting on unfair social conditions. Rather, it asks, "Why do we have this problem in the first place?" For example, when approaching the situation from an emancipatory perspective, you ask, "How can we create opportunities for women in the workplace?"; you also ask, "Why are women excluded from full access to employment in the first place?" As a nurse, you ask, "How can we overcome the stigma of human immunodeficiency virus/acquired immunodeficiency syndrome?"; you also ask, "Why is this condition stigmatized in the first place?" You ask, "How do we create tolerance for transgendered persons?"; you also ask, "Why does intolerance persist?" You wonder, "How can we end the unfair policy of mandatory overtime for nurses?"; you also consider, "Why has this practice emerged, and who benefits from this policy?" As we have said many times, after these questions are asked, emancipatory knowing demands that an individual work toward the elimination of these situations.

THE REBIRTH OF EMANCIPATORY KNOWING IN NURSING

There is a long history of nurse activists who have worked to change desperate social conditions in an effort to improve health. However, with the focus on scientific inquiry that took hold during the 1950s, an appreciation for other forms of knowing and inquiry was temporarily lost. During the 1960s and the 1970s, when different forms of scholarship became more legitimate, critical perspectives began to emerge. Much of this early critical scholarship was grounded in the work of prominent critical, liberation, and poststructuralist thinkers.

Critical Theory

In the discipline of nursing, the term *critical theory* refers to a foundational perspective that grounds emancipatory knowing. This term can be confusing in that it does not reflect the usual connotation of theory in nursing. The concept of *critical* has a range of common meanings that are not relevant in the context of critical theory. In this context, *critical* implies analysis that moves beyond the surface and beyond what is usually assumed. Generally, *critical theory* is a broad term that is used to describe both the process and the product of work that takes a historically situated and sociopolitical perspective and that challenges social inequities and injustices. Such theory is critical in the sense that it analyzes the roots and consequences of social inequities and injustices that privilege one group over another (Carnegie & Kiger, 2009).

As a method, critical theory has roots in the classic sociologic traditions of Karl Marx, Max Weber, and Emile Durkheim (Morrow, 1994). These early philosophic traditions were quite unfavorable to capitalist governments such as that of the United States and were viewed in the United States as being allied with communist ideology. The extreme anti-communist sentiments that prevailed in the United States during the 20th century made it difficult for U.S. scholars to engage in discourse surrounding the emergence of critical theory and philosophy. Scholars in countries that have strong social welfare policies and values have generally been more open and accepting of critical theory. As the political structures of the world began to change and the 40-year Cold War that began in the late 1940s abated, U.S. scholars gradually became more open to critical theory. This circumstance illustrates the tremendous influence of context on people's thinking in that fears of communism created barriers to understanding critical theory and suppressed openness to the possibilities offered by critical theoretic approaches.

Critical theory began to emerge as a specific approach to the study of society through the work of scholars who were exiled from Germany by Adolf Hitler in 1932. These scholars became known as the "Frankfurt School." Within the Frankfurt School, the term *critical theory* designated a form of sociologic theory that recognized society as evolving historically and that promoted a deliberate engagement with the problems of society and the processes of social transformation. Typically (but not always), when the term *critical theory* is capitalized, it refers specifically to the work of the Frankfurt School (Morrow, 1994). We use the lowercase format throughout our discussion to indicate a perspective that encompasses a broad range of philosophies, methods, and approaches that share a common fundamental engagement with the problems of society.

During the 1960s, Jürgen Habermas assumed a prominent position in shaping new conceptions of critical theory with broad interdisciplinary connections between the human sciences and philosophy (Morrow, 1994). In his critical social theory, Habermas (1973, 1979) posited three fundamental human interests, each of which demanded its own method, as follows:

1. *Technical interest* is the human capacity to create things and processes to understand the physical world; this requires empiric methods.
2. *Practical interest* is the human capacity to communicate and to get along within a social community; this requires interpretive and philosophic methods.
3. *Emancipatory interest* is the human capacity to see that something needs to change and to take action to change it; this requires critical and reflective methods.

Each of these interests is necessary for human survival. Although critical nurse scholars have grounded their thinking in the work of a number of critical scholars and philosophers, the influence of Habermas is significant.

Liberation Theory

Paulo Freire was an important liberation theorist whose ideas have also had a significant influence among nursing scholars. Freire was a Brazilian educator who championed critical approaches to education. His work was philosophically grounded in the ideas of Karl Marx, Friedrich Engels, Georg Hegel, Gyorgy Lukacs, Herbert Marcuse, and Erich Fromm (Freire, 1970). Freire's work grew out of a project to teach peasants in rural Brazil how to read. His ideas were not only specific approaches to teaching; they could also be used for any grassroots project of human liberation. Traditional education is based on the assumption that its primary purpose is to pass along the existing knowledge and values of the culture. Freire questioned this assumption, and in doing so, he formalized *liberation theory*, which considered education as a means of challenging the existing knowledge and values of the culture (Freire, 1970; hooks, 1993; Weiler, 1991). Because of the broad significance of his philosophy and the practical action-oriented perspective that he articulated, Freire's ideas have had a widespread influence that has gone well beyond the scope of education.

Poststructuralism

Michel Foucault's poststructuralist philosophy has also had a major influence on nurse scholars because of his insights with regard to the power imbalances that are embedded in and sustained by verbal and symbolic social discourses. *Social discourses* are whole systems of representation—writing, images, advertisements, artwork, and everyday verbal and nonverbal language—that create perceptions of social reality. For critical poststructuralists, there is no reality in an objective sense. Rather, what seems real is created for us by dominant social discourses. Verbal and symbolic discourses are powerful because they interconnect to both enable and limit what it is socially acceptable to know (Aston, 2008; Bradbury-Jones, Sambrook, & Irvine, 2008).

For example, discourses of beauty for young women suggest that a flawless face is more beautiful than a normally flawed and plainer face. Discourses also reinforce the idea that beauty of a certain type—that which is achieved by cosmetics and airbrushing—is attainable and a normal way to be. Because these messages appear everywhere, young women may only understand "beauty" as what is constructed and prescribed by these systems of discourse. Such discourses are powerful because they create barriers to societal resources for some as well as opportunities for others. Young women who cannot or choose not to achieve the popular standard of beauty may develop low self-esteem, and they risk being denied social resources, such as popularity among peers and the social interactions for which most young people yearn.

This same example could be applied to young men, for whom popular discourses prescribe what is considered a typical movie-star appearance (being handsome, having well-defined muscles, and wearing well-fashioned clothing) as opposed to that which is considered "geeky" or "nerdy" (being thin, wearing glasses, and having casual, disheveled, or mismatched clothing). It is in this way that discourses construct "realities" that create power imbalances (in our example, between young women and men who are "beautiful" or "handsome" and those who are not). As alternative discourses that counter notions of beauty begin to undermine dominant discourses, they begin to lose their power to control how young people spend their money and time (Phillips, 2006).

As a poststructuralist, Foucault viewed language and discourse, including theory, as systems of representation that are necessary in the social order in that they produce meaning or ways to comprehend the world. However, as the examples of discourses related to beauty illustrate, these systems of language and discourse also limit what is understood, known, or perceived in a way that has lasting negative consequences. According to Foucault, we can only know things as they have meaning, and it is systems of discourse that produce or construct meaning (Hall, 2001). Critical poststructuralism analyzes how discourse functions to create imbalances that disadvantage whole classes of persons, in an effort to illuminate possibilities for change (Doering, 1992; Foucault, 1980, 1984).

Nursing's Early Literature Related to Emancipatory Knowing

During the latter half of the 20th century, a growing number of nurse scholars and activists began to develop disciplinary perspectives that are clearly connected to an emancipatory pattern of knowing. During the 1960s, Lydia Hall, who declared that there is no "shortage of nurses" but rather a "shortage of nursing," established the Loeb Center for Nursing and Rehabilitation at Montefiore Hospital in the Bronx, New York. Her ideas and what proceeded from them are notable examples of emancipatory knowing in nursing. Believing that nursing was the chief therapy for those recovering from chronic illness, Hall established the Loeb Center as a place where nursing (rather than medicine) could be practiced and where physicians were under the direction of nurses (Hall, 1966). Hall envisioned the Loeb Center when she noticed that nurses were taking on medical tasks and becoming what she called "physician extenders" rather than providing bodily care and nurturing the cores of individuals after medicine's curative role. Hall's model of nursing at Loeb was revolutionary because it differentiated nursing from medicine and allowed nurses to practice in an environment that did not require the performance of curative tasks associated with the growth of medical technology during the 1960s.

Early literature in nursing that reflected emancipatory knowing also grew out of feminist perspectives. As reluctant as nurses were in general to accept feminist ideas and to align themselves with the women's movement of the 1960s and 1970s in the United States, some spoke out and published ideas that challenged the status quo. One of the earliest writings that reflected an emancipatory perspective was a 1973 article in the *American Journal of Nursing* by Wilma Scott Heide (1973), who made a case for the importance of feminist ideas for nursing. In *Hospitals, Paternalism, and the Role of the Nurse,* basing her argument on historical evidence, JoAnn Ashley (1976) contended that the prevailing apprenticeship system of education in nursing situated nurses and nursing in a context that not only exploited the labor of women in hospitals, but also undermined the fundamental values of nursing related to health and health care. Her feminist analysis drew the essential connection between a misogynist (woman-hating) society and the resulting health policies and practices that constricted the role of nurses in the delivery of health care (Kagan, 2006).

Another significant publication that reflected nursing's development of emancipatory perspectives was the 1983 article "Oppressed group behavior: implications for nursing."

Drawing on Freire's work and from literature about colonized Africans, Latin Americans, African Americans, Jews, and women, Susan Jo Roberts made the case that nurses also can be viewed as an oppressed group. Emphasizing that this insight can lead to substantive action to change nursing and health care, she concluded the following:

> Nurses are an oppressed group with characteristics similar to those of [other oppressed] groups. It is hoped that with this understanding nurses can learn from the experience of others to liberate themselves and develop an autonomous profession that can greatly contribute to the improvement of health care. (Roberts, 1983, p. 30)

Cassandra: Radical Feminist Nurses Network was founded by a group of nurses at the American Nurses Association convention in Washington, DC, on June 30, 1982, which was the expiration date for the ratification of the Equal Rights Amendment to the U.S. Constitution. The Cassandra founders were astonished to see no acknowledgment at the convention of the political significance of the date and the major events being held throughout the District of Columbia to commemorate the death of the amendment.

The women who formed Cassandra divided their time between various convention activities and events throughout the city to celebrate a renewal of their commitment to continue the struggle for women's full equality in U.S. society. Cassandra was formed to bring critical and feminist insights to the forefront in nursing and to use critical feminist insights as a basis for change in nursing. They named themselves after Florence Nightingale's essay titled "Cassandra," in which she asked the question that opens this chapter. The network's news journal was published until 1989, and although not widely distributed, it provided a significant source of affirmation for many practicing nurses and nurse scholars who were beginning to develop an emancipatory perspective (Chinn, 2009).

By the close of the 1980s and the beginning of the 1990s, nursing literature was beginning to reflect the strong presence of works informed by emancipatory perspectives, including critical, feminist, and poststructuralist theory (Bunting & Campbell, 1990; Doering, 1992; Muller & Dzurec, 1993). These early writings remain important foundations for nursing's emancipatory scholarship. These authors explained the particular critical perspectives from which they drew, and they offered critiques of nursing and nursing knowledge in addition to proposals for shifts in nursing practice and education, health care, and society that could address persistent and seemingly intractable problems in nursing.

By the mid-1990s, emancipatory perspectives appeared more frequently in nursing literature. Although remaining on the margins of dominant scholarly discourses in nursing, these perspectives gradually gained depth and quality that were increasingly recognized as noteworthy. These writings describe the nature of problems identified from an emancipatory perspective and the types of actions required to create the envisioned change. These scholarly writings challenge prevailing hegemonies and identify critical problems that typically are taken as simply "the way that the world is." These authors describe how the problems that they addressed came to be, who is advantaged and who is disadvantaged by the status quo, and how social practices intersect to keep the status quo in place; they also envision changes and the actions required to make such changes to the status quo (Falk-Rafael, 2006; MacDonnell, 2009; Messias, McDowell, & Estrada, 2009; Racine, 2009).

At present, there is a strong tradition of critical analysis in nursing, as well as a conceptualization of emancipatory nursing practice that is grounded in emancipatory knowing (Kagan, Chinn, & Smith, 2014).

THE DIMENSIONS OF EMANCIPATORY KNOWING

The dimensions of emancipatory knowing include critical questions; creative processes of critiquing and imagining; formal expressions; authentication processes; and the integrated practice expression of emancipatory knowing, which is praxis.

Critical Questions: Who Benefits? What Is Wrong with This Picture?

The creative processes for developing emancipatory knowledge grow from the critical questions of emancipatory knowing shown in Figure 3-1. These questions can be asked in a variety of contexts and situations, including the context of care. The questions on the model are suggestions, but any question that focuses on bringing social injustices into awareness is also a critical question. For example, critical questions can inquire about barriers to freedom, about why certain information remains invisible or hidden, or about why some people enjoy freedoms that others do not. When nurses question why something seems unfair, they are operating under the assumption that all persons deserve the freedom and opportunity to develop their full potential. Such critical questions also assume that developing and exercising one's potential is not solely a matter of individual will or desire, but that culture and society create conditions and structures within which people can thrive or fail to thrive. This is an important idea to remember when it comes to understanding emancipatory knowing.

When you ask the critical questions associated with emancipatory knowing, an underlying assumption is that people are not radically free to choose from among an unlimited variety of options, and that things need to change to make new options accessible to everyone. To assume that people are radically free places the responsibility for developing one's full potential totally with the individual. Critical questioning assumes that freedoms are situated, which means that the possibilities for freedom and the development of individual potential are determined by a person's situation. In other words, from a critical perspective, a person's situation is assumed to be constructed by social practices that create disadvantage for some and privilege for others. From an emancipatory perspective, any conditions that limit people from developing their full human potential can be made visible, what is imagined can become real, and humans have the innate capacity to bring about changes to improve the human condition. Asking a critical question such as "What is wrong with this picture?" requires a lens that sees beyond the obvious and beyond one's own personal experience. This makes it possible to discern problems that may exist with what people assume to be true.

Critical questioning requires a deep sort of awareness that is not easy to cultivate or to internalize. Developing this awareness requires seeing beyond your personal experience and moving beyond the tendency to measure the situation of others in relation to your own personal experience. For example, if you are from an economically and socially disadvantaged background but managed to "make good" by going to college, working hard, and having a good job, you may be unwilling or unable to notice how and why others in similar situations may be unable to do the same.

Recognizing injustices and inequities can create major personal and professional dilemmas. Most people are socialized to accept an unfair status quo as the way things are (hegemony) and not to question the uncomfortable fact that some people are privileged and others are disadvantaged. To bring this kind of awareness to the surface and to act on it requires great courage, persistence, and the support of colleagues and allies who remain committed to action (Georges, 2013; Giddings, 2005b). Taking action often disturbs the status quo in ways that are not only uncomfortable but that prompt harsh and swift action to keep prevailing hegemonies in place. Nonetheless, critically questioning the status quo is an initial and critical feature of emancipatory knowing that sets the stage for praxis.

Think About It

Consider a nursing situation that you observed and believed to be unfair or wrong, and then ask, "Who benefits from this situation?" Does your idea about how to change the situation change when you explore the answer to this question?

Creative Processes: Critiquing and Imagining

The creative processes of emancipatory knowing are critiquing and imagining. Again, these dimensions of emancipatory knowing require an awareness that something is not fair or just. These two creative processes tend to happen in a circular fashion; as you realize that something is not right and needs to change, this realization brings to mind things that are wrong (critique) and how things should really be instead (imagining).

Critiquing involves analyzing the status quo from multiple points of view. For example, you deliberately examine a situation from the point of view of race, ethnicity, sexual orientation, class, gender, or any other factor that limits human possibilities and creates inequities. The more comprehensive the critique, the more likely it is that the choices selected for action will be effective.

Imagining is the creative process that sets forth possibilities of how the world could be better, more equitable, and just. As with critiquing, the process of imagining benefits from a thorough examination of injustices from a variety of perspectives. We use the word *imagining* to describe a process of imaging and seeing possibilities and not to refer to simply dreaming about or making up scenarios without critique and examination. These dimensions of emancipatory knowing are carried out through dialogue and information sharing that lead to formal knowledge expressions of emancipatory knowing and praxis.

Within the context of emancipatory knowing, critiquing and imagining are *activist* in nature and grounded in the situation of those who experience a particular injustice. Someone else cannot impose emancipatory processes on people who seek or need liberation. *Emancipation,* or liberation from a situation that limits one's humanity, depends on the insights, understandings, and interpretations of those who are most deeply affected, those who are disadvantaged, and those who are oppressed. It is those who are disadvantaged by a situation who must take steps to change the situation. Others who sense that the situation is unjust can assist and encourage those who come together to share their stories and to engage in processes of critiquing and imagining, but they cannot direct the course of action or do what needs to be done other than in a supportive way. Those most directly affected by an unjust situation are sometimes referred to as "those who are oppressed"; we refer to them simply as "people seeking liberation." Those who join with the people seeking liberation to develop insight and knowledge and ultimately to support action for change are the allies of these individuals.

Activist projects bring together those who are most directly affected by injustices and their allies so that they can discuss, identify, and define what is problematic; imagine ways to create sustainable change; and plan ways to bring about the changes that they imagine. Because the conditions of people's lives are often taken for granted as the way things are (hegemony) or assumed to be unique to the individual, the processes of critiquing and imagining occur in group settings, where individuals share with one another the conditions of their lives and come to realize that they are not alone and that their situations limit their humanity.

As mentioned previously, the people seeking liberation are the experts regarding how their particular injustice is experienced. Allies often bring skills and insights about the situation that can inform the process, but they remain fully respectful of the perspectives of the people seeking liberation. Allies can be powerful agents of change by bearing witness to the situation of those who are disadvantaged. Those who participate in the process of change may not totally fit within the roles of "people seeking liberation" or "allies." Allies often have some connection to the experience of the people seeking liberation, whereas the people seeking liberation often bring insights, understandings, and ideas that come from experiences outside the realm of the oppressive situation.

The creative processes of imagining and critiquing can occur in a variety of in-person and virtual group settings. The Nurse Manifest project involved both in-person and virtual groups; nurses shared their stories by email "to raise awareness, to inspire action, and to open discussion of issues that are vital to nursing and health care around the globe" (Jarrin, 2006; Nurse Manifest, 2002) and also met in face-to-face groups (Jacobs, Fontana, Kehoe, Matarese, & Chinn, 2005). In the Nurse Manifest project, the people seeking liberation were the nurses actively engaged in direct patient care and employed in these roles. Some of the practicing nurses had been educators in the past and had returned to clinical practice. The allies in this project were nurse educators who had not been involved in clinical nursing for several years but who knew the experience well and who engaged with the clinical nurses to explore the experience of practicing nursing.

To be effective, the group process must provide a safe context that encourages people to discuss openly the circumstances of inequity or suffering in their lives and to talk about what would make their lives better. Members of the group share a mutual interest in changing a problematic status quo and use discussion to raise awareness of the conditions that sustain that status quo. As sharing and awareness occur, the group collectively criticizes that which limits full human potential and identifies what needs to change to create a more nurturing future.

The group process that is basic to emancipatory knowing is grounded in Freire's approach (1970), and the specifics described here were developed by Chinn (2013). These approaches to the group process are suggested as a way to assist activist groups to move effectively into the creative processes of critiquing and imagining. Groups of people seeking liberation may or may not include allies. When a group comes together out of a shared awareness that something is awry, its members are typically unclear about exactly what is wrong. They may have wrongly blamed themselves for the problem, or they may have attributed the problem to some condition that, with critique, turns out to not have contributed to the problem in a significant way. Initially, group members may not be aware that others share similar experiences. As the troup process proceeds, everyone respectfully listens to each other's stories, asks questions of one another, and suggest possible reasons for their condition. This discussion creates a "background awareness" of the complexities of the situation and the differences and similarities among the members' various perspectives. It also often brings to the fore some of the most creative (and sometimes outrageous) imaginings for change that might be made.

This process begins with examining and discussing *codifications* (i.e., pictures, stories, and images) that represent what the people are experiencing. Codifications help to make visible and to bring to awareness what is problematic in a situation when it is not readily apparent. This awareness leads the group to consider possible circumstances that create and sustain the situation as it is. Through discussion in which every voice is heard, the group members come to clarify and identify in new ways what is wrong with their situation (problematization), and they begin to imagine what might occur instead. The members also begin to imagine how they might bring about various possible alternatives, discussing the merits and limitations of each action that might bring about change.

Various actions for change that are identified are seen as "untested feasibilities." Each action is "tested" by exploring its merits and limitations for action that brings about change. This emergent pattern is not orchestrated or in any way controlled or directed by any one member of the group. Rather, it is a process that emerges spontaneously in the group and emanates from the human emancipatory interest (Habermas, 1979; Hagedorn, 1995). When leadership is needed, it arises from individuals in the group who are able and willing to assume leadership for the task at hand, not from socially prescribed roles that privilege some individuals over others.

Typically, group participants come together several times over weeks or months. Because the issue of concern in groups that involve people seeking liberation is an oppressive social process and not a particular individual's experience, anyone who has experience with the oppressive social process can contribute to critiquing and imagining. Individuals may or may not attend every meeting, and new members can join the group at any time. Continuity is maintained by summarizing the critiques and imaginings that involve the oppressive social process at the end of each group meeting, and then bringing that summary forward at the beginning of the next meeting. In the case of virtual groups, the group process outcome related to critiquing and imagining is archived electronically, which gives everyone access to all contributions of all participants. All participants involved with in-person groups can make notations and personal journal entries to retain ideas and insights during the discussion and to provide a point of reference for reflection between group meetings. The process of critiquing and imagining is circular rather than linear, which means that, regardless of who is present, a constant process of reflection, reconsidering, and rethinking ideas is valued, with new critiques and imaginings coming from each circular "turn" made in the process of discussion and analysis.

As discussion progresses, participants begin to explore dominant themes that characterize the focal problem as well as the links between themes. These individuals begin to situate the themes in their historical, cultural, political, and socioeconomic contexts. From these themes, the participants also explore the circumstances that maintain the status quo: the existence of persons or circumstances that directly or indirectly benefit from the status quo and of persons or circumstances that are negated and disadvantaged by the status quo.

It is from these explorations that praxis—the integrated expression of emancipatory knowing in practice—begins to happen. Early actions are often changes that people seeking liberation begin to make in their own lives, followed by collective actions that the group pursues as a group or as individuals. Freire called this process in its entirety *conscientização,* a Portuguese term that "refers to learning to perceive social, political, and economic contradictions, and to take action against the oppressive element of reality" (Freire, 1970, p. 19). Activist projects may or may not generate formal expressions of knowledge because of the primary commitment to act and to move emancipatory insights directly into actions that remove barriers to human freedom. However, formal expressions of emancipatory knowing may be formulated from the critique and imagining process, as described later.

Creative Processes and the Fundamental Patterns of Knowing. Although activist groups and their allies may have no knowledge of the fundamental knowing patterns, the creative processes of imagining and critiquing often overlap with processes within the empiric, ethical, personal, and aesthetic knowing patterns. For example, empiric methods can be used to document the extent of a problem or the nature of a structure that sustains the status quo, thereby forming a more thorough understanding of the problem. In this way, empirically based information provides data and substance that are useful for more fully critiquing and imagining possibilities for change.

For example, in a critical study seeking to understand girls' experience of menarche and create change toward a more healthy experience, a group of adolescent activists used a survey method to determine what menarche education approaches were being used in schools throughout a certain school district. The researchers also examined corporate reports to uncover the extent of profit being made by menstrual care product manufacturers who also produced the educational materials used in the schools. The participants used this information to affirm what they had suspected: that menarche education was not adequate to meet the girls' real needs but rather served the interests of powerful corporate entities. In this study, the context was a high school setting in which adolescent girls came together to explore their experiences of menarche and the meaning of those experiences, as constructed by larger sociopolitical circumstances. The study also relied on an academic ally who guided and supported their activism and published the adolescents' insights and knowledge, thereby moving it into the dimension of formal expression, where it became available to a larger professional audience (Hagedorn, 1995).

The creative processes of ethical knowledge—valuing and clarifying—can be used to better understand the nature of injustices (see Chapter 4). The manifesto of the Nurse Manifest project was developed primarily from the extensive values of clarification, dialogue, and justification (Cowling, Chinn, & Hagedorn, 2000). As the members of this group critically questioned why nurses experienced so much moral distress, their discussions focused on critique that further raised awareness of a deep conflict between the values strongly held by nurses and the values enacted by the systems in which they are employed. This underlying conflict of values was identified as the problem that was fundamental to the shortage of nursing. The manifesto project led the authors to imagine ways in which nursing values could be more fully realized—or manifested—in the practice of nursing. This project began with a focused critique of the ethical dimensions of nursing's core values and the exercise of those values in practice. Subsequently, other nurses joined the project, which resulted in a more complete critique of the experiences of practicing nursing in the context of an acute nursing shortage as well as a richer set of imaginings of a desired future.

The personal knowing processes of opening and centering are vital to the emancipatory knowing dimension of critiquing and imagining (see Chapter 5). These creative processes bring to the fore the experiences of those who are most deeply affected by injustices and provides the substance required to critique the problem and imagine alternatives. For example, in a critical feminist study of the experience of nursing practice, nurses brought to their first group meeting an object or symbol (i.e., a codification) that represented their personal experience of practicing nursing. They shared the personal meanings embedded in these symbolic objects and discussed the connections that their personal experiences revealed. A food strainer brought to the group by a participant represented her feelings of a loss of control of nursing practice, which was a feeling that other nurses in the group also shared. As these nurses shared their feelings about losing control, they came to realize that this problem was not a personal failure but rather a significant injustice that came from systematic structural problems in the ways that nursing was institutionalized and practiced. Out of their sharing and critique, these nurses imagined how personal growth toward authenticity and their collective actions could change the circumstances of practicing nursing (Jacobs et al., 2005). In the Nurse Manifest project, the research team developed fictionalized stories of nursing practice from actual stories told by nurses. These fictionalized stories are an example of formal expressions of personal knowing.

The aesthetic methods of envisioning and rehearsing can be used to critique the depth of human suffering sustained by an unjust status quo and then to imagine alternatives (see Chapter 6). The items, as codifications, brought by the nurses in the study can be seen as a type of art form that illustrated their feelings and served as a basis for the creative processes of emancipatory knowing. Simple objects (e.g., a food strainer) are important in that they codify and therefore symbolize complex human experiences (Jacobs et al., 2005). Such codifications engender a rich dialogue that is useful for fully understanding the problem. In the Nurse Manifest project, Cowling created works of art as formalized expressions of aesthetic knowing that synthesized the powerful experiences reflected in the stories of nurses from around the world (Nurse Manifest, 2002). Such artistic renderings can be used to further critique and imagine solutions to the problems of injustice represented.

Formal Expressions of Emancipatory Knowing: Action Plans, Manifestoes, Critical Analyses, and Visions for the Future

As mentioned previously, praxis may begin to occur as a direct result of critiquing and imagining processes, depending on the emancipatory interest of the activist group. However, formal expressions are often required to keep the emancipatory interest clearly in focus or to communicate to others the nature of injustices and what is needed to rectify those injustices. These formal expressions of emancipatory knowing (i.e., emancipatory knowledge) can take a number of forms. In Figure 3-1, four formal expressions of emancipatory knowing are identified: (1) *manifestoes,* which are action-oriented and impassioned portrayals of that which is problematic, the actions required to effect change, and descriptions of the ideals that are envisioned; (2) *critical analyses,* which examine what is, how it came to be, and who is disadvantaged; (3) *vision statements,* which describe in detail an envisioned future; and (4) *action plans,* which also describe an envisioned future, as well as what is required to reach that future. Although we have identified four formal expressions of emancipatory knowing, formal expressions can take many other forms, including drawings, sculptures, fictionalized stories, poems that portray the distress of disadvantage, and blueprints for the future. Any credible formal expression that is created to assist in some way with the liberation of oppressed groups can be a formal expression of emancipatory knowing.

As stated previously, formal expressions of emancipatory knowing can arise directly from an emancipatory project. Activist groups may create various formal expressions, including action plans, manifestoes, or visions for the future, depending on the nature of their emancipatory project. In addition to formal expressions that may emerge from the work of activist groups, scholars who have a direct or indirect experience with a situation of oppression can also develop formal expressions that synthesize theoretic and empiric insights related to an unjust situation. These formal expressions can subsequently be used to raise awareness in students, mentees, and peers with regard to the source of, extent of, and remedies for social inequities. Although ideas about who can and should generate formal expressions of emancipatory knowing vary, we believe that all sources of formal expressions with an intent to correct unjust positions are valuable to the pursuit of liberation.

Fundamentally, all formal expressions of emancipatory knowing, including critical analyses, are grounded in critical social theory in a broad sense. Critical social theory in this broad sense focuses on illuminating the processes that create social injustices as well as the changes required to move toward justice and freedom for oppressed people. Within the broad perspective of critical social theory, nurse scholars generally have approached problems of social injustices with the use of the lenses of critical feminism and critical poststructuralism (Grace & Perry, 2013; Pitre, Kushner, Raine, & Hagedoren, 2013).

Critical feminism perspectives focus on social and political structures that sustain injustice and how these structures interact with gender to limit full human potential (Alex, Whitty-Rogers, & Panagopoulos, 2013; Almutairi & Rodney, 2013; Pauly, MacKinnon, & Varcoe, 2009). This approach to creating a critical analysis draws from the perspective of critical social theory as well as from any or several of the various approaches to feminism. For example, a critical feminist approach to a problem that involves economics may draw on the insights of socialist feminist thought, in which the foundation of gender inequality rests with the nature of economic structures in society.

The model of social consciousness of Giddings (2005b) is an example of a critical feminist analysis that emerged out of an activist research project (Giddings, 2005a). Giddings interviewed nurses in the United States and New Zealand who identified with the dominant Eurocentric culture, the experience of being lesbian, or the experience of being a racial minority (i.e., African American in the United States or Maori in New Zealand). The nurses were invited to participate because of their reputations as people who actively engaged in advocating for others who were disadvantaged. The purpose of the study was to explore how these nurses became aware of the plight of disadvantaged persons, how they came to speak up and act on their behalf, and what their experience of doing so in nursing had been. On the basis of the life stories of these nurses, Giddings developed a model of social consciousness that provided explanations of the challenges and barriers to nurses acting from their awareness of injustices in health care.

Similar to critical feminism, *critical poststructuralism* offers an important approach for the critical work of nursing scholars (Bradbury-Jones et al., 2008). Critical post-structuralism focuses on the role of language and discourse in the creation of oppressive conditions. Poststructuralist theory deals with how language and discourses determine or construct what is a normal and natural way to be. Discourse includes such things as representational art, advertising images, music lyrics, interview text, and written or oral accounts that reflect social processes (Georges & Benedict, 2008; Montgomery, McCauley, & Bailey, 2009; Pauly et al., 2009). When there is no language or discourse regarding alternative ways of being and acting, those alternatives simply do not exist. Analyzing what is not said, what is not represented, and how representations intersect and converge to maintain what is constructed as truth can also facilitate the emergence of ideas for changing the status quo.

For example, when the word "man" was used as a generic term to include women and other gender configurations, the subjugation of women as an outcome of this language practice was simply not recognized or perceived, and it was often denied as a possibility. In cultures in which there is no language for lesbian, gay, bisexual, or transgendered experiences, these experiences are not perceived as existing or even being possible. When the term *nurse* is taken to mean "female nurse," the possibility of a man who is a nurse is not perceived, and the qualifier "male" is required to bring this particular situation into awareness.

Critical postcolonialism and critical ethnography are other forms of critical scholarship that are used to produce formal expressions of emancipatory knowing. *Critical postcolonialism* approaches tend to focus on injustices that are created as a result of one culture taking over and subjugating another culture for its own gain. *Critical ethnography* suggests an anthropologic approach that examines structures and practices that sustain social inequities within a culture.

In critical analyses, including poststructuralist and feminist forms, multiple sources of data or materials that reflect oppressive situations can be used and combined with other sources of data to yield the most comprehensive picture of the situation (Georges & Benedict, 2008; Montgomery et al., 2009; Pauly et al., 2009). A scholar often begins with one data source for analysis and then turns to others in an effort to create the most complete analysis possible. Critical approaches require crossing disciplinary and academic lines that have falsely fragmented and continue to falsely fragment knowing and knowledge and that have not served the best interests of society. Academic and disciplinary lines have also sustained the academic heritage of the "ivory tower," which distances academic thinking and processes from the grassroots experiences of people in society. Without denying the valuable contributions of various disciplines to society and human welfare, the realization remains that academic disciplinary lines have tended to limit the creative process and formal expressions of emancipatory knowledge that lead to praxis, thereby resulting in limited solutions for many of the world's most persistent social problems.

Regardless of the specific methods used, critical analyses are characterized by a perspective that does the following (Fontana, 2004; Freire, 1970; Morrow, 1994):

- Trusts and remains loyal to people seeking liberation without assuming the right to speak for them
- Uncovers hidden ideologic premises (hegemony) embedded in social structures
- Examines what is assumed or presupposed in what is taken as knowledge or truth to reveal assumptions that are false
- Unveils conventions of language and symbols that limit the true representation of the situation
- Challenges current institutionalized power relations
- Projects actions and processes for changing the status quo to create equitable social relationships
- Calls forth a self-reflective attitude that constantly challenges one's own understandings
- Requires those participating in the work to disclose their personal perspectives and intentions related to their work

Taken together, these traits reveal the explicitly political and values-laden stance of critical analyses while maintaining the high standards of academic rigor. From a critical perspective, all academic processes that are used to develop knowledge are inherently laden with value, despite traditional scientific claims to the contrary. Critical analyses require that those who participate in these analyses bring to conscious awareness and disclose their own personal perspectives and share their intentions related to their work. By making these perspectives clear, the values that underpin the work are made accessible for challenge, discussion, and debate. The overriding intention is to deepen explicit ethical commitments to full human health and well-being for all and to act on those commitments (Fontana, 2004; Freire, 1970).

Integrated Expression in Practice: Praxis

All the processes within the dimensions of emancipatory knowing—critical questions, creative processes of imagining and critiquing, and formal expressions of emancipatory knowing—contribute to the creation of a new lens with which to view the world. This lens reveals something that is not perceived because it may seem natural, or because it is difficult to see beyond those things that are assumed to be true. When what has not been perceived before is seen, it seems to become perfectly obvious. Ways to effectively change the situation begin to make sense, and action occurs. As each action is taken, other insights and understandings begin to come to awareness, and new actions are taken. This circular emerging process of acting, gaining new insights, and acting again is *praxis*. The process of praxis is ongoing and begins as soon as critical questions are asked; it gains momentum as creative process and formal expressions are critically reflected and acted on and more critical questions are generated. The lines between the processes of emancipatory knowing are blurred and blend together in reality, but we identify and name them here as a way to explain the nature of praxis.

Consider This Example

The life and work of Karen Silkwood (portrayed by Meryl Streep in the 1983 film *Silkwood*) reflect the emancipatory knowing processes, including praxis. Silkwood was employed at a facility that manufactured radioactive materials for nuclear power plants. She became a union representative and was requested to investigate (ask critical questions) regarding health and safety at the plant. As a result of this "critical questioning," poor respiratory equipment, improper storage facilities, and violations of health rules were discovered (were imagined and critiqued, and requestioned) that should have protected workers from radioactive contamination. Silkwood testified (a form of action plan) along with other union members to the U.S. Atomic Energy Commission (AEC). Ultimately, in an effort to publicize the radioactive contamination of herself and other workers, she compiled a document (manifesto, action plan, critical analysis) that detailed violations at the plant. Driving to meet with a newspaper reporter, she was killed in an automobile crash of questionable origin, and the documents she planned to share were not found. After her death, the plant was federally investigated, and Silkwood's allegations were found to be true. Subsequently, the facility was closed (The mysterious death of Karen Silkwood, 2010).

The work of Karen Silkwood illustrates the process of praxis. It is important to note that praxis was occurring throughout the example. Her story illustrates the integrated expression of emancipatory knowing in practice. Silkwood began to recognize, understand, analyze, solve, and publicly act to expose and mitigate the radioactive contamination, an unjust practice that exploited plant workers. Although the closing of the facility might be considered the final event, the process embedded in this example continues in relation to similar unjust and unfair circumstances.

A contemporary example of praxis as the integrated expression of emancipatory knowing is the formation of the Rebellious Nursing group. These nurses, having recognized (critically questioned) unjust practices in their lives and in health care practices, have come together as a group to interact and plan (imagine, critique, formulate action plans and visions for the future) for changes that could eliminate those injustices. This group recently convened outside their ongoing practice environment to contemplate barriers, changes, and problems in health care and who benefits, undoubtedly returning to the context of care, raising more critical questions, and making changes in the work environment. The following statement describing their purpose illustrates the emancipatory intent of their work:

> We seek to create a world where all people receive and have a say in competent, compassionate, and respectful care in their communities. As opposed to a world where nurses are divided by education and training, as well as structural forms of oppression that pervade society, such as racism and sexism, we seek to include all nurses in our organizing on equal footing, by confronting what divides us. As opposed to a world where a wall is placed between healthcare providers and patients and their friends and families, we envision a world where caregiving is a communal activity. As opposed to a world where access to care and education is determined by money, we seek a future where we all contribute according to our abilities and everyone receives care according to their needs. (About RN!, 2013)

In summary, praxis is ongoing reflection and action; it is both an individual process and an interactive process. As nurses practice, they notice (critically question) situations that are not just or fair (reflection) and then begin to take whatever steps possible to eliminate those injustices (action). When this begins to happen, other nurses, health care providers, and persons in the situation are called on to participate. Nurses can initiate change in groups by coming together to share and explore the nature of an unjust situation (reflection) and begin to initiate changes (action). Fundamental changes in social structures cannot occur without collective participation. No matter how the process begins, it sets into motion an ongoing cycle of reflection and action, which is the hallmark of integrated expression in practice. Social change requires that, as each step toward change is taken, reflection on what is happening leads to the next stage of action.

Authentication Processes: Social Equity, Sustainability, Empowerment, and Demystification

The disciplinary processes for authenticating emancipatory knowing and knowledge include challenging and affirming the *sustainability* of real change and transformation and determining the extent to which *empowerment* and *social equity* for oppressed groups occur, as well as the extent to which previously hidden circumstances that have created injustices have been *demystified*. These processes are in boldface in Figure 3-1, and they extend through all layers of the emancipatory knowledge model.

Methods for authenticating emancipatory knowledge can be drawn from any of the fundamental patterns of knowing. Analyses, action plans, vision statements, and manifestoes can be examined with the use of the processes of dialogue and justification to determine how responsible and right they are for changing oppressive conditions. Confirmation and validation can be used to review empiric data that reflects the extent of change. Response and reflection can be used to examine and increase the degree of self-authenticity and personal change, whereas inspiration and appreciation can contribute to an understanding of the effectiveness of transformative change.

However, the process of praxis itself, when it is engaged in a collective sense, is the most important form of authentication. When authentication processes are used with a reflective eye toward uncovering and understanding injustices and acting to rectify unfair social practices, praxis simply *is:* it occurs, it is enabled, and it exists. Praxis ensures a constant process of engagement in thoughtful reflection and action to transform the world. With each turn of reflection and action, at least four ideals are used as a benchmark for determining the worth and validity of emancipatory knowledge, as follows:

Sustainability: how well the envisioned social change survives and thrives

Social equity: whether there is a demonstrable elimination or reduction of conditions that create disadvantage for some and advantage for others

Empowerment: the growing ability of individuals and groups to exercise their will, to have their voices heard, and to claim their full human potential

Demystification: the extent to which things that were formerly hidden from understanding are made visible and openly disclosed

Think About It

To deepen your appreciation of emancipatory knowing, consider the following questions related to the content of this chapter:

1. Recall a situation in which you recognized that someone was being treated unfairly. How did others in the situation react? Did anyone speak up at the time? If they did, how did others respond? What could have happened to change the situation? What needs to happen differently in other similar circumstances? What could prevent this from happening in the future? What was at the root of this unfair treatment?

2. What do you know about the experience and perspective of others who would identify as having a different sexual orientation or identity, a different gender, a different racial or ethnic heritage, or any other imaginable difference? Think about some ways in which you may gain a fuller appreciation and respect for those who would speak from these different perspectives. Why is it necessary for anyone to gain a fuller appreciation and respect in the first place?

3. Do you have a language for the experience of taking into account preferences or points of view that do not coincide with your own, and for working to achieve a solution to a problem that addresses all points of view? Consider a situation in which three nurses working together have very different ideas about caring for people who refuse treatment on the basis of their religion. What words can you think of to describe reaching a point of understanding among the three nurses that respects each nurse's point of view? What actions would each of these terms imply?

4. What do you think about the Rebellious Nursing statement (About RN!, 2013)? Are there ways that you can begin to make change like this happen where you work?

REFLECTION AND DISCUSSION – SUPPLEMENT ⊖

References

About RN! (2013). Retrieved January 9, 2014, from http://rebelnursing.org/about-rn/.

Alex, M., Whitty-Rogers, J., & Panagopoulos, W. (2013). The language of violence in mental health: Shifting the paradigm to the language of peace. *ANS Advances in Nursing Science, 36*(3), 229–242.

Almutairi, A. F., & Rodney, P. (2013). Critical cultural competence for culturally diverse workforces: Toward equitable and peaceful health care. *ANS Advances in Nursing Science, 36*(3), 200–212.

Ashley, J. (1976). *Hospitals, paternalism, and the role of the nurse.* New York, NY: Teachers College Press.

Aston, M. (2008). Public health nurses as social mediators navigating discourses with new mothers. *Nursing Inquiry, 15*, 280–288.

Bradbury-Jones, C., Sambrook, S., & Irvine, F. (2008). Power and empowerment in nursing: A fourth theoretical approach. *Journal of Advanced Nursing, 62*, 258–266.

Bunting, S., & Campbell, J. C. (1990). Feminism and nursing: Historical perspectives. *ANS Advances in Nursing Science, 12*(4), 11–24.

Carnegie, E., & Kiger, A. (2009). Being and doing politics: An outdated model or 21st century reality? *Journal of Advanced Nursing, 65*, 1976–1984.

Chinn, P. L. (2009). *Cassandra: Radical Feminist Nurses Network: 1982–1987.* Retrieved from http://www.peggychinn.com/cassandra.html.

Chinn, P. L. (2013). *Peace & power: Creative leadership for building communities* (8th ed.). Boston, MA: Jones & Bartlett.

Cowling, W. R., Chinn, P. L., & Hagedorn, S. (2000). *A nursing manifesto: A call to conscience and action.* Retrieved from http://www.nursemanifest.com/manifesto_num.htm.

Dock, L. L. (1902–1903). Sanitary inspection: A new field for nurses. *American Journal of Nursing, 3*, 529–532.

Doering, L. (1992). Power and knowledge in nursing: A feminist poststructuralist view. *ANS Advances in Nursing Science, 14*(4), 24–33.

Falk-Rafael, A. R. (2006). Globalization and global health: Toward nursing praxis in the global community. *ANS Advances in Nursing Science, 29*(1), 2–14.

Fontana, J. S. (2004). A methodology for critical science in nursing. *ANS Advances in Nursing Science, 27*(2), 93–101.

Foucault, M. (1980). *Power/knowledge: Selected interviews and other writing 1972–1977.* New York, NY: Pantheon Books.

Foucault, M. (1984). *The Foucault reader.* New York, NY: Pantheon Books.

Freire, P. (1970). *Pedagogy of the oppressed* (M. B. Ramos, Trans.). New York, NY: Seabury Press.

Georges, J. M. (2013). An emancipatory theory of compassion for nursing. *ANS Advances in Nursing Science, 36*(1), 2–9.

Georges, J. M., & Benedict, S. (2008). Nursing gaze of the eastern front in World War II: A feminist narrative analysis. *ANS Advances in Nursing Science, 22*(13), 139–152.

Giddings, L. S. (2005a). Health disparities, social injustice, and the culture of nursing. *Nursing Research, 54*, 304–312.

Giddings, L. S. (2005b). A theoretical model of social consciousness. *ANS Advances in Nursing Science, 28*, 224–239.

Grace, P. J., & Perry, D. J. (2013). Philosophic inquiry and the goals of nursing: A critical approach for disciplinary knowledge development and action. *ANS Advances in Nursing Science, 36*(2), 64–79.

Habermas, J. (1973). *Theory and practice* (J. Viertel, Trans.). Boston, MA: Beacon Press.

Habermas, J. (1979). *Communication and the evolution of society* (T. McCarthy, Trans.). Boston, MA: Beacon Press.

Hagedorn, S. (1995). The politics of caring: The role of activism in primary care. *ANS Advances in Nursing Science, 17*(4), 1–11.

Hall, L. E. (1966). Another view of nursing care and quality. In K. M. Straub, & K. S. Parker (Eds.), *Continuity in patient care: The role of nursing* (pp. 47–60). Washington, DC: Catholic University Press.

Hall, S. (2001). Foucault: Power, knowledge and discourse. In M. Wetherell, S. Taylor, & S. J. Yates (Eds.), *Discourse theory and practice* (pp. 72–81). Thousand Oaks, CA: Sage.

Heide, W. S. (1973). Nursing and women's liberation. *American Journal of Nursing, 73*, 824–827.

hooks, b (1993). bell hooks speaking about Paula Freire—The man, his work. In P. McLaren & P. Leonard (Eds.), *Paulo Freire: A critical encounter* (pp. 146–154). London, England: Routledge.

Jacobs, B. B., Fontana, J. S., Kehoe, M. H., Matarese, C., & Chinn, P. L. (2005). An emancipatory study of contemporary nursing practice. *Nursing Outlook, 53*, 6–14.

Jarrin, O. F. (2006). Results from the Nurse Manifest 2003 study: Nurses' perspectives on nursing. *ANS Advances in Nursing Science, 29*, E74–E85.

Kagan, P. N. (2006). JoAnn Ashley 30 years later: Legacy for practice. *Nursing Science Quarterly, 19*, 317–327.

Kagan, P. N., Chinn, P. L., & Smith, M. C. (2014). *Philosophies and practices of emancipatory nursing: Social justice as praxis*. New York, NY: Routledge.

MacDonnell, J. A. (2009). Fostering nurses' political knowledges and practices: Education and politial activation in relation to lesbian health. *ANS Advances in Nursing Science, 32*, 158–172.

Messias, D. K. H., McDowell, L., & Estrada, R. D. (2009). Language interpreting as social justice work: Perspectives of formal and informal healthcare interpreters. *ANS Advances in Nursing Science, 32*(2), 128–143.

Montgomery, P., McCauley, K., & Bailey, P. H. (2009). Homelessness, a state of mind? A discourse analysis. *Issues in Mental Health Nursing, 30*, 624–630.

Morrow, R. A. (1994). *Critical theory and methodology*. (Vol. 3). Thousand Oaks, CA: Sage.

Muller, M. E., & Dzurec, L. C. (1993). The power of the name. *ANS Advances in Nursing Science, 15*(3), 15–22.

The mysterious death of Karen Silkwood. (2010). *Legends & legacies*. Retrieved January 9, 2014, from http://www.legacy.com/news/legends-and-legacies/the-mysterious-death-of-karen-silkwood/135/#sthash.a7YL7N5J.dpuf.

Nightingale, F. (1979). *Cassandra*. New York, NY: The Feminist Press (Original work published 1852).

Nurse Manifest Project (2002). *Research study report*. Retrieved from http://www.nursemanifest.com/research_reports/2002_study/2002_study.htm.

Pauly, B., MacKinnon, K., & Varcoe, C. (2009). Revisiting "Who gets care?" Health equity as an arena for nursing action. *ANS Advances in Nursing Science, 32*, 118–127.

Phillips, D. A. (2006). Masculinity, male development, gender, and identity: Modern and postmodern meanings. *Issues in Mental Health Nursing, 27*, 403–423.

Pitre, N. Y., Kushner, K. E., Raine, K. D., & Hegadoren, K. M. (2013). Critical feminist narrative inquiry: Advancing knowledge through double-hermeneutic narrative analysis. *ANS Advances in Nursing Science, 36*(2), 118–132.

Racine, L. (2009). Applying Antonio Gramsci's philosophy to postcolonial feminist social and political activism in nursing. *Nursing Philosophy, 10*(3), 180–190.

Roberts, S. J. (1983). Oppressed group behavior: Implications for nursing. *ANS Advances in Nursing Science, 5*(4), 21–30.

Schön, D. (1983). *The reflective practitioner: How professionals think in action*. New York, NY: Basic Books.

Weiler, K. (1991). Freire and a feminist pedagogy of difference. *Harvard Educational Review, 61*, 449–474.

White, J. (1995). Patterns of knowing: Review, critique, and update. *ANS Advances in Nursing Science, 17*(4), 73–86.

White, J. (2014). Through a socio-political lens: The relationship of practice, education, research and policy to social justice. In P. N. Kagan, P. L. Chinn, & M. C. Smith (Eds.), *Philosophies and practices of emancipatory nursing: Social justice as praxis*. New York, NY: Routledge.

Ethical Knowledge Development

> *Certain fundamental ethical principles are universal and unchangeable, but the interpretation and application of truth changes and different people arrive at truth by widely different methods.... Adults who are dominated by the opinions of the herd may be morally retarded. We do not act morally unless we act from a sense of conviction and reason, guided by our own conscience.*
>
> **Isabel Stewart (1921–1922, pp. 906, 909)**

The opening quote suggests that, although certain ethical and moral directives seem universal, when they are used in clinical settings, the ways in which to use them are not always clear. Moreover, the quote assumes that a moral truth does exist, at least in given situations, and that knowing ethical and moral truth requires not only our conscience and conviction but knowledge of moral and ethical directives. According to Stewart, moral and ethical truths are not necessarily what everyone else believes.

Ethical matters can be complicated; what to do is often not clear, and the information needed to make a sound decision may not be available. For example, consider the ethical directive "do no harm," a commonly understood ethical principle. On the surface, this may seem like a truth that is easily honored, but how is it applied in a clinical setting?

Consider This Example

Jill and Armando are expecting their first child, and they know that they may be carriers of the gene for cystic fibrosis. However, they seem to be unaware that an opportunity for genetic testing exists. You know that, in this situation, genetic testing would confirm or negate the parents' carrier status, and should they be found to be carriers, the fetus can be assessed prenatally to determine if he or she has inherited the genetic mutation from each parent. You also know that, if this fetus has inherited both genes, the child will most certainly develop the condition, but its severity cannot be predicted. You wonder what you should say to Jill and Armando about genetic testing. When considering this situation, you recognize that the parents are devout Catholics who likely would not want to terminate a pregnancy for any reason. Moreover, you know that there are risks to the fetus associated with prenatal diagnosis, should they choose this. In addition, you can provide no assurances about the quality of life of the child should he or she develop the disease, because the condition could be severe or milder. Knowing this, you wonder if you should encourage genetic testing, and what ethical principles could guide your actions.

According to the quote from Stewart, as the nurse working with Jill and Armando, you will eventually resolve this ethical dilemma by considering the principle "do no harm" as well as by involving your own reasoning. When making your decision, a whole host of contextual factors will be considered, including legal or policy requirements for information disclosure, what you believe the parents' response would be if genetic testing were strongly encouraged, and what you believe constitutes caring in this situation. You will make a decision, and whatever decision is made will be the best you can do given the circumstances. What the "right" decision is may never be totally clear. You understand that, in this situation and countless others, "do no harm" becomes a complex and uncertain directive to enact.

In this chapter, we focus on methods for creating ethical knowledge. Figure 4-1 shows the quadrant of our model that pertains to the development of this pattern of nursing knowledge. Nurses, regardless of setting, bring to practice the heritage of their own moral development and understandings, as well as knowledge of ethical and moral practice obtained through formal education. With this background, as nurses practice and reflect on their practice, they begin to ask critical questions such as "Is this right?" and "Is this responsible?" These questions set into motion the creative processes of clarifying values and exploring alternatives. As these questions are answered, knowledge that can be shared and used in practice is developed, such as ethical principles and codes. Through the collective disciplinary processes of dialogue and justification, ethical knowledge is authenticated and understood in relation to practice.

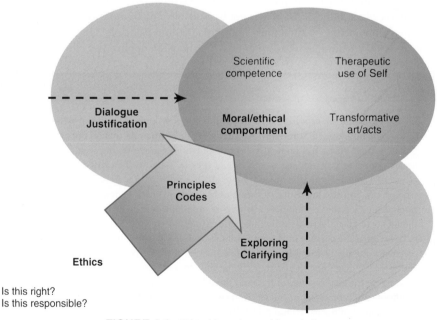

FIGURE 4-1: Ethical knowing and knowledge.

According to our model, nurses who make use of ethical knowledge that has been strengthened through the authentication processes of dialogue and justification can be expected to increasingly practice with *moral/ethical comportment,* the integrated expression of ethical knowing. In practice, further questioning occurs, and the stage is set for reinitiating the ongoing creative processes of clarifying values and exploring alternatives.

This chapter begins with a discussion of the nature of ethical and moral knowledge in nursing. We then consider the dimensions of ethical knowledge development in nursing shown in the model.

ETHICS, MORALITY, AND NURSING

Clearly, nursing is a profession that requires ethical knowledge to guide practice. Whether an individual is a seasoned nurse or a beginning student, and whether a nurse working in a high-tech intensive care environment or in an isolated rural elementary school, care outcomes depend on the nurse's ethical knowing and morality. According to Levine (1989), all nursing actions are moral statements. We would add that all nursing actions also are ethical statements. But what constitutes ethical behavior? How is morality determined? These are difficult questions to answer, and even when every effort is made to address ethical issues fully and appropriately, there is no guarantee that the right decision will be made.

Whether the business of ethics really is more complex today than it was historically is questionable, but the need to make ethical decisions has *always* been part of the modern nurse's role. Ethics is now receiving renewed emphasis, and nursing organizations are deliberately focusing on the need to attend to ethical issues. Certainly the complexity of the current health care arena has raised questions about what is ethical behavior. Advances in technology, concerns about the proper care of marginalized groups, laws that regulate disclosure in health care and research practices, a focus on the rights of individuals in the health care system, and technologic advancements are among the factors that have contributed to the complexity of ethical decisions, thereby creating confusion about what is the morally right thing to do.

Ethics and *morality* are commonly interchanged terms that are sometimes used synonymously in the nursing literature. We see ethics and morality as being enmeshed, and we use both terms together in this chapter and elsewhere in this book. The distinction between ethics and morality reflects the tension between epistemology and ontology and the difficulty of separating what we know from who we are. In general, ethics relates to matters of epistemology, or knowledge, whereas morality focuses on ontology, or being. Ethics is a discipline that structures knowledge, a branch of inquiry that tries to make sense of what is right or wrong. Ethics, then, is more like "head work," the products of which include ethical principles, theories, rules, codes, and laws; lists of obligations or duties; and descriptions of moral and ethical behavior.

There are two branches of ethics: descriptive and prescriptive. *Descriptive ethics* is an empiric endeavor that systematizes what people believe ethically and how they behave in relation to those beliefs. For example, suppose you conducted a survey of your student peers and asked the following: (1) "Is it wrong to use purchased term papers about nurse theorists and their work to fulfill course requirements?" and (2) "Have you ever done this?" Collating and reporting their answers would be in the realm of descriptive ethics. *Prescriptive,* or normative, *ethics* is concerned with the "oughts" of behavior. With the use of cognitive reasoning processes that incorporate emotional and other nonrational sources of behavior, prescriptions for ethical behavior are put into language and set forth as theories, codes, duties, principles, and so on.

Using the student peer survey as an example, you might reason how and why it is not permissible to purchase term papers to meet college course requirements by invoking a rule that deception is wrong. In this example, such a practice could be understood as deceiving faculty who expect you to do your own work. It also might be understood as self-deceit, because thoroughly learning about a theorist's work is short-circuited by simply reading a paper rather than composing it. As a result of your logical thought processes, you might propose an addition to the student code of ethical behavior in your school. In this example, the use of descriptive ethics (i.e., what is, with regard to beliefs and actions about term paper purchase) might reveal that prescriptions for ethical behavior need clarification because they are being violated (i.e., that such practices are deceitful and therefore wrong).

Notice that, in this example, the need for ethical directives around purchasing papers on the Internet would not have been necessary or even seen as a possibility 50 years ago. In this text, our focus is on prescriptive ethics, but it is important to recognize the value of descriptive ethics for examining the nature of ethical knowledge in nursing.

By contrast, morality is expressed in behavior and grounded in values. If ethics is head work, you might think of morality as "heart work" that is expressed by doing. Morality refers to our day-to-day living expressions of what we believe to be good, beliefs that are firmly embedded in our character. When people consistently behave in concert with their values, moral integrity is shown. When moral behavior is blocked by situational factors in a way that matters to persons, moral distress results. Peter and Liaschenko (2013) say moral distress results when the moral identities and responsibilities of nurses are constrained. For example, ethically you may believe that it is important to obey Provision 1 of the American Nurses Association Code of Ethics for Nurses (2010), which states that you should practice with compassion and respect for the dignity and worth of every individual. However, because time constraints imposed by a heavy patient load prohibit you from doing this in ways that really matter to you, you experience moral distress.

Morality is determined largely by situational and background experiences. Although people can appeal to ethical codes or principles to justify their actions, more often morality is shown on a less deliberative and conscious level. Daily expressions of belief about the right, the good, and the decent are filtered through lenses that are influenced by a host of factors, including family, friends, religion, gender, and developmental stage. Thus, what constitutes moral behavior varies, and what is important in one society (e.g., being on time out of respect for others) may be unimportant in another. A religious affiliation associated with one community may provide a lens that justifies war, whereas another may offer a lens that justifies pacifism.

Think About It

Consider a situation you have encountered in nursing that involved decisions of "right" and "wrong." What was your own judgment about what happened, or what was done? What in your experience shapes what you think of as "right" or "wrong" in such a situation?

Morality and ethics interrelate in that ethical knowledge can provide a basis or template for judging and evaluating moral standards and behavior. Conversely, moral or immoral behavior can provide a template for judging ethical knowledge. Consider the example of the U.S. Patients' Bill of Rights in Medicare and Medicaid (finalized in 1999) with its eight directives, summarized as follows:

- The right to information
- The right to choose
- Access to emergency services
- Being a full partner in health care decisions
- Care without discrimination
- The right to privacy
- The right to speedy complaint resolution
- Taking on new responsibilities for maintaining good health

The following is an example of ethical directives (ethical knowledge) being used to judge behavior as ethical or not. The right-to-privacy directive in the Patients' Bill of Rights states in part that patients have the right to confidentiality. Suppose that, as you worked your shift one day in a long-term care facility, you overheard a well-meaning social worker talking with a nursing attendant in a hallway. The social worker was helping the attendant understand the nature of a resident's dementia while visitors and other residents walked by. Because the resident who is demented was identified by name in the conversation, this activity clearly constitutes a breach of confidentiality as guaranteed in the Patients' Bill of Rights. Because the right to privacy (the ethical directive) was breached, the behavior of the social worker and the attendant could be judged as immoral. Within some systems of ethical reasoning, the intent of the participants is important to ethical decision making. In this situation, the social worker had good intentions of helping the attendant better care for the resident. Might the extent that the social worker's actions would be judged immoral change if the participants knew better but just didn't care? Regardless of how an incident such as this breach of confidentiality would be judged in relation to morality, it does violate a justifiable ethical directive. Several courses of action might be appropriate, including posting the Patients' Bill of Rights in a public space as a reminder of its meaning, or approaching the social worker and the aide and bringing to their attention the inappropriateness of their behavior in reference to privacy protections.

Conversely, the following example involves behavior being used to judge the adequacy of ethical knowledge. In the Patients' Bill of Rights, another ethical directive states that patients must take more responsibility for maintaining good health. On your same shift in the long-term care facility, you notice that a newly employed nursing attendant has taken this directive to heart and is encouraging a resident with compromised cognitive function to take more responsibility for his self-care. Given the resident's cognitive state, you understand that the attendant is asking the resident to do things that are physiologically impossible, resulting in the resident's health being compromised. In this example, the attendant attempts to behave morally in light of the directive, but unknowingly is compromising other ethical principles generally accepted in health care, such as the prescription to "do no harm." In this instance, the attendant's moral expression of the ethical directive is helpful for realizing that the directive needs to be changed or clarified for persons whose cognitive function is not intact.

Knowing how to act ethically is often not so clear. Rather, moral behavior is fluid; it occurs in the moment without time for contemplation, and it depends on situational understandings and circumstances. For example, suppose you feel justified in providing information to a patient who asked you about alternative health care practices, when you know that the primary physician is unwilling to supply information about their use. When the physician discovers you have provided this information and asks to talk with you, it turns out that both she and you believe that your respective actions are morally right. You believe the patient has the right to know and thus use the precepts that surround a patient's right to information to justify your action. The physician, on the other hand, provides reasons that indicate that her intent is to do no harm. The physician states that, in the past, she had given the same information to the patient, who had not acted on the information and subsequently became extremely anxious about making treatment choices. In short, your action of providing information on the basis of the patient's right to know (autonomy) was judged as the "right thing," whereas the physician, by withholding information, was also doing the right thing by protecting the patient's vulnerabilities (doing no harm) on the basis of a reasonable knowledge of the patient's condition. In this situation, the understanding that would arise from your conversation with the physician provides you with a perspective about the right thing to do that you can draw on in the future.

Sometimes, when the moral positions of physician and nurse collide, both positions are reasonable, and both parties to the moral positions hold strong beliefs about their correctness. Differences of opinion about the best course of action in a given situation are often grounded in a preference for different ethical precepts. For example, the desire to be beneficent by ensuring that what you do results in something good for the patient or client may conflict with the equally reasonable precept of individual autonomy, or the right of patients and clients to be self-determining. Both positions may be morally justifiable but may lead to different outcomes. Moreover, the outcome of acting in relation to one or the other ethical precept cannot be known. Physicians and nurses, because of their educational experiences and health care roles, may tend to use differing and conflicting ethical precepts in approaching some care situations.

In these situations, there may be no clear answers about how to proceed, and it becomes important to identify the political processes that are operating. If the client's welfare is the concern for both parties, the nurse and physician should be successful in engaging in dialogue that questions how right and responsible any decision is. Through this process, both the physician and the nurse (and the client, when feasible) can more fully understand the nature of the decision to be made and its potential outcomes. If the nurse's or the physician's attitude reflects more of a controlling or paternalistic position in relation to the client, other strategies may be warranted. In this instance, nurse and physician should recognize the nature of power imbalances and how these are sustained, and they should seek avenues related to emancipatory knowing that fundamentally will undermine or circumvent paternalistic patterns of control.

Legal requirements may also create moral distress and ethical conflict. Although appeals to ethical knowledge can be used to challenge and justify morality, they do not supersede the law. For example, if you have a strong moral disposition toward counseling an underage woman about her options for birth control, but such information is prohibited by state statute, an appeal to ethical knowledge (e.g., a code of rights) will not free you from legal responsibility in a court of law. In these cases, you have the choice to break the law, engage in deliberate civil disobedience to make a political statement, or work within professional organizations and local political circles to change oppressive laws.

What it is important to understand is that you, as a nurse, may act morally in relation to strong ethical precepts and end up in a court of law because your actions were illegal. Historically, changes in ethical and moral traditions have been made because people were willing to risk their lives and their personal freedom and security to ensure a broad base of human rights for others. Taking such a risk to make a political statement and to press a community to consider ethical and moral alternatives requires courage and strong moral conviction. It is also the case that ethical principles, held historically, may eventually become law. An example is the Health Insurance Portability and Accountability Act (HIPAA), which passed into law directives that protect the privacy of personal health information (Health information privacy, 1996). With regard to this act, doing what was once only the "right thing to do" is now legally required.

Ideally, whatever constitutes moral behavior in nursing (elusive though that may be) needs to be in place, understood, and grounded in ethical knowledge that supports and justifies yet challenges that morality. Nursing, similar to other professions, has a unique set of values and a particular culture and practice that affect the ethical decision-making processes. The goal to be approached by nurses is moral and ethical coherence that is supported by laws and other societal contexts that do not prohibit but rather allow for the expression of nursing's highest moral and ethical ideals.

OVERVIEW OF ETHICAL PERSPECTIVES

Within philosophic ethics, various theoretic perspectives have emerged that attempt to set forth the foundation on which to base ethical action. These approaches to ethics have been important for nursing as it attempts to create an ethical perspective on practice. The four perspectives that usually appear in nursing literature are briefly examined here: (1) teleology, (2) deontology, (3) relativism, and (4) virtue ethics.

Teleology and Deontology

Teleology and deontology are two common labels that characterize ethical systems. Most ethical codes and principles as well as systems of ethical reasoning and decision making can be broadly classified into one of these two types. In *teleology*, what is right produces good. Teleologic systems view the ends produced by a course of action as the measure that determines the action's goodness. What a right course of action yields is expressed in a familiar phrase: "the greatest good for the greatest number of people." Taken to extremes, teleologic systems could be used to justify behavior that is deemed harmful to a societal group if the harm that was done produced good for the rest of society. With the use of teleology, one could justify stripping a wealthy person of personal assets for redistribution to those who are poor and thereby producing a greater good for a greater number of people.

In *deontology*, what is right may not necessarily produce a good outcome; in other words, deontologic systems separate right from good. In deontologic systems, ethically right actions may have an undesirable outcome, as expressed by the following phrase: "the end does not justify the means." In deontologic frameworks for ethical decision making, knowledge forms such as external rules and codes determine what is right, regardless of the outcome produced. An extreme view of deontology is exemplified by someone who, because he or she is required by rule or precept to tell the truth, does the morally right thing and tells the truth, thereby causing great emotional distress to a client and that client's family (i.e., a bad outcome).

Deontologic systems suggest that the rules and the makers of the rules are in charge of ethical decision making, whereas teleologic systems assign decision-making authority to persons who make reasoned judgments about what constitutes the greatest good. Both deontologic and teleologic systems focus on the individual as a decision maker who is autonomous in action.

Relativism

Relativism exists in many varieties and basically is the claim that what is morally and ethically correct varies across cultures and societies. In relation to ethical systems of reasoning, relativists would argue that universal generalities about what constitutes moral action cannot be made. In relativism, ethical behavior and moral viewpoints are justified by, or relative to, any one of many viewpoints or standards. What is considered moral behavior and ethical knowledge is determined by the framework used when making a judgment, and no standard or viewpoint is privileged over any other.

In relativism, any one standard of morality is as good as any other, and all ethical precepts are equally true, assuming that these can be justified with the use of an acceptable framework (Blackburn, 2005). A relativist position may argue that an ethical system grounded in deontology is just as good as one that is grounded in teleology. For relativists, ethical systems and morality depend on historical timing, the culture and language within which the justification system is embedded, and the particular group and individuals involved in decision making (Bandman & Bandman, 2001; Mappes & DeGrazia, 2006).

Relativism may be a comfortable position to take because it circumvents a responsibility to know how to behave with some degree of certainty in the face of moral and ethical dilemmas. Under the extreme relativist view, incorporating any idea of moral and ethical comportment into a knowledge development model becomes something of a nonissue; moral and ethical comportment would be relative to every possible ethical situation, and thus standards for behavior could not be generalized to all nurses. Relativist claims also preclude the advancement of ethical knowledge because no standpoint for judging behavior is taken to be better than any other.

However, some dimensions of relativism are useful and seem necessary. Nurses often face tremendous clinical complexities as part of ethical decision making that prevent knowing with much certainty the best course of action. Although moral/ethical decision making involves uncertainties with regard to taking action that cannot be solved by *a priori* knowledge of what is moral and ethical, we believe we can move toward a shared idea of what constitutes moral/ethical comportment for nursing.

Virtue Ethics

Virtue ethics introduces the character of the person as an important determiner of moral/ethical decision making. Virtue or individual character is unimportant within the frame of reference provided by deontology and teleology. If ethical behavior could be reduced to the application of rules or calculations of good, character would be irrelevant. Character, however, determines how we perceive or frame situations, so a focus on the virtues of the nurse is critically important. Virtue ethics also offers a structure for moral/ethical comportment that can balance relativism by suggesting that a virtuous person will behave in a moral/ethical way. Virtue ethics allows flexibility when approaching moral/ethical situations, which deontologic and teleologic systems do not offer.

However, virtue ethics can be a particularly dangerous ethical system for a profession that is gendered in traditional female roles. Some focus on the cultivation of virtuous behavior seems important to ethical knowledge and knowing. Historically, however, for women to be virtuous meant to embrace a feminine ethic of being submissive, obedient, and self-sacrificing. It is important to question who defines what is virtuous and who benefits from the particular way in which the word *virtuous* is defined.

Our system for knowledge development includes aspects of both teleologic and deontologic perspectives. It also includes dimensions of relativism and virtue ethics. Although the knowledge forms include principles and codes, they are not taken to be infallible or to be adhered to at all costs. The creative processes of clarifying values and exploring alternatives can help to elucidate the situational contexts and decision-making frameworks that are important considerations for the modification of principles and codes. The authentication processes of dialogue and justification can function to temper rules and precepts and to sensitize them for different contexts. In addition, as the nurse acts, moral behavior and ethical knowledge are integrated with the other knowing patterns, including personal knowing, to create the best possible decision. This in turn can be further examined by questioning whether the action is right and responsible (rather than assuming that it is).

Our model incorporates a focus on virtues through the pattern of personal knowing, which grants the individual nurse the responsibility of examining what is virtuous. Emancipatory knowing suggests focusing on how and why particular virtues of nurses (e.g., caring, being on the job for patients despite heavy patient loads) may operate to maintain a problematic status quo (i.e., inadequate staffing that maximizes profits for hospital corporations to the detriment of caring nurses). The processes within the ethical knowledge quadrant help to ensure that, within the discipline, individual practitioners reflect on, discuss, and debate that which is virtuous in the context of nursing. As moral/ethical comportment is integrated in practice with other knowing patterns and subsequently examined by the critical questions ("Is this right?" and "Is this responsible?"), we expect that the growth of the discipline will evolve toward action and reflection that are consistent with praxis.

NURSING'S FOCUS ON ETHICS AND MORALITY

The virtues of a dutiful nurse were the focus of much literature about ethics during the first half of the 19th century (see Chapter 2). The historical work of Reverby (1987) underscores the nature of the nurse's duty to care while being denied the means to effect or create an environment in which caring is valued and possible. More recent nursing literature has shown increasing interest in the concept of *caring* as a centrally important focus for the development of both empiric and ethical theory. Much of the literature regarding the ethics of care centers on the relative merits of an ethic of caring compared with an ethic of justice, and how moral behavior relates to both (Barnes & Brannelly, 2008; Bell & Hulbert, 2008; Care Ethics, 2012; van Hooft, 2011; Vanlaere & Gastmans, 2011).

Nursing's focus on the caring perspective owes much to work that evolved from Carol Gilligan's critique (1982) and challenge of Kohlberg's theory of moral development (1976). Kohlberg's work staged moral development with the use of only male research participants, and Gilligan challenged its validity as a normative template for judging moral development in women. Gilligan found that women tended to care about relational concerns that focused on the needs and feelings of major players involved in the dilemma. By contrast, autonomy in decision making was a central feature of Kohlberg's theory.

Kohlberg's theory supported a morality in which actors could remain detached from the situation and appeal to rules or calculations of good as a guide to action. An approach that emphasizes detachment and objectivity in ethical decision making has been linked to traditional medical ethics approaches and critiqued as inappropriate for nursing. Fry (1989), for example, has suggested that the context of nursing practice requires a moral view of the person rather than a theory of moral action or a system of moral justification. For Fry, caring as a moral value ought to be central to any theory of ethics. Others have noted that concerns about autonomy and justice central to biomedical ethics traditionally have been male-gendered traits. Not only do these imply a separate-from or autonomous stance toward ethical challenges, but they also may be inappropriate for nursing, where gendered traits are typically female (Condon, 1992).

Historically, feminists have cautioned nurses about the alignment of moral decision making in women with care perspectives because of its potential to further entrench oppressive values (Hoagland, 1990; Houston, 1990; Liaschenko, 1993; Noddings, 2003; Tong, 2009). A central criticism of care ethics for women is that it represents a type of slave morality (Sander-Staudt, 2011).

Publications about the dangers of caring theory for nurses may have waned, but we believe the previous cautions of feminist writings are still pertinent. Feminist authors have chronicled the political reality of caring and urge caution lest we embrace a feminine—rather than a feminist—ethic (Liaschenko, 1993; Tong, 2009). Although it can become difficult to differentiate feminine and feminist ethics, writers such as Liaschenko suggest that a *feminine ethic* reflects the uncritical acceptance and embracing, often unknowingly, of traditionally feminine values that surround caring. Embracing a feminine ethic of caring means promoting as ethical the enactment of the virtues associated with caring: altruism, acceptance, loving unconditionally, and other stereotypic feminine traits.

Although this type of caring may seem to be a perfectly good thing to do and to exemplify a very good way to be, such feminine virtues associated with caring may preclude nurses from understanding how this type of caring benefits the health care industry to the detriment of nurses' salaries, working conditions, and social value. Whereas a feminine ethic is associated with the uncritical acceptance of stereotypic female caring as a template for judging moral behavior, a *feminist ethic* is associated with critically understanding the sociopolitical contexts that have gendered caring as feminine, and why and how this is problematic in relation to changing the situation of nurses within the health care system. In short, a feminine ethic of caring proclaims the importance of caring as being consistent with female-gendered virtues.

A feminist ethic would recognize that morality and social lives are interconnected, and that nursing's lack of power shapes our morality by determining whose ethical vision is authoritative (Tong, 2009). Feminist ethics require critical analyses that help nurses understand how to create contexts that would actually allow nurses to care. The caution to embrace a feminist rather than a feminine ethic, for feminist writers such as Liaschenko (1993), is a plea to understand how blind adherence to the feminine virtues of caring can preclude caring by allowing for the continuance of conditions that exploit those who care. An ethics of care that does not ask who is caring for whom and whether care relationships are just is not liberatory (Sander-Staudt, 2011).

We believe that nurses must be concerned with issues of both care and justice if nursing's purposes are to be realized. Walker (1993) suggested that nurses' moral expertise is not a question of mastering codes and laws but rather a matter of being architects of moral space within the health care setting and mediators in the conversations that are taking place. To do this requires paying attention to the vulnerabilities of both an ethic of care and an ethic of justice. As Cooper (1991) explained, we must take seriously the moral demands of care in the development of ethics. Doing so requires radical responses and moral courage as well as political astuteness. Ethical choices should be guided not only by rules and principles but also by the thoughtful analysis of feelings, intuitions, and experiences (Noddings, 1999; van Hooft, 2011).

DIMENSIONS OF ETHICAL KNOWLEDGE DEVELOPMENT

Our view of ethics is in concert with Carper's original conceptualization of the ethical pattern, which included dimensions of both morality and ethics intersecting with legally prescribed duties. Moreover, no single ethical or moral view is embraced, but nurses need to be constantly vigilant about the sociopolitical context in which they function. According to Carper (1978), "The ethical component of nursing is focused on matters of obligation or what ought to be done. Knowledge of morality goes beyond simply knowing the norms or ethical codes of the discipline. It includes voluntary actions that can be judged as deliberately right and wrong" (p. 20).

When examining the nature of ethical knowing and knowledge, the following questions naturally arise: Toward what end should ethical knowledge be developed? What ought to be done in practice to earn the label *ethical* or *moral*? What values support nursing's ethics and morality? Toward what clinical ends should ethical theories, reason, and ethical principles move us? What sort of moral development perspective should we embrace and encourage?

We might ask the following questions:

In the context of teleology: How do we know what the greatest good is?

In the context of deontology: How do we know which rules are good and which are not?

For virtue ethics: Which virtues are worthwhile for us to cultivate?

Such questions relate to the final value from which no others can be derived and that centers our knowledge development efforts and professional activities. Although we will not answer these questions, we do provide guidelines for ways to create answers in your own situation. Because our model combines aspects of each of these positions, these are central questions that require thoughtful consideration.

As the dimensions of the model are discussed in the following sections, some answers are provided, but additional questions are raised. For us, the merit of ethical knowledge will be judged based on the extent to which ethical codes and principles contribute to our collective ability to reflect and act in such a way that what we think and know is fully consistent with what we do. This implies increasing the reflective awareness or consciousness on the part of nurses as nursing is practiced. It implies a move toward action that is grounded in an open awareness and choice for both the client and the nurse, in other words, a move toward health. It implies a move to reduce the moral distress that nurses face as they encounter and negotiate ethical and moral dilemmas.

The pattern of ethics focuses on nurses' day-to-day moral decision making. Ethics goes beyond what many tend to think of as ethics (i.e., the weighty, dramatic decisions that often involve end-of-life contexts or controversial political and social issues). Rather, important ethical knowing is used and created in everyday incidents and in the work of nurses (Liaschenko, Oguz, & Brunnquell, 2006). According to Thompson (2007), bioethics may be only marginally meaningful to most nurses; the language of bioethics deflects attention from the political organizations of care and the challenges of day-to-day nursing care. Ethical knowing in nursing is reflected in the decision to ignore a comment or to attend to it, in considering what to say and what not to say during everyday conversations, or in deciding whether to keep information to oneself or reveal it. Ethical decisions that are made around a conference table by an ethics committee, although important, are not our major focus or the major domain of nursing's morality and ethics. Rather, ethics arises from the work that nurses do and is about everyday uses of morality and ethical knowledge, as expressed in moral/ethical comportment in typical practice settings. Nursing's morality is largely an everyday ontology.

Critical Questions: Is This Right? Is This Responsible?

In our model for knowledge development, ethical knowledge is generated with the following critical questions asked of ethical knowledge and moral behavior: "Is this right?" and "Is this responsible?" As you work as a nurse, this type of questioning is in the background whether you realize it or not. Without such questioning, you would be unable to make day-to-day moral/ethical moves.

We assume that nurses bring to their work some base set of values that guide their ethical decisions and moral behavior. As they work within the everyday world, their moral/ethical selves are challenged every day. For example, a nurse might ask the following: Should I reveal to an elderly woman that her family is cleaning out her apartment and does not intend to allow her to return home? Should I share my views about what is responsible childbearing with a young couple who discover that they both have diabetes? Would this cause more harm than good? What would be gained? Who would gain? If you reflect for a moment, several instances in which you have faced such ordinary decisions should come to mind. You will probably notice that your decisions were made relatively quickly, without obvious reference to ethical codes or principles, and that you did wonder what was right and responsible. As you consider these questions in the moment of practice, you act in relation to your knowledge about what is ethical with consideration for other patterns of knowing. You will also reflect on the principles, codes, and other ethical knowledge forms that guided your actions apart from actual practice, in an attempt to understand more fully what was done and what should have been done in the situation.

Creative Processes: Clarifying Values and Exploring Alternatives

As you or others inquire about how right and responsible your decisions are within your particular context, different perspectives on ethical decision making will become apparent. Clarifying values and exploring alternatives are the creative processes that begin to answer these questions. Simply stated, as you consider whether your moral/ethical behavior (as guided by disciplinary ethical knowledge) is right and responsible, you clarify the values that come into play as the situation unfolds, particularly those that create a dilemma. During this process, you are drawn to consider and explore various actions and options that flow from each value, which leads to the further clarification of the values themselves. Moreover, you and others can revisit and revise ethical knowledge forms to make them better guides for moral/ethical comportment.

Values Clarification. Values clarification processes deliberatively question and raise awareness of the personal values that undergird action. In this way, these processes have the potential to improve the moral/ethical correctness or "rightness" of a decision. The specific values that give rise to a nurse's moral/ethical decisions and actions (and subsequently ethical knowledge expressions) are often hidden. Values can be viewed as the background information or assumptions that create moral and ethical questions and actions. Values provide a lens that brings into focus certain aspects of a moral problem while at the same time distancing or blurring others. Values vary among individuals and reflect the contexts of our experiences with family members, friends, social institutions, gender boundaries, and age. The questioning of values with the use of formal techniques of clarification assumes that values may not always be "good." It also assumes that a disjunction exists between the values that we believe are important for influencing our actions and those that actually do influence what we do and say.

There are various techniques for values clarification (Bandman & Bandman, 2001; Catalano, 2008; Simon, Howe, & Kirschenbaum, 1995). Fundamentally, these processes involve the use of rational thought and emotional awareness to understand and examine the values that guide your actions. Approaches can involve the use of real or contrived dilemmas, group or individual work, self-analyses, interviews, or any number of other methods that free individuals to examine and embrace their values. The clarification of values is often an emotionally charged activity that involves deeply held personal beliefs. Individuals or groups who engage in values-clarification processes need an environment that allows for the freedom of value choices and for the affirmation of the values clarified. Regardless of the techniques used, values clarification is an individual process that seeks to unveil deeply held values that are often taken for granted. Values clarification is important because it emphasizes affective thinking and behavior-motivated choice and allows you to question how responsible your moral/ethical decisions are.

Various approaches for values clarification generally follow some basic general guidelines. First, it is important to select or create a moral/ethical dilemma that you and those working with you will emotionally relate to and that you will not see as fictitious to your practice. Although common approaches (e.g., Which person would you throw from the sinking boat?) may suffice, we believe that it is more beneficial if the situations relate to actual or potential nursing practice. Second, it is important to focus on clarifying individual values that emerge from the process, regardless of the process used for clarification. When performing values clarification, there may be a tendency to avoid what is difficult. Lively discussions about what should be done are not a substitute for a deliberative focus on one's personal values. A third guideline emphasizes writing about or listing personal values that emerge. *Journaling* about your values helps you make values explicit and clarify what the values are, and it provides a forum for examining how and why values change. Because it is difficult to provide a public forum in which nurses can freely examine their values, journaling is a particularly important tool, especially when the moral/ethical dilemmas that are the focus for deliberation are derived from practice situations that you are likely to encounter.

Exploration of Alternatives. The exploration of alternatives is an important process for understanding the moral/ethical correctness of a decision. Unlike values clarification (i.e., an attempt to understand emotionally, clarify, embrace, and perhaps change individually held values), an exploration of alternatives seeks to more objectively understand and analyze the values inherent in a certain situation and the various actions that flow from those values. During the process of exploring alternatives, you examine how different courses of action might flow from or challenge your values. As you explore what is or what could be happening morally and ethically in a situation, you begin to see alternative actions and even alternatives to your personal values. In addition, you begin to recognize the merits and pitfalls of different approaches to moral and ethical decision making. You strive to set aside your own values as much as possible and to view value structures—both your own and those of others—from different perspectives. During the process of exploring alternatives, you strive to gain clarity on an issue and examine various points of view, both factually and logically, as well as different approaches to resolving a dilemma.

As with values clarification, the situations that you choose for the exploration of alternatives arise from your practice. You explore the values that are important to the situation and the various actions that flow from those values. If factual evidence for one point of view is provided, that evidence is examined for accuracy. An ethical decision that is arrived at logically is then tested in some manner (e.g., by looking at its consistency with a principle or code for ethical behavior). However, when you are exploring alternatives, you are concerned not only with factual evidence but also with the preferences and beliefs of those who are involved in the situation. For example, when people are involved in end-of-life care, each individual will have personal beliefs and preferences about how best to care for the person who is dying. Each person's personal beliefs and values regarding death, life, and life after death influence how he or she approaches the situation. The facts about the dying person's physical condition, physiologic indicators that the end of life is near, and observable behaviors are all factors that influence the situation. However, many alternative actions can be taken, even when all the facts remain constant. As you explore all the alternative actions that arise from the various values of those involved and the dilemmas that arise from competing ethical values, you gain insight and understanding of the situation, ultimately with increased clarity about those actions that are right, good, just, and responsible.

Values Clarification and Exploration of Alternatives Using Ethical Decision Trees. A number of sources suggest the use of decision trees as an approach to ethical decision making (Burkhardt & Nathaniel, 2007; Ellis & Hartley, 2004; Frame & Williams, 2005). Although the elements that constitute ethical decision-making trees vary somewhat, fundamentally they are depicted as flowcharts or a series of ordered questions that begin with the identification of the ethical issue or problem. After the problem is identified, the user is guided linearly through a number of steps that, when followed, suggest an ethically correct decision.

Ethical decision trees call for the gathering of facts about the situation in relation to the ethical framework that is being used. Options are considered, situational factors are identified, and an evaluation of various courses of action is required before a decision is proposed. Some decision trees prescribe, at least in part, the ethical framework to be used, whereas others expect the user to designate or choose the framework that is relevant to the situation.

Ethical decision trees are particularly useful when there is enough time for effective consideration and clarification of the requisite details within the elements of the tree before a decision is made. Ethical decision-making trees reflect what Liaschenko and Peter (2004) identify as a *disciplinary* type of ethics that suggests the professional activities of nurses that are understood in a certain way are inherently moral. They propose that approaches that limit what counts as a moral or ethical concern and that authorize how these concerns are resolved—as decision trees often do—incompletely reflect the complexity of contemporary health care.

However, decision trees can be useful as a learning tool. As with the nursing process, ethical decision trees offer a system that, once learned, helps nurses more quickly integrate the details involved in ethical situations and make an appropriate decision. The trees also make the factors and processes involved in ethical decisions less opaque and help learners understand what is and what is not ethically justifiable.

Completing decision trees can be useful for values clarification and the exploration of alternatives. Case studies of ethical problems can be organized into decision trees rather than being discussed directly. Decision trees can be completed by individual participants and then examined with the use of questions for values clarification, such as those posted on the *Evolve* website. In addition, as participants individually complete decision trees, details that are important to consider within various elements required by the tree (e.g., the consequences of an action) will not be self-evident. When placing details of an ethical situation within a decision tree, it is important to notice which details require deliberation before making a choice and which can go unquestioned.

During this process, individual values tend to be clarified. As different members of the group suggest what must be included as relevant, the validity of various views within the group is likely to be challenged. Some members may notice that certain details were omitted that, in their view, should have been included. Others may not have even considered certain details as being relevant, whereas still others may offer reasons for omission as well as for inclusion. As discussions and disagreements occur, underlying values are made more visible to individual participants within the group. In addition, when individuals separately or groups collectively reflect on the extent and conditions of their agreement with a completed decision tree, values are clarified and alternatives explored.

Finally, changing the details that are entered in the elements of a decision tree and noticing how it affects both the processes and the outcomes of decision making is a useful clarification technique. Similar processes can assist in exploring alternatives using completed decision trees. Elements required within the trees as well as the details in completed trees can be questioned for underlying assumptions and conditions of context that have precluded the possibility of making some decisions. As participants notice the details within various elements as well as the elements themselves, the underlying values and how these are operating come to light.

Both values clarification and the exploration of alternatives are important processes for understanding the nature of right and responsible moral/ethical decisions in relation to the knowledge form that is generated. The juxtaposition of personally cherished but problematic values (from values clarification) and possible alternative values (from the exploration of alternatives) deepens an individual's understanding of what is possible and what is necessary for nursing practice. When problematic value positions are challenged by a person who sees that alternative positions are possible in certain situations, personal values can change.

The creative processes of clarifying and exploring include (whether recognized or not) references to justice and care perspectives that involve ethical decision making, as well as to ethical principles and codes that are consistent with the deontologic and teleologic perspectives. Within our model, therefore, exploring and clarifying processes occur when questions are raised about what is right behavior and what is responsible behavior. From these creative processes, formal expressions of ethical knowledge are created and recreated, and the integrated expression of ethical knowledge in practice as moral/ethical comportment is promoted.

Formal Expressions of Ethical Knowing: Principles and Codes

The formal expressions of ethical knowledge that we have identified are principles and codes, which are common in nursing (Numminen & Leino-Kilpi, 2009). However, other forms do exist. Ethical knowledge may be sets of rules; statements of duties, rights, or obligations; theory; or laws. The Nightingale Pledge (which, we would like to add, was not created by Florence Nightingale) and the Hippocratic Oath also are forms of ethical knowledge. An individual nurse or a group of nurses setting forth an ethical position for disciplinary use could put that position in the form of an article, a case analysis, or even a poem.

We choose principles and codes as generic forms of ethical knowledge because they are attainable and common forms of ethical knowledge in nursing. For example, the American Nurses Association has created a Code of Ethics for Nurses (2010). Nurses are also taught to operate within common forms of ethical knowledge, such as principles of autonomy and beneficence. We prefer to avoid associating ethical knowledge forms with theory to prevent confusion about the differences between ethical and empiric theories. Regardless of its form, we believe that, eventually, ethical knowledge can be reduced to principles and codes, which are shorthand ways of expressing ethical knowing.

Integrated Expression in Practice: Moral/Ethical Comportment

The integrated expression of ethics in practice is moral/ethical comportment. The term *comportment* basically refers to how people behave and, in this case, how they behave in relation to what they do morally and what they know ethically. Moral/ethical comportment requires the consideration of all other knowing patterns in the moment of practice. In the example of Jill and Armando at the start of this chapter, the nurse had to integrate her empiric knowledge of genetics; her personal feelings that Jill and Armando's fetus ought to be genetically tested and the pregnancy terminated if both parents carried the gene for cystic fibrosis; her aesthetic knowing to be sensitive to how Jill and Armando might respond if offered genetic testing; and her emancipatory knowing that testing is expensive and that, unfairly, Jill was not eligible for insurance coverage because of a preexisting condition. As this and other information are considered during the moment of ethical decision making and the decision is made, the nature of one's moral/ethical comportment becomes clear. How nurses act and the decisions they make in the complex contexts of practice ultimately contribute significantly to the processes for development of ethical knowledge (Doane, Storch, & Pauly, 2009).

Authentication Processes: Dialogue and Justification

It is within the model's processes of dialogue and justification that knowledge is more deliberatively examined with reference to the perspectives of justice and care. Through these processes, ethical knowledge is examined and refined, and it becomes part of the disciplinary heritage that individual nurses subsequently carry into practice. This knowledge is revisited and challenged as the need arises by asking the critical questions: "Is this knowledge right?" and "Is it responsible?" With these questions, nurses consider whether disciplinary forms of ethical knowledge guide right and responsible ethical decisions. These questions engage the clarifying and exploring processes that we have described with the use of dialogue and justification.

Dialogue requires a community of those who are challenged by an ethical problem. They come together as a community—face to face, online, or through exchanges in the professional literature—to examine established ethical perspectives, principles, and codes (Btoush & Campbell, 2009; Freysteinson, 2009; Quaghebeur & Gastmans, 2009). As a group, they strive to understand alternative points of view more fully. On some issues, they come to a point where they can accept, reject, or modify the knowledge form. On others, the dialogues continue over long periods of time.

Traditionally, ethical knowledge forms have been examined for internal logic as a standard of validity. Although internal logic is important for coherence, it is an insufficient standard for establishing the value of ethical knowledge in nursing. With dialogue, ideally multiple voices over time will be integrated into justification processes. The choice of the word *justification* suggests no particular framework for establishing the value of an ethical knowledge form.

Justification processes for ethical knowledge forms in nursing can appeal to the authority of historical values associated with nursing, existing moral/ethical knowledge, currently held values, and values and moral knowing consistent with an envisioned future. For example, the value of caring might be cited as an important historical factor that can be used to justify caring in nursing; in other words, caring as a historically embedded duty justifies caring as a contemporary value. Principles of nonmaleficence or autonomy, as baccalaureate students generally learn, might be called on to justify ethical knowledge. In addition, an envisioned future may form a critical template against which to reflect ethical knowledge. This occurs when we question whether caring is an ethic that will help us to achieve professional autonomy and identity. It is assumed that the collective voice of nursing will be the best hope for the emergence of appropriate and productive justification frameworks as the basis for re-envisioning the form of ethical knowledge.

We have chosen an eclectic approach to forming and justifying ethical principles because we believe no single perspective is entirely useful for all situations. Rather, the more likely scenario is that multiple justification perspectives will be used. Care must be balanced with a concern for justice; rules must be used in the context of doing the least harm or benefiting people in some way. Read the example in Box 4-1 to consider how this process unfolds. Although this example is somewhat contrived, the message is that dialogue and justification led the team to question the initial thinking about what was

BOX 4-1	Dialogue and Justification: An Example

As an example of how care and justice might emerge with the use of the processes of dialogue and justification, suppose that you and your peers are examining a situation beginning with a deontologic perspective that provides a rule for ethical action. The situation involves a mother who is suspected of inflicting physical harm on her young child.

The 2-year-old girl, who is currently being hospitalized for an emergency appendectomy, has bruises and marks that you believe are the result of being struck. However, the mother attributes them to the caregiver, who, you subsequently learn, is the child's grandmother. Although old and new bruises are seen, the child has no broken bones and appears to be quite healthy otherwise.

Assume that the rule being discussed is that of *nonmaleficence:* doing no harm. This is a principle that is generally followed by you and the professional group with whom you work. You and others initially suggest that doing no harm in this case means establishing the source of the child's bruises and subsequently protecting the child from further injury. As the dialogue proceeds about how to report concerns to child protective services or to ask the mother more pointedly about the bruises and their source, the dialogue and justification processes take an unexpected turn, and you begin to realize that doing no harm in this situation is becoming fairly complex.

The social worker on your team reveals that the mother is unmarried, must work outside the home to support herself and her child, and out of necessity is leaving the child in the care of the grandmother to minimize child care expenses. The mother cannot afford paid child care because she needs her income to meet expenses, including renting an apartment that keeps her whereabouts hidden from a former partner who abused both her and the child in the past.

A staff nurse states that he has talked with the grandmother during a recent visit. He offers the information that, although the child's grandmother is well meaning and loving, she was recently confined to a wheelchair because of a progressive, long-term debilitating muscular disease. The staff nurse believes that that the grandmother may bruise the child inadvertently by bumping her against the wheelchair or other household items as she provides care. An intern on the team shares that the grandmother had voluntarily offered in a conversation with her that, on occasion, the child had slipped from her arms to the floor, and the grandmother was worried that this may have caused the child's appendicitis. The intern, from talking with the grandmother, believes that generally she manages to care for the child properly, and certainly she intends to be a good caregiver to help her daughter.

Given the ongoing dialogue, it is becoming apparent that it might actually be harmful to the young child not to allow the grandmother to provide care during the day, if it means the child's return to the mother's care, the loss of the mother's income, the discovery of the mother and child by the abusive partner, and the risk of harm to both.

right, in that unconsidered approaches to protecting the young child from harm could likely result in unintended consequences of harm.

Justification and dialogue raise the question of what should prevail. What about the rule of doing no harm? Should the rule be violated to produce a greater good? The answers are never totally clear, but open, reasoned, and knowledgeable dialogue seems to be an effective approach to making the best decision. For the situation in Box 4-1, perhaps the best decision might be—assuming that the bruises are unintended, not seriously life threatening, and occurring because of the grandmother's physical condition—to let the grandmother continue to care for the child and to teach her care techniques that minimize the risk of physical harm to the child. As the situation changes (e.g., if the child is or may be seriously injured while in the grandmother's care), a different decision will emerge from the justification and dialogue processes. In the example, it is knowledge within the pattern of emancipatory knowing that would be a core solution. Such knowing would require critical analysis and action involving, for example, the sociopolitical context that contributed to the situation of a single parent with no options for financial support or safe child care.

Many different groups with a variety of justification perspectives carry out the justification and dialogue processes to develop ethical knowledge over time. Ethical knowledge is often communicated in a vacuum, and we know little about how it is actually used or applied. Arguments for one type of approach versus another are academically interesting, but positions become blurred, and the conditions within the work environment of nurses are often ignored. As analyses and understandings subsequent to the process of dialogue and justification find their way into the disciplinary literature and other venues where dialogue can occur, ethical knowledge forms will achieve legitimacy in relation to practice. It is unlikely that anything that could be considered "final" will ever evolve, because ethical knowledge is never used in the same context. However, the ideal of generating ethical knowledge from practice and refining that knowledge, with the intent that it will be returned to practice, needs to be the goal.

Through dialogue and justification, many perspectives can be brought to bear on ethical knowledge. The open questioning and dialogue that considers the context of working nurses is nursing's best hope for usable and effective ethical knowledge and moral behavior. It is through justification processes that an understanding of ethics and morality in nursing will be approached and will allow the knowledgeable and committed action required for praxis to emerge.

Think About It

To deepen your appreciation of ethics, consider the following questions related to the content of this chapter:
1. How have you integrated the patterns of knowing when making ethical decisions? Describe the situation and how the various patterns were reflected in it.
2. Consider a situation in which you experienced moral distress (i.e., you were unable, through no fault of your own, to do the right thing). What needs to happen so that the next time you are in a similar situation, you will not experience moral distress?
3. What aspects of your work environment—patterns of control, rules, and prohibitions—positively or negatively affect your ethical decision making?

REFLECTION AND DISCUSSION – SUPPLEMENT ⊖

References

Bandman, E. L., & Bandman, B. (2001). *Nursing ethics through the life span* (4th ed.). Upper Saddle River, NJ: Prentice Hall.

Barnes, M., & Brannelly, T. (2008). Achieving care and social justice for people with dementia. *Nursing Ethics, 15,* 384–395.

Bell, S. E., & Hulbert, J. R. (2008). Translating social justice into clinical nurse specialist practice. *Clinical Nurse Specialist: The Journal for Advanced Nursing Practice, 22,* 293–301.

Blackburn, S. (2005). *Truth: A guide.* New York, NY: Oxford University Press.

Btoush, R., & Campbell, J. C. (2009). Ethical conduct in intimate partner violence research: Challenges and strategies. *Nursing Outlook, 57,* 210–216.

Burkhardt, M. A., & Nathaniel, A. K. (2007). *Ethics and issues in contemporary nursing* (3rd ed.). New York, NY: Delmar.

Care ethics (The ethics of care). (2012). *A presentation of the northeast Ethics Education Partnership and Ethical Awareness for International Collaboration.* Brown University. Retrieved January 23, 2014, from http://www.brown.edu/Departments/Environmental_Studies/QuigleyPowerPoint/TheEthicsofCare_pptTM_Updated10122012.pdf.

Carper, B. A. (1978). Fundamental patterns of knowing in nursing. *ANS Advances in Nursing Science, 1*(1), 13–23.

Catalano, J. T. (2008). *Nursing now: Today's issues, tomorrow's trends* (5th ed.). Philadelphia, PA: Davis.

Code of Ethics for Nurses with interpretive statements. (2010). Retrieved January 10, 2014, from http://www.nursingworld.org/MainMenuCategories/EthicsStandards/CodeofEthicsforNurses/Code-of-Ethics.pdf.

Condon, E. H. (1992). Nursing and the caring metaphor: Gender and political influences on an ethics of care. *Nursing Outlook, 40*(1), 14–19.

Cooper, M. C. (1991). Principle-oriented ethics and the ethic of care: A creative tension. *ANS Advances in Nursing Science, 14*(2), 22–31.

Doane, G. H., Storch, J., & Pauly, B. (2009). Ethical nursing practice: Inquiry-in-action. *Nursing Inquiry, 16,* 232–240.

Ellis, J. R., & Hartley, C. L. (2004). *Nursing in today's world: Trends, issues and management* (8th ed.). Philadelphia, PA: Lippincott, Williams & Wilkins.

Frame, M. W., & Williams, C. B. (2005). A model of ethical decision-making from a multicultural perspective. *Counseling & Values, 49,* 165–179.

Freysteinson, W. (2009). The twins: A case study in ethical deliberation. *Nursing Ethics, 16*(1), 127–130.

Fry, S. T. (1989). Toward a theory of nursing ethics. *ANS Advances in Nursing Science, 11*(4), 9–22.

Gilligan, C. (1982). *In a different voice: Psychological theory and women's development.* Boston, MA: Harvard University Press.

Health information privacy. (1996). Retrieved from http://www.hhs.gov/ocr/privacy/.

Hoagland, S. L. (1990). Some concerns about Nel Noddings' caring. *Hypatia, 5*(1), 109–114.

Houston, B. (1990). Caring and exploitation. *Hypatia, 5*(1), 115–119.

Kohlberg, L. (1976). Moral stages and moralization: The cognitive-developmental approach. In T. Lickona (Ed.), *Moral development and behavior: Theory, research, and social issues* (pp. 31–53). New York, NY: Holt, Rinehart & Winston.

Levine, M. E. (1989). The ethics of nursing rhetoric. *Image—The Journal of Nursing Scholarship, 21,* 4–6.

Liaschenko, J. (1993). Feminist ethics and cultural ethos: Revisiting a nursing debate. *ANS Advances in Nursing Science, 15*(4), 71–81.

Liaschenko, J., Oguz, N. Y., & Brunnquell, D. (2006). Critique of the "tragic case" method in ethics education. *Journal of Medical Ethics, 32,* 672–677.

Liaschenko, J., & Peter, E. (2004). Nursing ethics and conceptualizations of nursing: Profession, practice, work. *Journal of Advanced Nursing, 46,* 488–495.

Mappes, R. A., & DeGrazia, D. (2006). *Biomedical ethics* (5th ed.). New York, NY: McGraw-Hill.

Noddings, N. (1999). Care, justice, and equity. In M. S. Katz, N. Noddings, & K. A. Strike (Eds.), *Justice and caring: The search for common ground in education* (pp. 7–20). New York, NY: Teachers College Press.

Noddings, N. (2003). *Caring: A feminine approach to ethics and moral education* (2nd ed.). Berkeley: University of California Press.

Numminen, O., & Leino-Kilpi, H. (2009). Nurses' codes of ethics in practice and education: A review of the literature. *Scandinavian Journal of Caring Sciences, 23*, 380–394.

The Patients' Bill of Rights in Medicare and Medicaid. (1999). Retrieved from http://www.medcareservice .com/DC/Medicare-Information/The-Patients-Bill-of-Rights-in-Medicare-and-Medicaid.cfm.

Peter, E., & Liaschenko, J. (2013). Moral distress reexamined: A feminist interpretation of nurses' identities, relationships, and responsibilities. *Journal of Bioethical Inquiry, 10*(3), 337–445.

Quaghebeur, T., & Gastmans, C. (2009). Nursing and euthanasia: A review of argument-based ethics literature. *Nursing Ethics, 16*, 466–486.

Reverby, S. M. (1987). *Ordered to care: The dilemma of American nursing, 1850–1945.* Cambridge, United Kingdom: Cambridge University Press.

Sander-Staudt, M. (2011). *Care ethics.* Internet Encyclopedia of Philosophy. Retrieved January 10, 2014, from http://www.iep.utm.edu/care-eth/.

Simon, S., Howe, L., & Kirschenbaum, H. (1995). *Values clarification: A handbook of practical strategies for teachers and students* (Rev. ed.). New York, NY: Hart.

Stewart, I. M. (1921–1922). Some fundamental principles in the teaching of ethics. *American Journal of Nursing, 21*, 906–913.

Thompson, J. L. (2007). Poststructuralist feminist analysis in nursing. In C. Roy & D. A. Jones (Eds.), *Nursing knowledge development and clinical practice* (pp. 129–143). New York, NY: Springer.

Tong, R. (2009). *Feminist thought: A more comprehensive introduction* (3rd ed.). Boulder, CO: Westview Press.

Van Hooft, S. (2011). Caring, objectivity and justice: An integrative view. *Nursing Ethics, 18*(2), 149–160.

Vanlaere, L., & Gastmans, C. (2011). A personalist approach to care ethics. *Nursing Ethics, 18*(2), 161–173.

Walker, M. U. (1993). Keeping moral space open. *Hastings Center Report, 23*(2), 33–40.

Personal Knowledge Development

Chapter

5

http://evolve.elsevier.com/Chinn/knowledge/

Self is a dynamic concept, ever deepening as we expand and broaden our relationships with others. The Self is created in relation to others.

Beverly Hall and Janet Allan (1994, p. 112)

The opening quote for this chapter suggests that people know who they are through their relationships with others, and that who a person is changes over time. In this context, the idea of relationships does not imply only close or intimate relationships, as with a partner. Rather, relationships include contacts and interactions with the people you relate to from day to day. These relationships can be close in varying degrees, casual, and even so subtle as to go unnoticed. In addition, in the context of personal knowing for this text, you can also have a relationship with your Self that reflects who you really are compared with the Self you project or you want others to see.

In a sense, all knowing is personal, because people can only know their own understandings, mental images, perceptions, experiences, memories, and thoughts (Bonis, 2009). However, for the purposes of this text and for the construct of patterns of knowing in nursing, we use the concept of *personal knowing* to refer to a process of self-knowing that is conscious; it is developed deliberately to know fully who you are and to understand your actions and relationships. Personal knowing is shaped by your relationships with others, and it also shapes your relationships when caring for others. As such, personal knowing is a conscious process that cultivates your wholeness and the wholeness of others.

Consider This Example

A young woman named Alia might be characterized a "jet-setter." Alia has much wealth at her disposal and has not had to work or become educated to maintain her standard of living. She is hospitalized because she was driving while impaired and sustained multiple injuries when her sports car ran off a cliff.

The nurse assigned to care for Alia—we'll call her Christie—has come to know her personal Self as a hardworking person who is responsible. Christie knows this largely because her parents and teachers have reflected to her and her brothers the importance of "making something of themselves." Her parents taught their children to work hard, to get a good education, and to contribute meaningfully to society. Christie did this, although it was not easy. Her parents also reflected to the children that those who have wealth and do nothing productive are undeserving if not contemptible. As a result, the nurse has a deeply held

continued

Consider This Example—cont'd

value that worthiness is a byproduct of being responsible and socially productive. At the same time, Christie was also taught in her nursing program that each person deserves to be respected and cared for as an individual, despite who they may be, and that each person is inherently valuable. Because of who Christie is, as a personal Self, if she did become aware that her nursing care for Alia was lacking in any way, she would be distressed.

As Christie cares for Alia, it is inevitable that who Christie is as a person—her core Self—will affect her nursing care. Without fully realizing it, because of her background, experiences, and values, Christie might be slightly punitive and withhold comfort measures just a little while longer than she otherwise would, or she might conveniently forget to call the kitchen when a special menu request is made, explaining to Alia that she became busy with another patient. She might not make an effort to understand anything about Alia as a human being, but rather focus on her care as just another situation to tolerate and get through. In this example, the Self of Christie and her care would benefit by a focus on personal knowing.

Personal knowing requires that you be in touch with who you are and understand that who you are as a person affects your behavior, attitudes, and values both positively and negatively. Through personal knowing, you live your life with deliberate intent; your actions come to be in harmony with your deepest intentions. In short, personal knowing is the dynamic process of becoming a whole, aware Self and of knowing the other as being valued and whole. It brings you to a place of knowing what you do and doing what you know.

Personal knowing is the basis for the expression of an authentic or genuine Self. It is also essential for a healing relationship and fundamental to the essence of what it means to be human (Green, 2009). Returning to our example, assume that the nurse was able to tolerate Alia despite her feelings toward her patient and thus was able to provide acceptable care. Tolerance alone does not engender the growth of personal knowing. However, if the nurse began to reflect on how she truly felt about Alia, she could then begin to recognize the basis of her feelings and how those feelings affect her nursing care. As the nurse reflects on her background and how it influences who she is, she can make a conscious choice about the person that she wants to be as a nurse. Through this process, the nurse becomes more genuine and authentic. Her actions grow to be more in harmony with what she would choose them to be: compassionate and caring toward Alia, just as they would be toward any other person.

Think About It

- How has what you know about your Self benefited or compromised your nursing care?
- Have you ever cared for someone like Alia in the example, or known another nurse who has? How was care affected?
- Is there anything about your Self that you know you would like to shift in order to be a better nurse?
- How difficult or easy would it be for you to change some aspect of your Self? What would it require?

PERSONAL KNOWING IN NURSING

Personal knowing as knowledge of the Self is perhaps the most difficult pattern to understand, because the nature of the Self and knowing the Self are elusive concepts. The ideal of personal knowing is to become a more whole and authentic Self. To know who you are, you need to embrace, internalize, and reflect on the responses that you receive from others as a clue to the Self that you are. As you more fully understand your Self, you realize possibilities for who you might become in the future as you grow and develop.

Personal knowing is expressed as the Self: the person you are. In other words, you are known to others because of who you are. Initially, people recognize you because you have a certain appearance; your face and other features of your physical Self are recognizable. People begin to know you by name. As they come to really know you as a person, people recognize not only your physical appearance but qualities of your Self that are expressed through your actions and the daily choices that you make. You might be known as someone who has a great sense of humor, who likes beans but not carrots, who loves to dance, or who is afraid of heights. All these things and many more constitute the "you" that others come to know, and these make you distinctly recognizable as you and not someone else. Others experience and know you as unique by virtue of your deeply personal qualities that are conveyed through being in the world within the context of the culture.

You know your Self as the person you are in part because of how others perceive you. You may not appreciate your sense of humor, for example, unless other people come to recognize this in you and give you feedback. You might not be aware that your food likes and dislikes are so obvious to others, and once you sense how they react to your being a certain kind of eater, you might decide to learn to change how you approach your food choices. At a deeper level, as you reflect not only on the reactions of others but also on how it feels to you *to be* you, you begin to make deliberate choices about the type of person you really want to be in the world. This process is what we refer to as *personal knowing*. It is an ongoing process that leads to change and growth toward wholeness, authenticity, mind-body-spirit congruence, and genuineness.

This chapter details the dimensions of personal knowing and provides examples of concepts related to personal knowing. Figure 5-1 provides an overview of the personal knowing pattern of our model for knowledge development in nursing. As shown, nurses bring to their practice the Self they are. As they care for others and reflect on their caring practices, knowing arises as they ask critical questions: "Do I know what I do?" and "Do I do what I know?" The creative processes of opening and centering flow from these questions, and these creative processes foster the development of formal expressions of personal knowing.

One formal expression of personal knowing is the *genuine* Self. The genuine Self conveys directly, without words, who one is. Personal or autobiographic stories are also formal expressions of personal knowing but are less direct than the actual Self (i.e., the person in the world). Personal stories are limited in their capacity to convey the fullness of the person, but they provide a means of communication with a wide audience and illuminate various paths to the creation of a more genuine Self.

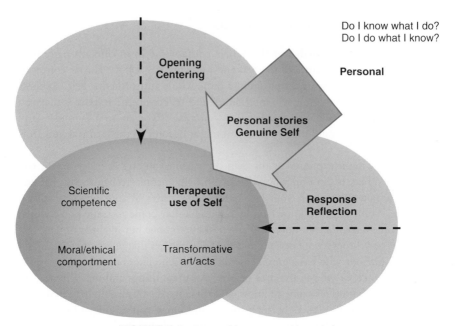

FIGURE 5-1: Personal knowing and knowledge.

Response and *reflection* are the authentication processes within the personal knowing pattern. Response and reflection in relation to personal knowledge expressions are necessary for us to know who we are as individuals, and they are the basis for continued growth. According to our model, nurses who practice using personal knowledge that has been strengthened through the authentication processes of reflection and response will increasingly improve with regard to the ability to use the Self therapeutically. As seen in Figure 5-1, the integrated expression of personal knowing in practice is the therapeutic use of the Self. This chapter opens with an exploration of the conceptual meanings of personal knowing in nursing and then details the dimensions of personal knowing identified in Figure 5-1.

CONCEPTUAL MEANINGS OF PERSONAL KNOWING

Carper's early description of personal knowing points directly to transcendent interpersonal encounters as central, defining qualities of personal knowing:

> One does not know about the self; one simply strives to know the self. This knowing is a process of symbolically standing in relation to another human being and confronting that human being as a person. This "I-Thou" encounter is unmediated by conceptual categories or particulars abstracted from complex organic wholes. The relation is one of reciprocity, a state of being that cannot be described or even experienced—it only can be actualized. (Carper, 1978, p. 18)

For Carper, personal knowing is connected to an "I-Thou" encounter that actualizes the Self in a way that is instantaneous and transcendent. If you have ever had an experience, most likely a powerful and memorable one, during which you "just knew" or "understood" something about another and your Self without contemplating or thinking about the person, you most likely have experienced what Carper conceptualized personal knowing to be. This sort of personal knowing happens in a compelling human-to-human moment, and it is both transcendent and immediate. For Carper, personal knowing actualizes the wholeness and integrity in each encounter and immediately knows and affirms the Self of the person.

Examples are difficult because personal knowing as conceptualized by Carper is not explained or recounted, it is only experienced. However, an encounter described by a young nurse serves as an example. A young man she was caring for was slowly dying from an abdominal gunshot wound sustained while committing a petty crime. One day, during the course of care, this young man motioned for the nurse to come to his bedside. As she approached, he held out his arms, pulled her in close to his face, and whispered, "You are the best nurse I ever had." In that moment, this young man was fully known not as a criminal or a dying man but simply as a person. It was an unmediated and unexpected knowing of Self and other that just was. To this day, the recollection of this moment that occurred more than 40 years ago is still vivid and powerful for this nurse. We believe that this type of in-the-moment knowing of another is the "I-Thou" experience that Carper associated with personal knowing.

Personal Knowing as Spiritual in Nature

Personal knowing has been linked with spirit and to what is sometimes referred to as *spiritual understanding* (Bishop & Scudder, 1990; Pesut, 2008; Pesut, Fowler, Taylor, Reimer-Kirkham, & Sawatzky, 2008; Stevens-Barnum, 2010; Register & Herman, 2010). *Spirit* is a term derived from the Latin word for "breath" and "breathing," which are basic to sustaining life and being (Huebner, 1985).

The term *spiritual* is often associated with religion, a tradition that Hall (1997) identified as deriving from the fact that Western culture limits the expression of what is known either to science or to religion. Because of this, alternative conceptualizations of the spiritual have not been as visible as those that associate spirituality with religion. Many people do connect their spirituality with religious beliefs; however, that which is spiritual does not of necessity link with religiosity (Campesino & Schwartz, 2006; McSherry & Cash, 2004; Pesut et al., 2008; Tinley & Kinney, 2007). Rather, the spiritual is a complex combination of values, attitudes, and hopes that is linked to the transcendent and that guides and directs a person's life. It is particularly associated with life experiences that bring one to the brink of uncertainty: the "existential boundary issues" of life and death, good and evil, hopes and dreams, and despair and suffering. Personal knowing, when viewed as being spiritual in nature, provides a way for people to understand and shape their lives as they confront difficult challenges. This form of spirituality helps people to face the inevitable realities of life that create vulnerabilities and that cannot be overcome. Spirituality nurtures a personal agency for relating to such vulnerabilities (Hart, 1997).

Hall (1997) presented a conception of human spirit and spirituality as reaching within to learn to accept, love, and value what you find there and learning to be yourself authentically and with confidence. What you find may not be what you want to find, but you either change or come to live with, accept, and love what is within. This spirituality is not a process of self-centered exploration, nor is it linear. Rather, it is an unfolding process that is grounded in the context of everyday experience in relationship with others.

Personal Knowing as Self-in-Relation

Hall and Allan (1994) explained the vital link between personal knowing and relationships with others in their concept of Self-in-relation. Personal knowing and wholistic nursing practice are possible through Self-in-relation, which is the core of caring and healing. These authors' ideas are grounded in traditional Chinese medicine, which philosophically views the mind, body, spirit, and environment as an integrated whole. The embodied Self is an open system that belongs to a social world. The caring relationships that nurses enter into can reflect four dynamics that nurture Self-in-relation, as follows:

Caring by giving requires being present and involved in relation with others. In this process, mutual sharing develops the Self and the other by giving to one another and by affirming the value and purpose of each life.

Empowerment develops a sense of the Self as being responsible for one's own health and involves the context in which health is possible for everyone. Empowerment in relationship gives rise to the ability to influence one's own health outcomes. When the Self is fully in relation with the other, both are empowered, and unconditional love occurs. Both learn the joy of reciprocity, which occurs when what each brings to the interaction is deeply valued.

Knowing the value of a human life comes from a mutual quest to find meaning in life. In a healing relationship, questions of living and dying come to the surface, thus inviting an openness to explore what is possible in a particular time and space. Openness while fully engaging with another person in this quest develops the Self in each.

Sense of community is the most important and yet the most elusive concept. Basically, this dynamic means that a supportive and caring community is required for the development of Self-in-relation.

Personal Knowing as Discovery of the Self and the Other

Moch (1990) defined personal knowing as the discovery of the Self and other that is arrived at through reflection, the synthesis of perceptions, and connecting with what is known. She identified three overlapping components of personal knowing: (1) experiential knowing, (2) interpersonal knowing, and (3) intuitive knowing.

Experiential knowing is the understanding and knowledge that comes from participating in the events of daily living; it is deepened by attending to the experience, studying the process of the experience, and connecting the experience to previous understandings. Attending to the experience involves being aware of what one is feeling and sensing and observing the Self and others. For Moch, both cognitive and spiritual processes contribute to deriving meaning from experience. *Interpersonal knowing* is increased awareness as a result of interaction or being with another. It emerges from intense attending to the moment, opening the Self to the other, and conveying feelings to one another. *Intuitive knowing* is the immediate knowing of something without the conscious use of reason.

Moch (1990) identified the following attributes of personal knowing:

- Personal knowing can be viewed only in the context of wholeness; there is no knowing apart from the knower.
- Personal knowing includes a process of encountering. The ideal encounter is one of mutual respect that affirms those involved in the encounter.
- Personal knowing involves passion, commitment, and integrity. Passion affirms something as valuable, commitment motivates the search for personal meaning, and integrity brings thought and action together as an authentic whole.
- Personal knowing is the instantaneous "aha" experience during which one's perspective shifts, either consciously or unconsciously.

Personal Knowing as Unknowing

Munhall (1993) reflected Carper's point that knowing the other sets aside personal assumptions and generalizations. She stressed the nature of a genuinely authentic encounter by conceptualizing a pattern of "unknowing" to signify the openness to the other that must occur during such an encounter. Unknowing creates a stance that is completely open to the experiences and perceptions of others as they experience them and not filtered by the nurse's own structures of understanding. Unknowing means setting aside all that is assumed to be known about the other, as well as previously held organizing structures that make sense of the world. This requires a "decentering" from the perspective of the Self and a movement toward considering the perspective of the other. This occurs when the nurse takes a deliberate stance of complete openness and receptivity to the unique subjectivity of the other and remains open to a deep knowledge of the other, to different meanings and interpretations, and to varying perceptions of the world. Unknowing is similar to the phenomenologic process of "bracketing" but specifically refers to a type of personal openness that is more than intellectual; it is a full mind-body-spirit openness that creates existential availability to know another deeply.

Summary: Common Meanings for Personal Knowing

Despite certain distinctions in each of these conceptualizations of the meaning of personal knowing, important threads are common to all. These threads form the conceptual understandings on which our approaches to developing personal knowing are based, as follows:

- Personal knowing grows out of relationships and interactions with others and out of deep reflection on experiences with others.
- Personal knowing goes beyond cognitive reasoning; it depends on deep reflection that brings about an awareness of meaning and direction in one's life.

- Personal knowing brings about congruence between one's actions and one's values.
- Personal knowing brings about a wholeness that embraces the entirety of existence and experience.

DIMENSIONS OF PERSONAL KNOWING

Personal knowing is fundamental to nursing because interpersonal relationships are inherent in nursing practice. Meaningful interpersonal connections do not occur in a vacuum and are not happenstance. Well-developed personal knowing is a requirement for being fully present with another.

The label "personal knowing" can be misleading in that it can imply a solitary and individual process that involves only the unique perceptions of the individual. However, as shown by our overview of the conceptualizations of personal knowing, relatedness is essential for the development of personal knowing. Personal knowing does require deep inner reflection that is sometimes solitary and that comes from within the individual; in other words, it involves a form of the Self in relation with the Self. However, personal knowing also requires openness to experience the world and to have mutual meaningful interactions with others. Contemporary popular notions of self-actualization and individuation reinforce images of the individual on a lone, often self-indulgent journey of discovery. Moreover, contemporary cultures that primarily value empiric knowing reinforce the limited and mistaken notion that people are essentially rational egos who seek individual autonomy, rights, and freedoms (Hart, 1997). Despite these dominant cultural contexts, personal knowing is not a quest of a rational, autonomous ego. Rather, personal knowing as we view it is intimately connected to relationships with others. In the following section, we focus on the epistemologic aspects of how we come to know and express the whole, genuine Self and enhance the authentic being of the other.

Critical Questions: Do I Know What I Do? Do I Do What I Know?

In our model of knowledge development in nursing, the pattern of personal knowing requires asking two critical questions: "Do I know what I do?" and "Do I do what I know?" These questions, as with the other patterns, can be asked apart from the context of practice or in the moment of practice. These questions assess the authenticity of the Self and the extent of the therapeutic use of the Self in care situations, and they initiate the process of personal knowing.

All nurses bring to their work an understanding of the Self that guides how they use that Self therapeutically. Think about caring for a person whom you typically view in a negative light. We use the examples of an older person with dementia, a morbidly obese woman with diabetes, and a homosexual man with acquired immunodeficiency syndrome. The care provided for people with traits such as these is often jeopardized and influenced by the typical stereotypes and stigmas associated with who they are and what they are experiencing. In such situations, asking the critical question "Do I do what I know?" creates an awareness of the values of the good nursing care that you believe in and reflection on the extent to which you are providing that form of care in this situation.

The critical question "Do I know what I do?" brings about reflection on what you know to be the care you are providing and the realization that perhaps your practice is falling short because of the stigma and stereotyping that prevail with regard to particular individuals.

Each of the critical questions points to important aspects of the experience and processes involved in developing personal knowing. As you honestly ask and answer these questions, you will uncover areas for growth of the Self toward authenticity so that you will move toward doing what you know and knowing what you do.

Creative Processes: Opening and Centering

As you or others ask the critical questions, the extent to which your knowing Self and your doing Self are congruent becomes clearer, and creative processes that acknowledge and develop your personal knowing can be initiated. The creative processes involved in developing personal knowing evolve in unique and individual patterns throughout a person's life, but there are ways to develop personal knowing that can be described and carried out.

The ability to grow toward becoming a more genuine and authentic Self requires deliberate preparation and intent. Figure 5-2 depicts the creative processes of opening and centering. Over time, these processes ground the individual in the center of the Self (represented by the heart in the figure) so that the Self is known, valued, affirmed, and loved for what it is. Specific opening and centering practices that can be used are journaling, meditation, and various body-mind-spirit practices such as yoga, tai chi, labyrinth walking, drumming, and chanting. These types of meditations bring mind-body-spirit into wholeness, create a

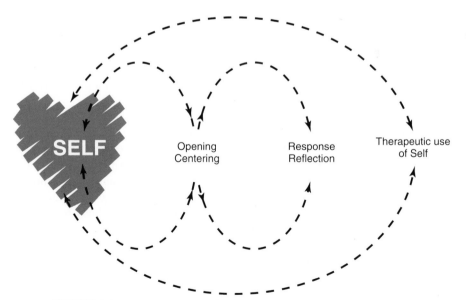

FIGURE 5-2: Creative processes of personal knowing: opening and centering.

time-space of inner calm and peace, and bring personal intentions and meanings to realization at a deep level that transcends consciousness. Such practices also make it possible to bring deeper meanings to conscious awareness to shape your actions in harmony with your inner intentions.

From time to time, realizations that come from private opening and centering processes enter into shared experiences with others, thus providing the opportunity to exchange responses and to integrate new perceptions and reflections. As you return to your private time-space of opening and centering, responses that you have received from others deepen and enrich your experience of your Self. In the figure, the inner dotted loops represent reflection as it moves through opening and centering, back and forth between the heart center of the Self and the interactive responses of others, to depict the circular movement among the aspects of opening and centering. Opening and centering provide the core strength and character that are necessary to enter into an authentic encounter in which the heart center or the Self of the person opens to be fully present with and for the other. The larger dotted oval represents how private opening and centering processes that are shared with others to create a more genuine and authentic Self in turn foster increasingly authentic encounters with others and support the therapeutic use of the Self.

Opening and centering to grow in personal knowing are different from therapy or counseling. Therapy can assist a person with his or her quest for personal knowing, but therapy involves other purposes that focus on returning one's Self from a troubled or disturbed situation to one that is less troubled and more able to cope with life's difficulties. Therapy often involves an unequal relationship in which one person provides therapeutic guidance and the other receives it. Many practices that are used for opening and centering (e.g., meditation, journaling, labyrinth walking, tai chi) can also be used for therapeutic purposes. However, opening and centering are vital processes that are required to fully know the Self and to constantly deepen inner knowing and self-wisdom, regardless of therapeutic or healing needs.

For some, opening and centering can be closely linked to prayer. However, prayer is generally a process of communing with a higher power, a divine being, or the universe, whereas meditative opening and centering are ways of listening to your own heart, your own Self, and your own inner wisdom (Hall, 2004).

The creative processes of personal knowing can be integrated into daily life and can provide a focus on knowing the Self as a whole, authentic being. These processes contribute to self-healing and focus the energy of the Self without interference from outside sources. Opening and centering can be facilitated by others or enhanced by joining with others to share in a particular self-healing practice. However, opening and centering require one's own deepest intentions and attention. When opening and centering to nurture self-knowing, the individual reaches into an attentive mind-body-spirit center to come to know and love what resides within.

Opening and centering are interrelated and occur in many different ways and in many different contexts. The processes of opening and centering focus on your lived experience and the meaning of that experience. These processes can be engaged spontaneously or can be deliberately scheduled as individual, solitary processes that contribute to self-knowing (Beckerman, 1994).

In the following section we discuss two specific practices that you can use for opening and centering: journaling and meditation. These practices nurture Self-knowing and prepare the Self for authentic encounters. Although we focus here on journaling and meditation, you may find and use many other approaches to the creative processes of opening and centering.

Opening and Centering Practices

Journaling and Meditation. Journaling is an avenue for opening and centering that nurtures self-knowing. It is a private encounter with the inner Self. Through journaling, you can be your Self without fear of judgment by others. You can acknowledge those things about your Self that might otherwise be hidden. Journaling provides a platform for understanding the Self, for growth, and for change (Banks-Wallace, 2008).

Meditation often goes hand in hand with journaling. Meditation requires clearing the mind and inviting a deep inner awareness to emerge. Both journaling and meditation benefit from consistent and regular practice, time devoted to the practice, and solitude away from other people and things. There are many different reasons for journaling. In the context of developing personal knowing, what you write is never to be shared with others unless you choose to do so. To be a useful practice for full discovery and knowledge of the Self, your journal should be something that you write with the intention of keeping it private to maintain your sense of safety for the expression of whatever feelings and perceptions emerge from deep within. In your journaling, you can let fears, anxieties, anger, and fantasies surface without even your own censoring. There are no critics peering into the inner Self; even your own critical judgment is withheld as you seek to know and understand your deepest Self.

⊖ Image Collection – Intentional Journaling

We reserve the term *journal* for the type of private opening and centering process writing that is not to be shared with others. If you do decide to share something from your journal but you are not comfortable sharing it in the form in which it appears in your journal, you can extract and revise segments from your journal with the intent of sharing with others for response. Alternatively, you might be required to write what someone refers to as a "journal" as an assignment that must be shared with one or more other people. When you write something that you are required to share or that you plan to share, consider starting with the kind of private writing that we describe here, to gain the deepest insights so that your inner knowing can flourish. You can then revise your private journal into a document that can be shared, and you can include only what you are willing to share with others (Nelson, 1994).

As you settle into a time for journaling, begin with meditation: sit still and quietly, turn your focus to your breath, and take several deep breaths. Let the sense of your being settle into a centered space. You can repeat a sound, a mantra, or an affirmation that brings your focus closer to your center and to your deepest intentions, hopes, and desires. Affirmations should begin with "I" and be stated in the present tense. In addition, they should be positive, reflect your personal way of talking, and be stated as if what you want to become has already happened. For example, you might repeat an affirmation such as "I am a loving and accepting person" or "I am at peace with the path of my life" (Chinn, 2007).

When you feel ready, move to your journal to begin to bring your inner perceptions to the page. Journaling can include recounting facts and events, but it should move beyond these to explore how you feel and what is going on inside of you. As other people enter your reflections, you can move back to your own center and explore your sense of being in the situation and the relationship. When journaling as an approach to personal knowing, it is important to let your innermost thoughts come to the surface, however difficult it may be. Acknowledging the nature of our deepest Self is critical to realizing our full, genuine, and authentic Self.

Journaling is a process of working from both the conscious and the subconscious and of engaging in an inner experience with the Self. The inner experience sensitizes your perceptions of events, people, and situations and brings you to a place of harmony and wholeness with who you are in relation to your world (Beckerman, 1994).

As you journal, abandon rules about written expression to express your feelings and perceptions fully. You can doodle, draw, and let nonverbal images find expression on the page. Let the unexpected emerge without censorship or judgment. Imagine what you hope and dream for and what your deepest desires are. If you feel drawn to analyze and judge what is coming forth, move back to nonverbal meditation, focus on your breath, and turn your attention once again to being open and feeling unconditional love and value for who you are. Insights will come from your journaling that enhance your ability to analyze and rationally think through problems, so you can let go of anything that is drawing your attention toward the rational processes of problem solving while you are journaling. Use journaling to deepen your own inner sense of worth and self-love, which will grant you greater clarity and strength to address the issues that you face day to day. While you are meditating and journaling, always treat yourself as if you totally love yourself (Nelson, 1994).

You can enter into journaling with a specific intent, or you can enter the time-space with no particular intent other than to let your perceptions of your inner being come to the surface. If you are new to journaling, or if you have had an experience or are involved in a situation that is saturating your consciousness, you can use a specific intent to focus your journaling and meditation. Again, the intent is not to solve problems but rather to explore a particular aspect of your inner Self. Images can also be used to focus your journaling and to draw you into your inner Self. Beckerman (1994) used works of art that depicted caring and focused her journaling on her perceptions of caring within the works of art. You can create an intention around your hopes and dreams, around memories, or around experiences. For example, you could write a prayer to express your deepest hopes and dreams. You could spend time journaling about different "selves" you have been throughout your life, such as your child Self, your afraid Self, and your confident Self. Typically, starting with a focus simply opens doors and begins the journey to deep reflection; the path of the reflection then moves in directions of personal change and growth.

The creative processes of opening and centering assist with the knowing of the genuine, authentic Self and with coming to understand and love who and what we are. It is this self-knowing and self-love that subsequently mobilize and allow us to continue to grow and change in ways that continue to heal and create wholeness in the Self and in others and to create a Self that is therapeutic in the context of care.

Formal Expressions of Personal Knowing: Personal Stories and the Genuine Self

Personal stories and the genuine Self are the formal expressions of personal knowing that emerge from the creative processes of opening and centering. The genuine Self, as Carper (1978) initially proposed, is the active, acted-in-the-world form of expression of personal knowing.

Personal stories provide a written form of expression of personal knowledge. Formally developed stories written in the first-person voice of the nurse provide a means of conveying personal knowing in a form that can be widely communicated within the discipline. Personal stories can recount an instance that occurred in practice that conveys to others something about the experience of the therapeutic use of the Self.

Personal stories developed from your journal are a way of sharing insights that come to you from journaling while keeping your journal a protected and private document. You may have journaled about feelings and emotions surrounding a situation without writing the story of the situation. As you identify what you want to share, you might not include anything from your very personal journaling, but rather use your journal to bring you back to the experience as a way to develop the story for sharing. Your journal will also draw you into deeper reflection regarding the meaning of the situation, which you can weave into your story in language, metaphors, analogies, or symbols. In some instances, you may find excerpts that you do want to extract and share or to integrate into a written or verbal story (Nelson, 1994).

Personal stories provide a glimpse of who you are in a form that is not confined to the time and space of the moment. Personal stories are limited in their capacity to convey the fullness of the Self but provide a means of communication about who you are with a wide audience. Personal stories convey essences of experience that are not communicated in theories or clinical histories. Personal stories are not trivial pastimes or entertainment; they are vital within a discipline that depends on meaningful interpersonal connections. In addition, personal stories are important to the discipline to create a shared understanding of what it means to know and develop the Self. The written expression of personal knowing opens opportunities for responses from others as well as for possibilities for deeper reflection.

Personal stories are distinct from other types of stories in that they are personal accounts of your own experiences. They reveal the thoughts, feelings, insights, and values that come from your own inner Self. Other characters and players may enter into your story, but it is your own thoughts, words, and feelings that are the focus of the story. For example, if you compose a story about your encounter with a person who is dying, the story provides a window into your experience, not into the experience of the dying person. Your story might include dialogue with the person you cared for or may recount what you observed about that person, but the main content of the story is how you felt and what you experienced as you cared for this person. The story called "Regrets" on the *Evolve* website is an example of such a story. In this story, the nurse described not being able to communicate with her patient Dora because she could not speak Dora's language. However, the description of this fact focuses on the regret that the nurse felt because she was not able to talk with Dora and how she experienced trying to find some common ground for communication that transcended language.

In addition to personal stories as a form of expression of personal knowing, personal knowing is expressed as the genuine Self. In other words, who you are as a person and your being in the world is an ongoing and living expression of your personal knowing.

Think About It

Have you encountered a story about nursing that has stayed with you, a story that you cannot forget? Why is this story so powerful for you, and what does it reflect about the nature of nursing? What insights about the nature of nursing does this story reveal?

Integrated Expression in Practice: Therapeutic Use of Self

The genuine Self is conveyed most explicitly in nursing practice when the nurse engages in the therapeutic use of the Self. The therapeutic use of the Self is the integrated expression in practice that is at the heart of nursing's healing art. Although it is a somewhat elusive concept, the therapeutic use of the Self suggests the ability to engage authentically with the Self and the other to facilitate health and healing. At the heart of the therapeutic use of the Self is the assumption that it is critical to know the nature of the Self, to acknowledge the Self, and to put aside or change biases and attitudes that interfere with understanding and caring for others. As you come to understand yourself more fully, the therapeutic use of the Self in the context of nursing care is more fully actualized.

Authentication Processes: Response and Reflection

It is through the processes of response and reflection that the Self and personal stories that reflect the Self can be examined. Response and reflection in relation to the Self come from being in the world with others. The Self is perceived as unique by others and brings to each interaction a dynamic that is recognized and known. As people respond to one another, they give messages that affirm, disappoint, celebrate, or negate aspects of the expressed Self. Responses are taken in, felt, and internalized. When responses are internalized, reflection on their meaning can follow. The person may return to critical questioning and to the creative processes of opening and centering with the use of journaling and meditation. The person also may reflect on the responses in other ways and take in meanings that arise anew from the interactive experiences.

In addition to responses that are received from interactions that occur during the course of daily experience, insights from meditation, journaling, and other self-knowing practices can be shared with trusted friends and colleagues who are willing to listen and to respond to what is offered. Drew (1997), when exploring nurses' meaningful experiences and expanding self-awareness, found that sharing the story of an experience with another person enlarged, solidified, and deepened the meaning of the experience in a way that improved therapeutic interactions.

⊖ Image Collection – Personal Story

As formally developed personal stories are created and shared within the discipline, the insights conveyed in the stories give others in the discipline an opportunity for reflection and response that involves their potential for conveying the nature of the therapeutic use of the Self. When made available to others, these stories have the potential to enrich and deepen personal knowing as they inspire others to change the nature of the Self. Although written stories are in one sense limited in their capacity to convey the essence of a person, they are rich in that they convey inner processes and meanings that are not easily perceived as part of the interpersonal experience. These personal stories provide vicarious experiences that enrich those experiences provided by response and reflection in relation to the Self alone.

Think About It

To deepen your appreciation of personal knowing, consider the following questions related to the content of this chapter:

1. Think about a patient or family with whom you had a particularly memorable relationship. Write about this person or family and what you remember about your interactions with them. What did you learn about your Self in this situation?
2. Consider a time when you left a nursing care situation feeling great regret and sadness. What were your regrets, and what brought about your feelings of sadness? What from your own personal past made you feel a connection with this experience in practice?
3. Consider a nurse you have known and who you feel was fully authentic and genuine as a person. What about this nurse did you particularly appreciate? What have you learned from this person about what it means to be a nurse?
4. Does personal knowing lead to personal shifts in how you practice? If yes, how does this happen?

REFLECTION AND DISCUSSION – SUPPLEMENT ⊖

References

Banks-Wallace, J. (2008). Eureka! I finally get IT: Journaling as a tool for promoting praxis in research. *ABNF Journal, 19*, 24–27.

Beckerman, A. (1994). A personal journal of caring through esthetic knowing. *ANS Advances in Nursing Science, 17*(1), 71–79.

Bishop, A., & Scudder, J. (1990). *The practical, moral, and personal sense of nursing: A phenomenological philosophy of practice.* New York, NY: National League for Nursing.

Bonis, S. A. (2009). Knowing in nursing: A concept analysis. *Journal of Advanced Nursing, 65*, 1328–1341.

Campesino, M., & Schwartz, G. E. (2006). Spirituality among Latinas/os: Implications of culture in conceptualization and measurement. *ANS Advances in Nursing Science, 29*(1), 69–81.

Carper, B. A. (1978). Fundamental patterns of knowing in nursing. *ANS Advances in Nursing Science, 1*(1), 13–23.

Chinn, P. L. (2007). *Peace & power: Creative leadership for building communities* (7th ed.). Boston, MA: Jones & Bartlett.

Drew, N. (1997). Expanding self-awareness through exploration of meaningful experience. *Journal of Holistic Nursing, 15*, 406–424.

Green, C. (2009). A comprehensive theory of the human person from philosophy and nursing. *Nursing Philosophy, 10*, 263–274.

Hall, B. A. (1997). Spirituality in terminal illness: An alternative view of theory. *Journal of Holistic Nursing, 15*, 82–96.

Hall, B. A. (2004). *Surviving and thriving after a life-threatening diagnosis.* Bloomington, IN: 1st Books.

Hall, B. A., & Allan, J. D. (1994). Self in relation: A prolegomenon for holistic nursing. *Nursing Outlook, 42*, 110–166.

Hart, H. (1997). Conceptual understanding and knowing other-wise: Reflections on rationality and spirituality in philosophy. In J. H. Olthuis (Ed.), *Knowing other-wise* (pp. 19–53). New York, NY: Fordham University Press.

Huebner, D. (1985). Spirituality and knowing. In E. Eisner (Ed.), *Learning and teaching the ways of knowing* (pp. 159–173). Chicago, IL: University of Chicago Press.

McSherry, W., & Cash, K. (2004). The language of spirituality: An emerging taxonomy. *International Journal of Nursing Studies, 41*, 151–161.

Moch, S. D. (1990). Personal knowing: Evolving research and practice. *Scholarly Inquiry for Nursing Practice, 4*(2), 155–165.

Munhall, P. L. (1993). "Unknowing": Toward another pattern of knowing in nursing. *Nursing Outlook, 41*, 125–128.

Nelson, G. L. (1994). *Writing and being: Taking back our lives through the power of language.* San Diego, CA: LuraMedia.

Pesut, B. (2008). A conversation on diverse perspectives of spirituality in nursing literature. *Nursing Philosophy, 9*, 98–109.

Pesut, B., Fowler, M., Taylor, E. J., Reimer-Kirkham, S., & Sawatzky, R. (2008). Conceptualising spirituality and religion for healthcare. *Journal of Clinical Nursing, 17*, 2803–2810.

Register, M. E., & Herman, J. (2010). Quality of life revisited: The concept of connectedness in older adults. *ANS Advances in Nursing Science, 33*(1), 53–63.

Stevens-Barnum, B. (2010). *Spirituality in nursing: The challenges of complexity.* New York, NY: Springer.

Tinley, S. T., & Kinney, A. Y. (2007). Three philosophical approaches to the study of spirituality. *ANS Advances in Nursing Science, 30*, 71–80.

Aesthetic Knowledge Development

Chapter
6

http://evolve.elsevier.com/Chinn/knowledge/

The first requisite [of nursing] is the practical belief that the greatest likeness among humans is their difference. The unspoken lesson of anatomy, the autopsy room, chemistry lab builds up the insidious biological impression of the body as a predictable entity—no wonder normal and alike become confused!

Katherine Brownell Oettinger (1939, pp. 1224-1225)

This opening quote penned 75 years ago remains timeless. Oettinger acknowledged the core premise of aesthetic knowing: that situations and humans, while alike in general and predictable ways, remain unique and different. Aesthetics focuses on knowing how to understand and act in relation to those individual differences to create a positive outcome. Oettinger understood that those aspects of humanness that make people alike fall within the realm of empirics, and she cautioned that "alike" is not necessarily the same as "normal." Oettinger implied that, although humans do generally share things in common (e.g., certain features of anatomy and physiology), they are more alike in their uniqueness. Although empirics addresses what is common and predictable, it is aesthetic knowing that helps us know how to deal with circumstances that are unique to the situation.

Consider This Example

You are working with a certified nurse practitioner in an outpatient clinic when a scantily dressed 13-year-old girl we'll call Niki arrives and, after the usual preliminaries, is escorted to an examination room accompanied by her mother. As you and the nurse practitioner review Niki's intake questionnaire, you notice that she is complaining of urinary frequency and burning and that her urinalysis showed results typical of a urinary tract infection. A pregnancy screen also reveals that Niki is pregnant, although this is not acknowledged on her questionnaire. You discuss your approach to care with the nurse practitioner, recognizing the probable diagnosis and pregnancy.

In this situation, you will consider the *empiric data:* the urinary dipstick results, the pregnancy test, the reported symptoms, and the indicated treatments. You might also consider the *ethics* of questioning Niki about sexual activity or abuse given her young age and the presence of her mother. You acknowledge your *personal knowing* as someone who is somewhat intolerant of parents who would let a young girl dress so provocatively, and you

continued

Consider This Example—cont'd

tell yourself to keep those attitudes in check; you also are aware of a deep compassion for this child, who may be in a very precarious situation. You understand through *emancipatory knowing* that this type of dress is promoted as socially acceptable for young women despite its possible harmful consequences, but you do not believe that addressing Niki's appearance is appropriate until you have more information about the situation.

Before going into the examination room, you and the nurse practitioner briefly discuss your plan. The plan includes, in part, that you expect to work with Niki and her mother from a place of compassion for the plight of the young girl. You will do an assessment to uncover any other problems or issues that might require attention, and you will explore more about the situation in the home and at school. After you get a clearer picture of the situation, you will discuss a possible plan of care with Niki and her mother and finish with some preventive teaching about her pregnancy and urinary tract infection prevention. You have thought about the *aesthetics* of your encounter, and you plan to try to create the best outcome by gaining Niki's trust before broaching the subject of her sexual behavior or possible abuse when her mother is asked to go to another room, where she will talk with the nurse practitioner. You do not know whether Niki's mother knows that her daughter is pregnant, and you are not sure how best to reveal it, but you do know that knowledge of her pregnancy must come out during this visit. This type of planning integrates all the knowing patterns, whether they are recognized or not, and it considers what, in general, seems reasonable for this situation.

As you open the door and enter the room, you notice immediately that something is terribly wrong and that the situation is not what you expected. Your eyes immediately go to Niki, who has obviously been crying. The clothes she was wearing are awry, and she is huddled on the examination table as far away from her mother as possible. Her mother is looking rather angry. The look on your face and your hesitation registers your surprise at what you see, and, before you can say anything, Niki's mother angrily declares, "This little slut just told me she's pregnant."

You immediately move to deal creatively with the situation. The anger of the mother may be the first thing you attend to, but then you immediately consider other elements of the situation: how Niki looks; the fact that her clothes are awry, which suggests a minor physical confrontation; and the body language that indicates estrangement. You notice these as well as countless other details all at once. Your assessment is not linear or conscious, and you say and do something immediately to assuage the mother's anger. On the basis of the unique response that you receive after this action, you make other moves that include verbalizations and movements. You continue this sort of "artful dance," balancing and tempering your ongoing responses according to the responses received from Niki and her mother. Eventually, the situation calms down; this is the outcome that you envisioned and successfully created during this encounter.

Recounting the how, what, and why of your actions in a particular situation is not possible, because these occur immediately in the moment, with consideration of elements that were present but not consciously and deliberatively recognized. Basically, you act in a way that moves the situation to a desired outcome. This is the nature of aesthetics; it is artful, balanced, and in a sense beautiful, rather than clumsy or uncertain.

You complete a transformative art/act and transform a situation that is uncomfortable or undesirable into a situation of calm where healing can occur. As illustrated in the story of caring for Niki and her mother, you do this rather quickly by noticing and responding to the whole situation all at once. Each situation is totally unique and will never be duplicated exactly, and it can only be understood and managed in the moment. Moreover, although you know when you act artfully, you can never fully explain what you did. You can recount the situation in a story and describe how you felt, what you thought, and what happened, but it is not possible to describe fully the details of how you knew what you knew in the moment, that is, the fullness of aesthetic knowing that is essential to creating your actions in the moment.

As another example, some degree of postsurgical pain is an expected common human experience after hip replacement. However, the expression and experience of pain differ for those who believe it is something to be endured, for those who are fearful of addiction to prescription pain medication, and for those who believe that pain is necessary for healing. It is through the pattern of aesthetics that the nurse ascertains such nuances of meaning for the common experience of pain and creatively works within the situation. The nurse's goal is to transform artfully the experience of pain into a therapeutic level of comfort in persons regardless of their individual meanings for and responses to the pain experience.

Think About It

- What would you have initially said or done if, as the nurse in our example, you actually encountered Niki and her mother?
- What would have been the absolutely wrong thing to say or do in the situation with Niki and her mother? Why?
- Have you ever encountered an unexpected care situation that required you to respond immediately in a way you didn't anticipate? In retrospect, was your response a good choice, or could you have done something differently to improve outcomes?
- Do you think that aesthetic nursing practice could be considered a form of performance art?

This chapter details the pattern of aesthetics. Aesthetic knowing in nursing is the aspect of knowing that requires an understanding of deep meanings in a situation and that, on the basis of those meanings, calls forth the creative resources of the nurse that transform experience into what is not yet real but envisioned as possible. It is the dimension of knowing that understands how human experiences that are common (e.g., the teenage pregnancy of our example) are expressed and experienced uniquely. In practice, aesthetic knowing is expressed by means of *transformative art/acts*.

Figure 6-1 depicts the dimensions of aesthetic knowing. In our model, the aesthetic pattern of knowing in nursing requires asking the questions, "What does this mean?" and "How is it significant?" From these questions, the creative processes

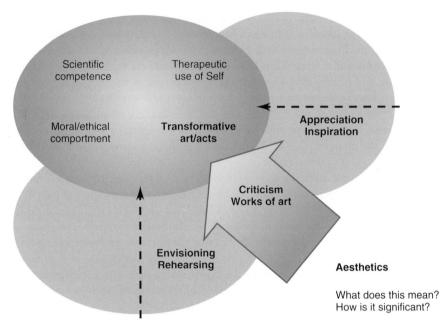

FIGURE 6-1: Aesthetic knowing and knowledge.

of envisioning and rehearsing nurture the artistic expression of aesthetic knowing. Aesthetic knowing can be shared to some extent through its formal expressions of aesthetic criticism and works of art. Poetry, stories, and photographs are also artful forms of expression for aesthetic knowing. These formal expressions provide for the discipline a source of appreciation and inspiration that further nurtures aesthetic knowing. In practice, aesthetic knowing is expressed in transformative art/acts, in which the nurse moves experience from what is to a new realm that would not otherwise be possible.

As nurses move into caring encounters, they have some idea of situational factors that might be present based on prior experiences with similar situations. In the example involving Niki, the nurse (i.e., "you") moved into the encounter having asked and answered the critical questions, "What does this (situation) mean?" and "How is it significant?" With the nurse practitioner, you made a plan based on your past experiences with similar situations. However, as soon as you entered the room, those same questions were asked again, all at once in the moment, although not deliberatively or with conscious intent. After the meaning that the mother was angry was apparent, you sensed (envisioned) what was required is to calm the situation and, in the moment, you selected a response. You had various responses stored up in your background of experience both in practice and from deliberate rehearsal of different kinds of responses that you could call forth in an unexpected situation that required a calming influence. Because you have practiced how to calm a situation and you knew that you could be effective when doing so, you acted in this situation with skill and confidence.

You continued to ask the critical questions and to envision a desired outcome, and select from various rehearsed possibilities all at once; this is the essence of the transformative art/act.

As you reflect on this situation, you could write about it to describe the situation and your own internal experience of the scenario as it unfolded. As you begin to explore what it all meant or could mean and how your education and experience inform your reflection of the situation, you create an aesthetic criticism. Such a written account will never be as rich as the actual situation, but certain elements can be expressed. Alternatively, you might write a poem or create a drawing that represents the situation. After such a work has been created, others can ask the critical questions, "What does this mean?" and "How is it significant?" as they review and study the formal expressions of your aesthetic knowing. They could ask themselves if your representations helped them to appreciate the meaning and significance of the situation, and if its meaning and significance inspire them in a way that would be helpful in their own practices. As a preceptor, mentor, or teacher, you might guide your students to rehearse and envision what they might do in a similar setting as a way to help them to cultivate aesthetic knowing. In these ways, others learn how to create transformative art/acts more effectively.

We begin this chapter with a discussion of the meaning of art and aesthetics as the background for our conceptualization of aesthetics in nursing. Next, we present a conceptual definition of the art of nursing and discuss our definition in the light of other conceptualizations of the art of nursing that have appeared in nursing literature. We then focus on the dimensions of aesthetic knowing as represented in Figure 6-1.

ART AND AESTHETICS

Aesthetics is a noun that derives from the Latin and Greek words that refer to perception. It has evolved to refer specifically to the study of and ideas about *artistically valid* forms. The adjective *aesthetic* identifies an object or experience as being artistically valid. That which is artistically valid is coherent in form and substance and thus conveys a meaning of a whole beyond the formative elements; the artistically valid also evokes a response. In the following sections, the terms *aesthetic* and *artistically valid* are used interchangeably.

Consider the famous painting *Mona Lisa*. Aesthetics would address theoretic and philosophic views about its artistic validity. If an art critic declared the painting to be artistically valid, it would mean, in the critic's view, that it had a coherence about it that conveyed some meaning that was understood across multiple critics. Coherence may be proposed because of color contrast and proportion within the painting that emphasize the subject's large figure and face. The response that is evoked is one of interest or mystique.

The Nature of Aesthetics

The aesthetic does not necessarily equate to that which is commonly viewed as beautiful or lovely. The standards by which something is taken to be appealing or beautiful vary widely in different disciplines and within different contexts and cultures.

Individuals, given their unique perceptions and tastes, respond differently to an art object or experience. In the philosophy of aesthetics, beauty is not taken as a matter of taste. Rather, it takes a form that brings forth a response that draws one in to notice what is expressed. The substance of what is addressed as beauty in philosophy may, in fact, represent something like shame, grief, or death. However, the form is considered beautiful in that it satisfies aesthetic criteria and thus is considered to be artistically valid.

There are general traits that distinguish what is artistically valid or aesthetic in form from what is not. That which is artistically valid places various elements into a pattern to form a whole that symbolizes meaning beyond the elements themselves. The form evokes a response, a feeling, an insight, or a sense of connection with the experience portrayed in the art. The response that art evokes is very often strong or even transformative, which means that the experience of the art is unforgettable, it leaves a strong impression, or it provides insight into the human condition (Archibald, 2012).

The meanings conveyed and the responses evoked are connected to the cultural heritage from which the art form arises. Those outside the culture may not fully recognize the meanings that are derived from the culture, but they can still recognize the work as artistically valid. They will recognize the wholeness of the form and see there is meaning in the work, although the meaning may differ from that in the culture of origin. The cultural heritage of nursing points to the primacy of interpersonal interactions, and thus nurses will tend to be drawn to works that evoke a sense of caring and meaningful interpersonal connection.

The Nature of Art

Art is both the process of creating an aesthetic object or experience and the product that is created. The process of creating and what is produced must display characteristics that are artistically valid to properly be called "art." Art is not limited to the fine arts or to what is often labeled as art. Rather, art is present in all human activities that involve forming elements into a whole (Chinn & Watson, 1994; LeVasseur, 1999; Sandelowski, 1995; Liehr, Morris, Leavitt, & Takahashi, 2013; Dean, 2013). In our example of Niki, the transformative art/act was art in action, and it was artful because the nurse's actions and being were in synchrony with all that unfolded as part of the situation. The nurse was an integrated part of a whole and created an unfolding of possibilities that would not otherwise have been possible.

Art is not defined by taste or by what someone likes. Matters of taste or preference, such as "I like that painting (or what that nurse did)" or "I do not like that painting (or what that nurse did)" do not define something as being art. Neither is art in the traditional sense considered art because it can be sold for profit. For example, a local "art show" might sell out of its posters of a popular rock band, but this does not mean the poster was in fact a work of art. Rather, the extent to which art as process is satisfying and the extent to which art the product assumes coherence as a whole and elicits a feeling response determines the extent to which the experience can be called "art" (Eisner, 1985).

Art as a process requires skill in the technical and mechanical aspects of working with the elements from which the product is formed. It also requires an ability to imagine the whole before it is expressed and creatively integrate elements of form into a whole. This process can be readily illustrated in the fine arts; for example, a musician acquires technical and mechanical skills with an instrument and learns to bring the elements of sound together into a musical performance that generates a response from the listener. Art as a product creates a response that can transform experience. This transformation of experience occurs when a person—whether an observer or a participant—is drawn into a realm that would not otherwise be accessible, such as the realm of chaos that a performance of Wagner's *Ride of the Valkyries* might engender.

In summary, art is the process and product of bringing diverse elements together into a whole that evokes a response and that moves one's experience or perception into a realm that is not otherwise possible. Aesthetics concerns the nature and characteristics of art as process and product to determine the extent to which what is said to be art is in fact artistically valid in form.

Art and Aesthetics in Nursing

Nurses have a notable history of appreciating art and creating aesthetically pleasing environments to enhance healing and well-being. Familiar examples include the use of music to create a sense of calm, visual arts to convey health and illness experiences, dance or free-form movement to enhance physical coordination and strength, and drawing as a therapeutic modality. Works of art have also been used to illustrate and interpret meanings of health and illness experiences in education and research (Chinn & Watson, 1994; Darbyshire, 1994; Lamb, 2009; Liehr et al., 2013; Dean, 2013; Pellico & Chinn, 2007). Although we acknowledge and encourage these therapeutic uses of artistic processes, this is not the focus that concerns aesthetic knowledge development, and this is different from what we are addressing as "the art of nursing." Rather, aesthetic knowledge development is directed toward those aspects of knowing that are essential to the "doing" of nursing itself, which is what we consider "the art of nursing."

Aesthetics is typically associated with what is typically seen as art. Perhaps because of this, aesthetics has not had much emphasis in nursing. However, aesthetics has always been integral to nursing practice. Aesthetic qualities can be seen as art in all aspects of nursing practice, from notes written in a chart to theoretic formulations, from a single brief interaction with an individual to sustained interactions with groups and communities, and from an unexpected encounter to a thoughtfully planned design for a system of care. In all these wide-ranging nursing experiences, nurses artfully draw on and use emancipatory, empiric, ethical, personal, and aesthetic knowing. It is the dimension of aesthetic knowing that endows nursing experiences with aesthetic qualities and that differentiates excellent and skilled nursing from the impersonal performance of technical acts and routinized procedures.

Moreover, things that ordinarily would not be labeled as "art" do have aesthetic characteristics (Liehr et al., 2013; Sandelowski, 1995; Wainwright, 2000). For example, an empiric theory is formed from conceptual ideas linked in a pattern having a meaning that the concepts alone could not convey. The appeal (i.e., a subtle feeling response) of a theory often derives from the *aesthetic shape* of the theory. Without this quality, the theory lacks a certain attractiveness or appeal to the community of scientists.

AESTHETIC KNOWING

Aesthetic knowing requires knowledge of the experience toward which the art form is directed as well as knowledge of the art form itself. For example, the poet requires knowledge of a life experience that is reflected in the poem, as well as knowledge of the art form in the manner of the techniques and methods used to create something that can be considered poetry (Kramper & Thawley, 2009). The visual artist requires knowledge of the experience or situation that will be visually presented as a painting or sculpture, as well as knowledge of the technical aspects of painting or sculpting required to achieve the desired visual representations.

In nursing, aesthetic knowing requires knowledge of the following:
- The experience of nursing (the art form)
- The experience of health and illness (that which nursing art/act transforms)

These two aspects of knowledge grow as nurses are educated, as they have experiences in practice, and as they learn about the experiences of other nurses. For example, nurses learn about the experience of dying by studying theories of death and dying, by reading or hearing stories about dying, and by caring for people who are dying and experiencing their feelings and those of their loved ones. Nurses learn about caring for someone who is dying as they are guided through this type of clinical experience in school, as they hear the stories of other nurses who have cared for people who are dying, and as they experience working with people who are dying.

Background knowledge of the experience of nursing and of the experiences of health and illness are essential, but they are not sufficient for aesthetic practice. For example, to bring an aesthetic quality into the experience of caring for someone who is dying, you also need to cultivate the ability to enact nursing's art form itself, which is the focus of this chapter, as shown in Figure 6-1. The following section details various conceptions of nursing art that form a foundation for our approach to developing aesthetic knowing and knowledge in nursing.

Conceptual Definitions of the Art of Nursing

As Johnson (1994, 1996) demonstrated, the idea of the art of nursing has had several different meanings reflected in the nursing literature since the time of Florence Nightingale. Although no single clear definition of the art of nursing prevails, nurse scholars have consistently recognized the art of nursing and emphasized how vital this aspect of nursing is in relation to who nurses are and what they do. Although historically nursing art referred largely to technical skills that were often learned in the "nursing arts laboratory," the art of nursing has taken on a meaning that is more closely related to art as aesthetic practice.

The art of nursing as aesthetic practice can be a difficult concept to understand. One difficulty is that the nurse's art is expressed in the knowing-being of the nurse. Briefly, nursing art does not simply reflect what and how the nurse knows (epistemology); it also refers to the nurse's being and doing (ontology). The embodied nature of "the art of nursing" is part of what makes it difficult to understand. The term *embodied* means that nursing art requires mind-body-spirit involvement in a creative experience that is transformative. The body moves through the nursing situation, the mind understands meaning, and the spirit feels—all at once—and artfully acts to transform experience. In this sense, nursing art is a form of performance art that involves the nurse and the person for whom the nurse is providing care. Like a theatrical production or an orchestral concert, the nurse's performance art can have various degrees of artistic validity. As with all art forms, artistic skill can be taught and learned. Even for those who are most talented in the art form, artistic competence requires discipline and practice; it does not come naturally.

Recognizing the challenges inherent in defining the art of nursing, we propose a definition that was derived from an aesthetic inquiry project that began as the result of conversations with practicing nurses who, without exception, recognized meaning in the phrase "the art of nursing." Conversations and storytelling among nurses focused on their experiences of the art of nursing, the various meanings that they saw in photographs, or in rehearsals or the role playing of various alternative approaches to nursing practice (Chinn, 1994, 2001). The conversations with nurses were supplemented with introspection and more formalized aesthetic inquiry techniques carried out by project leaders. Chinn, Maeve, and Bostick (1997) observed nurses as they practiced nursing, reviewed photographs of nurses as they practiced, and used journaling to explore deeper symbolic and personal meanings of the practices observed.

The following definition emerged from this aesthetic inquiry project and is used in this text:

> The nurse's synchronous arrangement of narrative and movement into a form that transforms experiences into a realm that would not otherwise be possible. The arrangement is spontaneous, in-the-moment, and intuitive. The ability to make the moves that are transformative is grounded in a deep understanding of nursing, including relevant theory, facts, technical skill, personal knowing, and ethical understanding; and this ability requires rehearsal in deliberative application of these understandings. (Chinn, Maeve, and Bostick, 1997, p. 90)

This definition identifies synchronous narrative and movement as the elements that nurses use to form the aesthetic experience, which is what in this textbook we refer to as the *transformative art/act*. *Narrative* includes words, gestures, and intonations of speech. *Synchrony* refers to the coordination and rhythm of the experience. Synchrony of intention and action is also implied. Synchrony and narrative must come together to form an integral whole. In the example of Niki, narrative would include elements such as what you said, the somewhat surprised look on your face when you entered the room, and the loudness or softness with which you spoke at different times when trying to restore calm. Synchrony refers to how you moved your embodied Self within the situation; who you approached and when; how and where you touched Niki or her mother with the intent to calm, as well as how you were synchronizing your words with what you were doing. Synchronous narrative and movement as the elements that form the aesthetic in nursing are critical features of the Chinn, Maeve, and Bostick (1997) definition that provide a basis for teaching and conveying aesthetic knowledge and knowing.

Johnson (1994) identified the following five conceptualizations for the art of nursing:

- The ability to grasp meaning during patient encounters
- The ability to establish a meaningful connection with the person being cared for
- The ability to skillfully perform nursing activities
- The ability to rationally determine an appropriate course of nursing action
- The ability to morally conduct one's nursing practice

Grasping Meaning During Patient Encounters. In our definition of the art of nursing, the ability to grasp meaning during a patient encounter is required if the nurse is to transform an experience from what is to what is possible. Our explicit reference to the intuitive, in-the-moment arrangement of movement and narrative refers to the intuitive element as it unfolds within the transformative art/act, not to intuitive elements that inform or point to a specific outcome or problem. In other words, as a nurse in the moment of care, you may not have an immediate grasp of what the moment means to a person or family and what to do about it. Rather, your intuitive sense detects all that is going on and calls forth a response, and you act spontaneously to care for the person or family in the moment (Billay, Myrick, Luhanga, & Yonge, 2007).

The focus from which your art form emerges is the intuitive use of your creative resources to form experience. You are open to making moves within an experience that you have not anticipated and planned, and you have not necessarily confirmed the patient's or family's perceptions of the situation. Rather, your moves come from a perceptual grasp of the various possibilities for forming the situation that resides within the experience. Your own creative energy moves the encounter forward as a work of art in process.

As a way to better understand what is meant by "grasping meaning in the situation," think about how you cannot really know how to be in a situation until you are actually in it. As an experienced practitioner, as you move into clinically complex care situations, you comprehend—all at once—what a situation is calling forth, and you respond wholly. As you respond, your being and your behavior call forth in the other or others a response that they in turn wholly understand and to which they respond. These sorts of all-at-once, instantaneous, and simultaneous response patterns, which transform the experience in the moment, constitute the *art/act*.

The intuitive aspect of creating form is what is referred to as *creativity.* It is a knowing in the moment of creating that enables the artist to express unique possibilities that fit together, make sense for the situation, and come together in the right relationship. It then follows that the intuitive perception of a right relationship within a nursing encounter depends on a deep grasp of the meaning embedded in the situation.

Although our definition is clearly applicable to patient encounters, it also applies to nursing actions that do not involve a direct patient encounter. The ability to design a system of care is grounded in a grasp of meaning in the experience of people for whom the system is designed. Here, spontaneous and intuitive aspects of the process of creating the design are part of the formative process. The nurse-designer does not intuit an end point or set about to design it. Rather, the nurse-designer is immersed in the experience of creating the design and remains open to a stream of possibilities that can only emerge as the design takes shape.

Establishing a Meaningful Connection with the Person Being Cared For. Our definition of the art of nursing assumes a deep and meaningful connection with the other. A transformative move requires presence with the other. To be transformative and artful, an art/act must be grounded in a profound level of connection between the nurse and the other. In the context of such a connection, there is a synchronicity or rhythmicity between the nurse and the other. The "synchronous arrangement of narrative and movement" in an interaction refers to the timing and flow among all elements in the situation and reflects a deep level of connection between the nurse and the person for whom care is being provided.

Skillfully Performing Nursing Activities. The performance of nursing skills is one of the earliest conceptualizations of nursing art, and it is an element of meaning often expressed by nurses in Chinn's aesthetic inquiry (Chinn, 1994; Chinn et al., 1997). Nurses first pointed to tasks and procedures that are required in the "doing" of nursing, noting that it is *how* they do what they do that characterizes their art. However, in our definition, skills alone do not constitute the art of nursing. Rather, skillful performance is expressed in the nurse's movement and narrative, which may or may not involve tasks and procedures. Skillful performance is developed over time from a background of practice (rehearsal) that makes possible what Heidegger (1962) identified as "ready-to-hand" knowing. Artful nursing includes and indeed often requires skilled technical performance. However, our definition implies an integration of skill with relevant theory, facts, and personal knowing as well as with emancipatory and ethical understanding.

Rationally Determining an Appropriate Course of Action. Research regarding clinical judgment and rational reasoning suggests that intuitive and aesthetic components are necessary for sound practice (Benner, Tanner, & Chesla, 1996; Mattingly, 1994). In our conceptualization of the art of nursing, rational reasoning is not a defining element. Rather, as with technical skills, rational thinking ability and clinical judgment processes create the background necessary for aesthetic capability. Nursing art as synchronous movement to transform experience is an art form; it is not rationally formed, and there is no "outcome" that is defined in advance. As in other art forms, the nurse has a vision or an idea of what improved health and well-being would be like for a person in a particular situation. However, the exact outcome of a particular situation is not projected in the moment of the transformative art/act. Rather, the direction of health and well-being is intuitively shaped and formed as it occurs. In this sense, the creation of health and well-being is a "work in progress."

For example, a composer makes use of accepted theories of rhythm when constructing a musical score and has an idea about what the music might be like in the end. However, during the process, she is inspired to integrate rhythmic variations that may defy common conventions, and the exact form of the music shifts as it unfolds. In the process, the composer places a unique signature on the work that gives it artistic character. The final score generally reflects what the composer envisioned, but it is not exactly what might have been predicted at the outset. Likewise, as a nurse, you call on your theoretic understanding of a particular type of illness experience when developing a rational plan of care to point toward appropriate nursing action. Although you do plan, you remain open to spontaneous events that create opportunities to change the plan as the caring process unfolds in synchrony with the person and family involved in a particular experience. It is this spontaneous unfolding of the process, when integrated with your prior rational understanding, that creates artistic form. The particular ways in which the nurse shifts or moves through the experience is the artistic signature that endows the experience with a particular and unique quality.

Morally Conducting One's Nursing Practice. Our definition of the art of nursing points to ethical understanding as background that is essential for aesthetic practice. A significant ethical dimension is inherent in the transformative art/acts that are basic to the art of nursing. Transformative art/acts create change with regard to what would otherwise happen. Nurses who participated in the aesthetic inquiry from which our definition was derived told many stories of their practices that involved ethical dilemmas and elicited actions that they associated with the art of nursing. There is a value component in the idea of transformative art/acts that implies a significant ethical dimension being inherent in the art of nursing, in that transforming creates a change in what something is to what it otherwise would not be. In the context of nursing, the change is, by definition, one toward a higher level of health and well-being. A transformative art/act could not be recognized as artistically valid if it violated ethical sensibilities. However, transformative art/acts alone do not convey ethical understanding (Vezeau, 1994). Rather, transformative moves can come out of significant ethical and moral dilemmas and contribute to the development of ethical sensibilities (Maeve, 1994).

THE DIMENSIONS OF AESTHETIC KNOWING

As seen in Figure 6-1, the dimensions of aesthetic knowing include the critical questions, "What does this mean?" and "How is it significant?" These critical questions engage the creative processes of envisioning and rehearsing possibilities. From these creative processes, aesthetic criticism can be constructed as a form of knowledge of the artistry of nursing that can be shared with others. Works of art also emerge as representations of what is known, and they are also a form of aesthetic knowledge that can be made available to the broader audience within and outside the discipline. Art forms that can be created in nursing to represent the meaning and significance of nursing and health experiences include poetry, photography and other visual art forms, story, drama, and dance (Chinn & Watson, 1994). The authentication processes of appreciation and inspiration examine the extent to which formal expressions of aesthetic knowing are aesthetic in nature and thus can be used to cultivate aesthetic knowing in nursing. Transformative art/acts are the integrated expressions of aesthetic knowing in practice. Synchronous movement and narrative that transform the health-illness experience, from what is into a realm that would not otherwise be possible, characterize these art/acts.

Critical Questions: What Does This Mean? How Is It Significant?

The critical questions for aesthetic knowing—"What does this mean?" and "How is it significant?"—can be asked of formal expressions of knowing or in the context of practice to create a transformative art/act. As a nurse engages in transformative art/acts, various possibilities emerge instantaneously in the moment, without conscious thought. Outside of practice, these questions initiate an envisioning and rehearsing process that is conscious and deliberative and that can be used to cultivate aesthetic knowing.

Creative Processes: Envisioning and Rehearsing

Envisioning and rehearsing are two interrelated processes from which creative products of aesthetic knowing emerge. Typically, envisioning and rehearsing have not been deliberately taught, nor do nurses identify these processes as something that they do. However, many of the practices that Chinn, Maeve, and Bostick (1997) came to view as envisioning and rehearsing were activities in which nurses engaged. Often these activities were hidden from view, engaged in during the nurses' time away from job responsibilities, and assumed to be insignificant and trivial yet often necessary to cope with difficult situations. For example, as nurses described situations that represented their art, they related how they shared stories about the situations in phone conversations after work, over a meal, or in a secluded area during a downtime. Their storytelling episodes always included an account of the response of the listener and the ways in which their interactive talk formed and re-formed how they saw similar situations and how they came to trust their own intuitive senses. When the nurses associated these and similar activities as being necessary and important aspects of developing an aesthetic knowing of their art form, the importance of these activities was immediately grasped.

Envisioning involves imagining a typical end point scenario or a response that one hopes to elicit by the performance or display of the art form. For a comedian, the envisioned obvious end point is the audience's laughter; a less obvious but hoped-for end point is that the audience will catch subtle meanings conveyed in the comedy (i.e., "get" the point of the joke). For a musician, the envisioned end point for a particular piece of music might be to convey a sense of longing, a sense of joy, or a sense of excitement. For a novelist, the envisioned end point is transporting the reader into a realm outside that reader's own experience and into the realm of the characters and situations depicted in the novel. For a nurse, envisioned end points are those that represent health and well-being, such as calm, relaxation, comfort, and the ability to navigate a certain health-related situation.

Rehearsing is either a physical or a mental walk-through of the skills required for the performance or display of the art form, ultimately involving the presence of a coach, teacher, or critic. The writer presents excerpts or pieces of writing to reviewers for critique and feedback. The comedian engages small audiences to listen and respond to segments of a routine. The musician performs for a teacher or mentor.

A useful analogy for understanding the processes of envisioning and rehearsing in nursing is *improvisation.* In an improvisational art, which includes the art of nursing, the display (or performance) is possible because the performer is skilled in the various moves and sequences that improvisation requires. The skills are developed through repeated practice, thus making it possible for the performer to call these skills forth in a unique situation. Repeated and intense rehearsal and the development of a wide range of finely tuned skills makes the skills fully embodied. Over time, the artist must also rehearse imagined improvisational scenarios before a coach or critic to receive direction that allows the artist to refine his or her ability so that intended meanings are conveyed.

For example, in improvisational drama, the actor (nursing student) practices sequences of movements (techniques), postural and facial expressions (body language), and voice intonations (soft and soothing or loud urgent speech) that convey wide ranges of emotion (from calm to immediacy). They also practice and narrate lines ("Shh, it's OK" or "Hurry with that crash cart!") that give verbal expression to a possible experience (this is going to be frightening for the patient or the patient is going to arrest). The director (critic, coach, or teacher) gives the actor (nursing student) feedback and guidance that lead the actor into new territory. The director (teacher) may also guide the actor (nursing student) to repeat and perfect the sequence of movements to bring them to a refined, embodied level. Eventually, the actor's skills are so finely tuned that the actor's focus remains on the process that is emerging in the improvised situation rather than on the technical skills required for the process of improvisation.

In the following sections, we describe three practices for envisioning and rehearsing narrative and movement as elements that are basic to nursing's art: (1) creating and recreating storylines, (2) creating and developing embodied synchronous movement, and (3) rehearsing and engaging a connoisseur-critic. The practices that we describe are not linear or sequential; they are interwoven and integral to aesthetic knowing. They are presented separately here to describe in some detail what they are and how they function to contribute to aesthetic knowing. Each of these practices fosters both envisioning and rehearsing.

⊝ Image Collection – Storyline Guidelines

Creating and Recreating Storylines. When nurses tell stories to one another, they move into a realm created from the imagination and not bound by the constraints of the workaday world. Even when the story begins with the intention of conveying an accurate account of a real experience, in the telling of the story, the narrator creates emotion, stresses points of emphasis, exaggerates or downplays selected elements of the story, and selects certain features to include or exclude. Often the desires of the storyteller come into the story in ways that surprise even the storyteller. For example, the storyteller may unexpectedly give an account of what he or she wishes had been done in the situation as if it actually happened, rather than accounting for what did happen. In this way, the storyteller forms various types of meanings and significances for the story, providing multiple possible responses to the critical questions of "What does this mean?" and "How is it significant?" If viewed through the lens of empirics, the story would have little or no worth. When viewed through the lens of aesthetics, however, the story has exquisite value as a frame from which to explore possible meanings and to create visions and possibilities for the future (Maeve, 1994).

To develop aesthetic knowing with the use of the creative envisioning and rehearsing processes, we recommend that the story be told in the voice of the person who receives nursing care. Stories that are told in the voice of the nurse are more often reflective of personal knowing and explore the nurse's personal meanings. Stories that are told in the voice of the person receiving nursing care inspire empathy as well as a deeper understanding of the experience that is the story's focus. Stories told from the perspective of the other also help to develop an embodied knowing of the other's experience. We recommend stories that illuminate some health or illness experience toward which nursing's art form is directed.

The story can come from actual experience, but aesthetic storytelling does not require adhering to the factual truth of a situation as does an empiric case study or anecdotal account. Rather, the storyteller purposely exaggerates, fictionalizes, emphasizes, and reshapes the actual experience to enhance listeners' perceptions of certain meanings that the storyteller intends to convey in the story. In this way, the story comes from the imagination more than from the actual experience, although the imagination is inspired by the actual experience. The well-developed story will reveal possibilities in human experience that often are not perceived empirically or understood rationally.

The storyline is the *plot* of the story. A plot requires that the essential characters of a story be placed in a situation that suggests a tension that builds toward an uncertain ending, thereby moving the story toward any one of several possible endings. The storyteller knows which of the uncertain endings will eventually emerge, but the listener or reader can only be drawn into the story if the ending remains uncertain. The listener or reader senses any number of possible endings, some dreaded and others hoped for. In the best of stories, the worst possible ending and the best possible ending both remain viable to the listener or the reader until the very end, thus keeping the reader engaged. Characters other than the essential characters can shift and move in and out of the story, but the main characters play essential roles throughout to maintain the tension of uncertainty. This tension of uncertainty is appealing in part because this is exactly the way one's own real-life story is emerging from day to day and even from moment to moment. Nurses move in and out of people's real-life stories, often playing essential roles that can and do influence movement toward a hoped-for future.

During the initial creation of a storyline, you typically begin by recounting an experience very much the way it actually happened in practice, with creative license to embellish along the way. Then, you recreate the situation by telling the story as you might have wished it to unfold. You retell the story and describe your actions (movements and narrative) as you might have acted in the situation, perhaps describing what you wish you had done instead of what you actually did. You continue to create different storylines that involve the same situation, inserting different imagined possibilities for what you might have done and said in ways that you can imagine would lead to a different possible ending.

In our opening example, when recounting the story of Niki, you might insert a different approach to your initial encounter with Niki and her mother, when you knew that the pregnancy test was positive but did not know if Niki or her mother knew this. You could create a storyline in which you candidly tell them about the results of the pregnancy test; you could then imagine how Niki and her mother would react at this point in the unfolding story and how you would handle such a scenario. You might create a storyline in which Niki did not know she was pregnant, one in which her mother was overjoyed, one in which the mother became very frightened, and one in which both immediately revealed incest occurring in the home and expressed despair regarding how to stop it. Each of these scenarios leads to mentally rehearsing possible creative possibilities that can be used in actual practice.

Creating and recreating storylines serve several purposes that are related to aesthetic knowing. Most importantly, from the perspective of aesthetics, each storyline brings forth new perceptions of meaning that could be possible in the situation. For example, the storylines in the case of Niki provide the opportunity to explore various nursing approaches to the situation and to imagine different responses from Niki and her mother and how you, or those with whom you share the story, would respond to each of the possible scenarios. The different storylines bring to awareness various meanings that could be present in a care situation. As various meanings come into awareness, new possibilities for creative engagement with each meaning can emerge. Stories elicit profound reflection on meaning that involves both personal meaning and the meaning for others in the story. In this way, the story brings to awareness the aesthetic knowledge that is embedded in experiences and that contributes to aesthetic practice.

Creating and recreating storylines also provide a means of rehearsing a narrative that in turn develops knowledge and skill that are basic to the art of nursing. The exact words that emerge during the processes of creating and recreating storylines are not suitable for the actual clinical situation. Rather, the storytelling process itself enhances the nurse's ability to use narrative effectively in practice.

The *narrative* used to tell a story places the plot within a context; it conveys the feel, attitude, and mood of the story, and it integrates the storylines to form a whole, vicarious experience that is located within the story's time and space. The narrative—those verbalizations, gestures, and voice intonations that are used in practice—serve the same functions. Narratives locate the isolated experiences of the person within a larger plot, contribute to the creation of an atmosphere within which the experience can unfold, and integrate the various elements of the experience into a whole that moves toward an imagined future. For example, as you imagine various storylines that involve the scenario of Niki and her mother, you form and "bank" any number of possibilities for managing an actual situation that can be called forth when needed. You also form various "moves" (i.e., words and actions) that will constitute who you are as a nurse in similar situations. Storylines are considered fiction because, although the initial story is based on a real event, the story is embellished and enhanced as it is told. In this way, stories provide a vehicle for the rehearsal of possibilities that you might be called on to actualize in your practice at some point in the future. Storylines become etched in your memory in much the same way that actual experience remains with you and that you can call forth at a moment's notice when needed.

When you create a storyline, you can develop your ideas in writing (Sorrell, 1994) or conversation. You might begin with an anecdotal account of a real experience. The experience can be your own or one that you observed or have heard about. The first account of the experience may seem relatively simple and inadequate for representing the significance of the experience itself, and it may sound clinical because of the culturally acquired propensity to focus on anecdotal accounts of a sequence of events or a clinical case study.

To make a first effort less clinical and more of a story, first explore what it is about an experience that compels your attention; identify the key characters involved in the experience; and imagine each character's perspectives, motives, and intentions. Explore the context within which the experience is set and the key elements of the situation that seem important to the unfolding of the story. Imagine various endings toward which your experience could have moved or may still move. Proposing various endings provides possibilities for building tension within the story that can be significant in different ways and lead to various endings.

Next, sketch out the essential characters that you want to place within your storyline. You can shift the characters as your storyline unfolds and changes, but the characters will remain central to the storyline. Begin to write as if you were these characters. As you write, include those elements you explored that will create richness to your story: the story's context; the character's motives, intentions, and perspectives; the key elements of the situation; and so forth. As you begin to write, the elements of the storyline will begin to emerge. Imagine several different possibilities for the movement of the storyline toward an ending, and let one of your imagined possibilities become part of your story. This first narrative will become material that you can work with to recreate the storyline with other possible endings. As other possible endings are created, a richness of meaning emerges.

Creating and recreating storylines provide aesthetic narrative skills that the nurse uses as a participant in the emerging real-life stories of those for whom care is provided. The story that unfolds clinically is shaped and transformed by emerging possibilities that are situated between the past and the future. Mattingly (1994) described this process as "therapeutic emplotment." The story that unfolds clinically is lived. The aesthetic challenge is to structure isolated episodes into a plot that moves the lived experience toward a hoped-for ending. In our example of Niki, you made a transformative move that fairly quickly brought an explosive situation to a calmer place. However, you are likely to have continuing contact with Niki, and your experience of creating transformative art/acts continues. As Niki returns to the clinic throughout her pregnancy and beyond, you will continue to participate as a player in shaping Niki's real-life story. As during that first encounter, you will use nursing as an art/act that moves the real-life story that is unfolding toward the best possible future.

In real-life stories, all participants are instrumental in the creation of the plot, the selection of the ending, and the actions that bring about changes and transformations. The plot does not happen by design; rather, it unfolds. The end that participants desire energizes movement toward that end. A nurse's ability to participate in this aesthetic process is nurtured by skills that are developed through the rehearsal of creating and recreating storylines.

Creating conversational or written storylines that move the situation toward a desired future provides a vision of what might be and an opportunity for the rehearsal of ways in which nursing care can be enacted to energize movement in a new direction. As the actual experience unfolds, what the person and his or her family envision is shaped by everyday experiences. For example, as a nurse assists a person with taking the first steps after a traumatic injury, the possibility for mobility begins to take form, and with this possibility comes the potential for returning to a job or reengaging in a desired activity. The imagined scenarios of one's new life story gradually begin to take shape as they are formed by the mutual interactions of nurses, family members, and others involved in caring for the person. See Box 6-1 for an example.

To summarize, the purpose of creating stories is twofold. First, your stories develop a deep sense of meaning and significance in human experience, and they provide a connection with human experience that only aesthetic expressions can convey. This sense of connection begins for you as you develop a story. The experiences in your stories can then become real for those who read or hear the stories that you create. Second, your stories can provide an avenue for you to explore and, in a sense, rehearse new possibilities—with new meanings and significance—for practice. If you place a dynamic in your story that explores a situation in practice that you had hoped for but never experienced, or that you imagine might be possible, your stories provide a way to experience what you have not yet come across in practice. Your stories provide a vicarious experience that helps to make potential nursing situations that have not yet been encountered seem more real.

BOX 6-1	**Creating and Recreating Storylines: A Clinical Example**

Consider the idea of working with someone who experienced a life-altering experience, such as a major trauma or a disabling illness. You enter the person's life story at a time when the future that the person had imagined is inalterably changed. The person and the family face a period of tension and uncertainty during which the new imagined future is a dreaded future that was never imagined before. As a nurse, you begin with small, everyday acts of nursing care. With each nursing interaction, you begin to create with the patient and family a new plot that cannot be fully anticipated in advance. On the basis of your experience and background as a nurse, you are able to help the patient and family imagine a new future. It may not be the ultimately desired future, but it may be one that they can begin to embrace. Some elements of the new future involve small, everyday things, such as learning to function with only one arm. Other elements of the new future are more complicated, such as imagining new options for making a living.

Creating and Developing Embodied Synchronous Movement. Movement is inherent to the practice of nursing, yet little attention is given to the systematic development of movement skills other than body mechanics. Movement is generally taken for granted; people enter nursing with a lifetime of experience with moving through space and with a cultural understanding of the symbolic significance of various moves, gestures, and postures. Within the art of nursing, movement takes on a different level of significance.

As an element of the art of nursing, movement becomes the medium for the expression of meaning that parallels visual representation in the fine arts. Like the picture that conveys a thousand words, your movements as a nurse express a multitude of meanings on many levels. The communicative power of movement includes what is popularly known as *body language,* which involves movements grounded in the culture that send messages without the use of spoken language. Movement communicates who you are as a nurse, the nature of your intentions, how you regard yourself, your genuineness as a nurse and as a human, your capacity for relating to another, and your level of technical and scientific competence.

Movement, including posturing, is important for synchrony with the narrative and movement that artful nursing requires. How you move in and around a situation sets a rhythm, a style, a dynamic, a pace, and an attitude that invites or disinvites engagement. It is a fundamental symbolic marker of your abilities as a nurse artist. For example, if the way that you move into a room conveys that you are in a rush or are impatient, people's reactions to your entry will reflect their personal response to the message conveyed by your movement. Some who perceive your impatience may be apologetic for bothering you; others may feel angry that you seem to be inconvenienced by what they legitimately need and to which they feel entitled. If you do not intend to show your sense of impatience or of being rushed, your challenge is to acquire ways of moving into a situation that do not convey this message to others.

Movement makes both physical and symbolic touch possible. Without movement, touch or even symbolic touch (i.e., "touching a person's life") does not occur. The meaning of touch, which is considered vitally important in nursing practice, is conveyed through the movement toward and away from physical contact. For example, consider a scene from the movie *Silence Like Glass.* Eva, a rising-star ballerina, faces a devastating malignancy and can no longer dance. Her dance partner, with whom she had dreamed of touring the world, comes to visit. As he is leaving, she reaches out to touch his hand in a loving gesture that also conveys the regret and sorrow of the moment. He quickly withdraws his hand from her touch, with a subtle upper body shift backward and a facial expression of repulsion. Here, if you observe just the moment of touch in a snapshot of her hand touching his, you might conclude that it was a gesture of caring and love; the fuller meaning of the episode—and his movement of withdrawal from her touch—would be lost.

Movement provides a means for a nurse to identify and define the time-space within which the care encounter will occur (Chinn et al., 1997). For example, as the nurse enters an encounter, body moves, gestures that often include touch, and visual scanning define the space within which the nurse functions during the encounter. The nurse's moves remain primarily within a defined space until near the end of the encounter, when there is a gesture or move that is often accompanied by words that signals a retreat from the encounter.

Movement is needed for actions that protect, assist, comfort, and heal. The intentions that bring such moves into the nursing encounter are inherent within the moves and serve to define such moves. For example, this means that moves that are intended to protect embody that intention and convey the essence of protection within the specific situation. When you consciously focus on movement, it can be deliberately shaped so that subtleties of posture and the sequence of the movement convey meanings that are intended. The intentions that energize and give meaning to movement can be perceived by others, because your intention is embedded in the style of the move and in the physical form and shape of your movement. In other words, if your movements are hurried and rushed, the form and shape of those movements suggest an intention of doing what must be done but exiting the situation as quickly as possible. Box 6-2 lists features of movement that contribute to its aesthetic quality.

BOX 6-2   **Features of Movement that Contribute to Its Aesthetic Nursing Practice**

Coordinated balance is the concurrent movement of all parts of the body within a whole, smooth, integral pattern. Coordinated balance includes breath patterns as a foundation for the coordination of muscle movement. Breath contributes to rhythm in movement. Coordinated balance within a sequence of movements requires embodied knowing. You may have cognitive awareness of the sequence of movement, but the more your moves arise from embodied intelligence and not from cognitively processing, the finer and more balanced your coordination will be.

Finesse is the refinement and versatility with which moves are made. Finesse depends on embodied familiarity with the environment and with the objects and processes with which you work. It requires integrating a knowing of the materials at hand with the capabilities of the body. Finesse comes with practice and experience and can be nurtured with rehearsal, but each individual has different aptitudes for developing finesse.

Style is the unique character that each individual brings to movement. It is the particular way that you use movement as you bring intention and action together. It is your unique artistic expression that emerges in the creation of an integrated whole. Style cannot be taught, but it can be encouraged. Style emerges as others respond to your unique ways of acting and being in the world. Style can be described, but it cannot be duplicated, because it is an integral element of a unique Self. There can be no value judgments with respect to style. Artistic value resides not in the style per se but in the form of the whole, the meaning that is conveyed, and the responses that are evoked.

Timing involves rhythm, the pace of movement, and the placement of various moves within a time sequence of an unfolding experience. The idea that "timing is everything" most certainly applies to the artistic validity of the nursing art. Timing is an important factor of narrative interactions just as it is important to movement; in other words, *when* you say something is vitally important. Timing is a key marker of intuitive ability, because timing cannot be planned in advance, and it is not cognitively processed. Rather, timing is determined in the moment as an experience unfolds.

Synchrony is the ability to bring together elements of the environment with the responses of others and to use movement and narrative to fashion an integrated whole. Synchrony depends on coordination, finesse, style, and timing.

Movement conveys the aesthetics of technical skill performance. Movement that just "gets the job done" is empty and mechanical. What creates an aesthetic performance is the nurse's intention to bring together the various elements of narrative and movement within the experience into a caring and healing whole in which all elements fall into the right relationship. Being able to do this requires practice (rehearsal) and well-developed skill, but without a caring and healing intention being inherent in the performance, the act of doing the technical task will be mechanical.

Intention saturates movements with meaning beyond accomplishing the skill. Intention finely tunes the style, timing, finesse, and coordination to convey artistic as well as scientific competence. Aspects of movement such as coordinated balance, finesse, style, timing, and synchrony can be rehearsed in deliberately planned exercises. Movement exercises are best rehearsed within the context of nursing, because they are guided by the situation.

Movement exercises, particularly meditative forms (e.g., tai chi, yoga), can also be used to develop the embodied movement skills of coordination, finesse, and style. The posturing and movements of such body meditations are also consistent with good body mechanics and the development of an embodied sense of balance, rhythm, and coordination.

In summary, movement is an important medium that shapes the emerging story of a lived experience. It is an avenue of communication that assists with and inspires a shift from one moment to the next. Movement is a foundational element of the art of nursing.

Rehearsal and Engaging a Connoisseur-Critic. Rehearsal can focus on specific aspects of narrative or movement, or it can focus on a real-life situation with all its complexity. Rehearsal of real-life situations can be performed either in a protected studio in which you role-play various situations or in a relatively safe, actual nursing situation. A *connoisseur-critic* is an experienced nurse well versed in the art of nursing and able to envision the form of artistic nursing practice. A connoisseur-critic is also committed to teaching and coaching others as they develop artistic abilities.

Engaging a connoisseur-critic to observe your rehearsal is a vital aspect of developing aesthetic ability. As the one who is performing, you cannot judge your own artistic ability. Only from an observer's critical perspective can artistic validity be perceived and judged. Through interaction with the responses of the critic, you gain insight into the integrity of your expression, deepen your knowledge of your art form, and discover avenues for moving your art into a new realm of possibility.

Connoisseur-critics have profound familiarity with and appreciation for the art form that they critique. A connoisseur has specialized knowledge of artistic expression, and his or her judgment of the practice of the art form is considered to be discriminating. Connoisseur-critics understand the technical expertise required for artistic expression. They have studied the field that pertains to the art form and have knowledge of what the art form is directed toward as well as of the art form itself. In the case of nursing, they have studied the field of nursing and understand that nursing's art is directed toward such ends as health and healing. They also understand the processes required to bring dimensions of health and healing into being.

Connoisseur-critics also know the history of the art form and understand how it has changed over time. They are familiar with the current cultural context for the art form and the possibilities for new directions that are emerging within the art form. Given their expertise, they have developed a keenly trained "eye, ear, and feel" for the art. The intention of the connoisseur-critic is to nurture the artist's ability to obtain a new dimension of expression. This intention and its translation into action create a safe environment that nurtures the artist's skill. A skilled teacher is a skilled connoisseur-critic, and a skilled connoisseur-critic is a skilled teacher.

Skilled critics nurture critical abilities in the novice artist and shape and support the development of the reflective capacities that are necessary to refine aesthetic ability. The primary function of the connoisseur-critic in a rehearsal context is to provide guidance that moves the art form to a new level. The critic provides substantive information about well-developed aspects of the performance and elements that show promise for development, with specific guidance for taking the performance to a new level of skill. Ideally, the critic works with the artist over time so that the critic becomes familiar with the performer's unique abilities and style. Over time, the critic becomes sensitive to signals of emerging ability and engages with the artist in ways that encourage a shift toward increasing artistic competence.

The critic does not give generalized value judgments of "good" or "bad." Value judgments are empty of substantive insight about the performance. However, the critic does provide authentic indicators of the feeling response that the performance elicited as well as substantive information regarding what aspects of the performance elicited that response. For example, in response to a nurse's unexpected move that clearly turned an evolving situation in a new direction, the critic might say, "When you did that, I was worried at first because it was so unexpected and seemed so daring and out of place. But as soon as I saw what happened next, I was overjoyed, because you clearly made a breakthrough when you did that." Here, the value-laden responses of fear and joy are grounded in the particular perspective of the critic and explicitly linked to the nurse's actions.

When the critic observes something that could change or that needs to change, rather than render a value judgment of "bad," the critic provides specific guidance for the next step and, if possible, places the element within the context of the performer's history. For example, in response to a move that is awkward and poorly timed, the critic might say, "I sensed that you were distracted and tense today when you did what you did. One thing you might try next time is to pause and just take a deep breath before you jump into this kind of challenge. Spend a moment getting clear about your intentions as you gather your equipment, and breathe!" Alternatively, the critic might respond, "Your finesse could have been better when you performed that action. Here is a sequence of moves that you can practice during the next week that I think will help. Start out slowly, and practice breathing and establishing a rhythm and a flow."

Connoisseurship requires creativity in that the critic engages in the rehearsal with a sense of openness to insights not previously conceived. It also implies that the critic has a disciplinary focus, because the critic offers a trained perspective and expectations regarding artistic validity within a particular field (Box 6-3).

BOX 6-3	Elements Critics Observe When Evaluating and Critiquing Artistic Validity

Voice intonation and expression in narrative. The critic notices the feeling that is elicited from the narrative and notes specific elements of expression that appear to be associated with the response.

Substance of the narrative interactions. The critic notices words, phrases, and narrative sequences and how they are framed within the whole.

Synchrony of movement. The critic observes how movement is situated within the context and provides guidance for developing skill in areas that interfere with synchronous movement.

Synchrony between movement and narrative. The critic observes the ways in which movement and words come together to form a whole within the interaction and the ways in which movement and narrative synchronize to create an artistic expression.

Perceived intention and emotion. The critic senses the intention that is communicated by the nurse, which may or may not coincide with the nurse's actual felt intention. When the perceived intention (as received by the critic) and the nurse's felt intention do not coincide, the critic suggests how the nurse's movement and narrative need to shift to convey adequately the felt intention.

Synchrony of interaction. The critic notices the responses of others in the situation, the rhythm and flow of the interactions, and how these reveal possibilities for the nurse to develop his or her art.

Formal Expressions of Aesthetic Knowing: Criticism and Works of Art

From the creative processes of envisioning and rehearsing, the formal expressions of aesthetic knowing emerge. These include works of art and aesthetic criticisms. Works of art as aesthetic knowledge can be made available to the broader audience within and outside the discipline. Works of art that are developed to show and symbolize artistic qualities expressed in nursing practice are an unwritten form of aesthetic knowledge. *Aesthetic criticism* is a written account that portrays the artistry of nursing. Because aesthetic criticism takes written form, it can also be shared with others.

Works of art can take a visual form, such as paintings, drawings, or photographs; a literary form, such as poetry or fiction; a more physical form that involves dance or music; or any other art form. Works of art embody and represent meaning in the experience of nursing as the artist perceives them, and they are a unique creation of the artist. Those who view, hear, or read what is expressed in a work of art also engage in the aesthetic experience of perceiving meaning in the art. The meanings perceived by the observer or reader may or may not be the same as the artist's meanings, but they can be valid meanings that inform a more complete interpretation of the art.

Aesthetic criticism, as a formalized written account of aesthetic knowledge, focuses on the transformative art/act enacted in nursing practice or on a tangible work of art representative of some nursing experience. Aesthetic criticisms highlight and bring to awareness aspects of the artistry that may not be readily perceptible to the casual observer. Aesthetic criticism provides insight into the art form, interprets the work of the nurse artist, and deepens appreciation of the nurse's art (Pellico & Chinn, 2007). Aesthetic criticisms are the product of a connoisseur-critic who selects the art of one or more artists as the focus for the critique. The critic reflects on the meanings as well as the technical adequacy of the art. A critique systematically explores the significance of one or more interpretations of the art and places the art in its historical and cultural context. Aesthetic criticism includes the following essential elements (Chinn et al., 1997):

- *Historical integration.* Historical integration includes the history of the art form and the personal artistic history of the artist. The critic examines evidence of change and continuity in the artist's history and interprets its meaning. The threads that comprise the artist's history are related to the art form, and the art form is placed within the context of those threads.
- *Comparative description of the art form.* The critic examines the form that the artist takes in the artistic process and compares the artist's work with known forms of the art. By drawing comparisons, the critic substantiates the unique aspects of the artist's work and the significance of the artist's work with regard to the discipline.
- *Consideration of plausible interpretations of meaning.* The critic considers a number of plausible meanings of the art and explores what the various meanings contribute to aesthetic understanding in the discipline. The critic may develop a preferred interpretation, but the stance remains open to multiple plausible interpretations.
- *Translation of future possibility.* The critic explores the directions that the artist might take and what the work of the artist contributes to the future development of the discipline. This aspect of criticism opens the way for appreciation and inspiration, for both the artist and the other members of the discipline.

Integrated Expression in Practice: The Transformative Art/Act

Transformative art/acts are the in-the-moment expressions of the art of nursing. Transformative art/acts require a certain quality of being and doing and of synchronous narrative and movement. This synchronicity proceeds as the nurse grasps the meaning and significance of a situation and responds in the moment. Transformative art/acts, which emerge from the situation, move the situation toward an ongoing future that would not otherwise be possible. Art/acts guide the experience of those involved from one moment to the next and help them to envision and create possibilities for the future (Benner & Wrubel, 1989). During the transformative art/act, everything about the situation comes together in synchrony, like a dance that works for everyone in the situation. The art/act has an element of mystery; it is perceived in the moment but not consciously or analytically understood. It creates a possibility that can never be deliberately planned or anticipated but that is sensed as being right for the moment.

Authentication Processes: Appreciation and Inspiration

As nurses share and communicate insights that are derived from the creative processes of envisioning, rehearsing, and then formally expressing the artistry of nursing, others in the discipline respond to the formal expression of art and the meaning that it provides in relation to the discipline of nursing. In the sphere of aesthetics, the authentication of aesthetic knowledge involves appreciation and inspiration.

Formal expressions of aesthetic knowing provide representations for the discipline that are unique in temporal time and space and that are grounded in the wholeness of human experience. The authentication processes of appreciation and inspiration are used to reflect back on the artistic experience that is represented and on the symbolized meanings inherent in its representation.

In the pattern of aesthetics, the authentication of aesthetic knowledge requires responses of appreciation and inspiration. Appreciation means that others affirm that they see meaning in the art/act or in the artistic representation, and that the meaning conveyed is appropriate and important for the discipline of nursing. Inspiration means that the work brings forth new meanings and possibilities for understanding the experience that it represents, and that it moves the viewer or observer toward the experience that is represented. In other words, observers are moved to bring something represented in the art/act into their own practices, or to draw on insights represented by the art/act to inform their own practices.

There are three guiding principles for the authentication processes of the appreciation and inspiration of aesthetic knowledge. These principles ask the following:

1. Is the artistic expression a unique, creative expression that is grounded in the immediacy and enduring wholeness of human experience?
2. Does the artistic expression expand and enrich the plausible meanings of the experience?
3. Does the artistic expression illuminate possibilities for the future?

Unique features serve to distinguish artistic expressions from any other type of expression and to reveal possibilities in human experience and expression that have not existed before and that will not be replicated. An expression of aesthetic knowing in nursing is authenticated when you and others in the discipline come to appreciate something about nursing not previously appreciated and are inspired to consider new possibilities for your own practice and for the nursing discipline. The expression is also authenticated if it inspires you and others to change the Self and learn in some way or to integrate new creative possibilities into your practice.

Works of art, as aesthetic expressions, are appreciated immediately—in the moment—and call forth human responses that inspire in some way. To say they are forms of knowledge that are responded to "immediately" means that you appreciate them all at once; they are not mediated by language or other symbols. For example, when you see a painting that connects with you about some aspect of nursing, the feeling response of "it just speaks to me" is immediate and in the moment. You do not read the painting line by line like you would a book. Rather, you notice a painting all at once. Your eye movements scan and interpret the painting, and it touches something within you that you appreciate as inspirational. You are drawn to dwell on the painting and begin to notice nuances of expression in the art. The capacity to call forth human responses in the moment and to draw the observer into a deeper experience of the art reflects a work of art's power to reflect something that is significant as well as common in the human experience.

Unlike works of art, aesthetic criticism usually takes a written form. These criticisms are authenticated in a way similar to that of works of art, but the whole of the criticism is not appreciated all at once in the moment as a painting or sculpture might be. However, authentic aesthetic criticisms can be both appreciated and inspirational. When you reflect on a well-written criticism, new possibilities for your nursing art and its possibilities for nursing come into awareness, just as they do when works of art are authenticated. Although aesthetic criticisms are formalized expressions of aesthetic knowing that are written, it should be noted that appreciation and inspiration could also come about when you and a connoisseur-critic engage in a nursing encounter. To summarize, a response that is elicited by an aesthetic art form—whether a work of art or an aesthetic criticism—deepens the observer-participant's appreciation of the experience that is represented and creates new meanings and possibilities for the expression of nursing art to an extent that would not otherwise be possible.

Think About It

To deepen your appreciation of aesthetic knowing, consider the following questions related to the content of this chapter:

1. What comes to mind when you hear the phrase "the art of nursing"? Do you think a focus on nursing as an art is important today? Why?

2. Consider a situation in which you felt that you practiced artfully by being deeply satisfied that you made a real difference in the turn of events. Why did you feel this way? What was it about the situation that made you feel satisfied?

3. What features of your nursing practice do you feel are particularly artful? Why do you feel this way? In what areas do you need to improve your art? How might you do this?

REFLECTION AND DISCUSSION – SUPPLEMENT ⊖

References

Archibald, M. M. (2012). The holism of aesthetic knowing in nursing. *Nursing Philosophy*, *13*(3), 179–188.

Benner, P. A., & Wrubel, J. (1989). *The primacy of caring: Stress and coping in health and illness*. Menlo Park, CA: Addison-Wesley.

Benner, P. A., Tanner, C. A., & Chesla, C. A. (1996). *Expertise in nursing practice: Caring, clinical judgment, and ethics*. New York, NY: Springer.

Billay, D., Myrick, F., Luhanga, F., & Yonge, O. (2007). A pragmatic view of intuitive knowledge in nursing practice. *Nursing Forum*, *42*(3), 147–155.

Chinn, P. L. (1994). Developing a method for aesthetic knowing in nursing. In P. L. Chinn, & J. Watson (Eds.), *Art and aesthetics in nursing* (pp. 19–40). New York, NY: National League for Nursing Press.

Chinn, P. L. (2001). Toward a theory of nursing art. In N. L. Chaska (Ed.), *The nursing profession: Tomorrow and beyond* (pp. 287–297). Thousand Oaks, CA: Sage.

Chinn, P. L., & Watson, J. (Eds.). (1994). *Art & aesthetics in nursing*. New York, NY: National League for Nursing.

Chinn, P. L., Maeve, M. K., & Bostick, C. (1997). Aesthetic inquiry and the art of nursing. *Scholarly Inquiry for Nursing Practice*, *11*(2), 83–96.

Darbyshire, P. (1994). Understanding the life of illness: Learning through the art of Frida Kahlo. *ANS Advances in Nursing Science, 17*(1), 51–59.

Dean, Patrick (2013). Nursing as Art-in-Action is Practical as well as Aesthetic. *Journal of Art and Aesthetics in Nursing and Health Sciences, 1*(1), 4–10.

Eisner, E. (1985). Aesthetic modes of knowing. In E. Eisner (Ed.), *Learning and teaching the ways of knowing (Part II)*. Chicago, IL: University of Chicago Press.

Heidegger, M. (1962). *Being and time* (J. Macquarrie & E. Robinson, Trans.). New York, NY: Harper & Row.

Johnson, J. L. (1994). A dialectical examination of nursing art. *ANS Advances in Nursing Science, 17*(1), 1–14.

Johnson, J. L. (1996). Dialectical analysis concerning the rational aspect of the art of nursing. *Image—The Journal of Nursing Scholarship, 28*(2), 169–175.

Kramper, M., & Thawley, S. (2009). Poetry and the art of nursing. *ORL Head and Neck Nursing, 27*(2), 6–11.

Lamb, J. (2009). Creating change: Using the arts to help stop the stigma of mental illness and foster social integration. *Journal of Holistic Nursing, 27*, 57–65.

LeVasseur, J. J. (1999). Toward an understanding of art in nursing. *ANS Advances in Nursing Science, 21*(4), 48–63.

Liehr, P., Morris, K., Leavitt, M. A., & Takahashi, R. (2013). Translating research findings to promote peace: Moving from "field to forum" with verbatim theatre. *ANS Advances in Nursing Science, 36*(3), 160–170.

Maeve, M. K. (1994). Coming to moral consciousness through the art of nursing narratives. In P. L. Chinn, & J. Watson (Eds.), *Art and aesthetics in nursing* (pp. 67–89). New York, NY: National League for Nursing.

Mattingly, C. (1994). The concept of therapeutic "emplotment." *Social Science Medicine, 38*, 811–822.

Oettinger, K. B. (1939). Toward inner freedom. *American Journal of Nursing, 39*, 1224–1229.

Pellico, L. H., & Chinn, P. L. (2007). Narrative criticism: A systematic approach to the analysis of story. *Journal of Holistic Nursing, 25*, 58–65.

Sandelowski, M. (1995). On the aesthetics of qualitative research. *Image—The Journal of Nursing Scholarship, 27*(3), 205–209.

Sorrell, J. M. (1994). Remembrance of things past through writing: Esthetic patterns of knowing in nursing. *ANS Advances in Nursing Science, 17*(1), 60–70.

Vezeau, T. M. (1994). Narrative inquiry in nursing. In P. L. Chinn, & J. Watson (Eds.), *Art and aesthetics in nursing*. New York, NY: National League for Nursing Press.

Wainwright, P. (2000). Towards an aesthetics of nursing. *Journal of Advanced Nursing, 32*, 750–756.

Chapter 7

Empiric Knowledge Development: Conceptualizing and Structuring

⊖ http://evolve.elsevier.com/Chinn/knowledge/

Looking at human behavior is like running into a cloud whose origins and direction is unknown. You can see the cloud, dynamic and three dimensional, but when you reach out to grab a handful to test you come away with nothing visible but a clenched fist. You may be buffeted by the forces within the cloud that moves on, still visible and dynamic and still three dimensional and you think "I can see the cloud, I can feel the forces it contains, but how do I study it when it refuses to lend itself to anything more than a fleeting encounter?"

Marjorie R. Wright (1966, p. 244)

The opening quote suggests that the discipline of nursing concerns phenomena that are rather elusive—phenomena that nurses know exist and deal with on a daily basis yet that are difficult to describe and fully understand. Nursing is often characterized as a *human science,* which means that its disciplinary knowledge focuses on phenomena and events that are very different from phenomena within the physical sciences. Understanding (and developing) shared knowledge about human responses to a life-changing event is much different than understanding how solid matter responds to the application of heat or force.

Research is the usual means by which nursing's disciplinary knowledge within the empiric pattern is developed. The suffix *re-* means "again" as well as "back," which implies that, in research, knowledge is generated by a backward look or "re-searching" in relation to the phenomena being studied. However, when one looks back at human behavior as described in a single research report, what was found often is no longer evident or has changed. Research findings change because human behavior is not static. To be sure, some phenomena in the human sciences are more "cloud-like" than others. Human behavior that is regulated by physical processes (e.g., behavior associated with cardiovascular function) may be more predictable than behavior regulated by perceptions of meaning. For example, we now understand that compromised circulatory function in the brain of an elderly person is likely to cause perceptible mental changes eventually. It is much more difficult to understand or know how a child whose parent has been diagnosed with a debilitating disease will experience hope and despair. This is because human behaviors related to hope and despair are closely linked with the child's perceptions of the meaning of the parent's illness; those perceptions in turn depend on factors that change over time.

This chapter deals with conceptualizing and structuring phenomena that are relevant to nursing as an approach to developing disciplinary knowledge. Nursing seeks to conceptualize and structure phenomena that are extremely elusive as well as phenomena more easily understood. As we explain in this chapter, however, even what seems to be easily understood can sometimes be elusive. The challenge when conceptualizing and structuring empiric knowledge is to realize that in nursing, regardless of what is studied, the focus is on human behavior and human responses, which are, as Wright establishes in her quote, rather cloud-like.

Figure 7-1 shows the empiric quadrant of our model for nursing knowledge development. As the critical questions, "What is this?" and "How does it work?" are asked, the creative processes of conceptualizing and structuring are initiated. As with the other patterns, these questions are asked in the moment of practice as empiric knowledge is integrated with the other patterns of knowing. The questions can also be asked of the formal expressions of empirics apart from the immediate practice situation. As these questions are responded to, the creative processes of conceptualizing and structuring are engaged. Out of these creative processes comes the generation or reconfiguring of formal expressions of empirics.

The formal expressions of empiric knowledge include theories as well as other structured descriptions of empiric phenomena. As formal expressions are authenticated by confirmation and validation processes, the potential for scientific competence (i.e., integrated expression of empirics in practice) is strengthened. In this chapter, we focus on the creative processes of conceptualizing and structuring empiric phenomena. Chapters 8 to 10 focus on other dimensions of the model's empiric quadrant.

The two processes used for conceptualizing and structuring empiric phenomena are (1) creating conceptual meaning and (2) structuring and contextualizing theory. In the

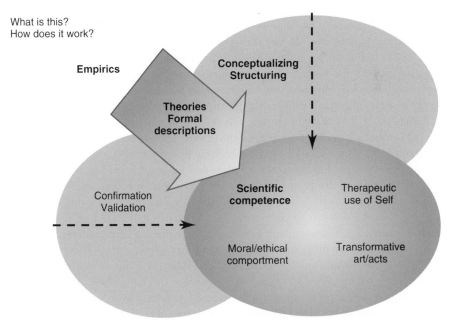

FIGURE 7-1: Empiric knowing and knowledge: conceptualizing and structuring.

discipline of nursing, *theory* is generally considered the most formal and the most highly structured of the empiric knowledge forms, and this type of theory is our focus here. However, these processes can also apply to many forms of empiric knowledge.

WHAT IS EMPIRIC THEORY?

The term *empiric* has a number of different meanings. From a traditional standpoint, *empiric* implies an objective, nontheoretic observation, which implies that meaning exists in what is observed apart from the interpretations of the observer. In a clinical context, *empiric* is used to specify a treatment or an approach that has been demonstrated to be effective. From a philosophic perspective, *empiric* refers to that which is accessible to sensory perception, either directly or indirectly. Our definition is grounded in the philosophic meaning of the term: knowledge that is grounded in perceptual experience. This would include knowledge that is developed with the use of controlled experimental studies as well as various naturalistic methods that rely on interacting with and understanding the nature of experience as it is perceived. In this and the following chapters, we discuss *empiric theory.*

As with *empirics,* the idea of *theory* can be defined in many different ways within and outside of the discipline of nursing. This can be confusing, because each definition can be functional, depending on how you are using the term. It is a challenge to select the best definition when you are developing theory, because your definition will guide your methods of theory development. Your definition will also reflect your underlying beliefs and values related to science, knowledge, and what constitutes an adequate empiric method. You will see our values and beliefs reflected in our explanation of how we came to the definition used in this text.

Theory has common, everyday connotations that are apparent in phrases such as, "I have a theory about that," or "My theory about *x* is. . . ." These uses imply that theory is an idea or feeling or that it explains something. In this text, we use a definition that is consistent with the more everyday meanings of theory: as a collection of ideas or explanatory hunches. However, our definition goes beyond this to a characterization of theory as something that is deliberately designed for a specific purpose.

Beliefs about the nature of empiric theory arise in part from the various fields of inquiry from which nursing knowledge is developed. Some nursing theorists come from traditions in which the ideal of theory is logically linked sets of confirmed hypotheses. Others view theory as loosely connected ideas that are conjectured but not confirmed. Still others think of theory as philosophically based sets of beliefs and values about human nature and action. As a result, the nursing literature contains varying definitions of theory, but this diversity serves to stimulate the further understanding and development of theory. The following four definitions in the nursing literature emphasize different perspectives and different underlying values that involve theory. These definitions each highlight important aspects of theory that we draw on in our own definition:

- *A logically interconnected set of confirmed hypotheses* (McKay, 1969). This definition implies a specific form of expression that is based on rules of logic. It also requires that the hypotheses be tested and confirmed with the use of methods of scientific-empiric research to generate theory.

- *A conceptual system or framework that is invented to serve some purpose* (Dickoff & James, 1968). This definition emphasizes the purpose for which a theory is created. The term *invented* implies a creative process, although this may not necessarily involve the type of testing and confirmation that McKay suggests. This definition emphasizes the importance of the theory having a purpose.
- *An imaginative grouping of knowledge, ideas, and experiences that are represented symbolically and that seek to illuminate a given phenomenon* (Watson, 1985). This definition also emphasizes creativity. For Watson, the purpose of creating theory is to enhance understanding of a given phenomenon. As Dickoff and James explain from their point of view, a theory's purpose should be a specific practice-oriented application. For Watson, a theory fulfills the purpose of understanding what a phenomenon is, which may or may not have direct application in practice.
- *Conceptual and pragmatic principles that form a general frame of reference for a field of inquiry* (Ellis, 1968). This definition does not address a specific type of purpose for theory, and it does not suggest any particular method for developing theory. For Ellis, theory provides a philosophic view that guides inquiry in a discipline. Theory contains abstract (conceptual) and pragmatic principles that provide a general frame of reference. To avoid redundancy in this chapter, when we use the term "theory," we are referring to empiric theory.

⊖ Image Collection – Empiric and Scientific Traditions

From our perspective, theory is a creative and rigorous structuring of ideas. The ideas are expressed by word symbols that form a conceptual structure. The structure is created with the use of a method that draws on the creativity of the theorist. The concepts contained within the theory must be defined, and they must have a logical relationship with one another to form a coherent structure or pattern. Empiric theory is purposeful; theorists create the theory for some reason. Theoretic purposes may take many different forms, but the purpose needs to be clearly evident.

Theory is not a finalized prescription or a formula for practice; it cannot describe exactly what can be objectively observed. Instead, theory projects tentative ideas that open new perceptions and possibilities with regard to what might be beyond the common surface understandings of the world. Theory is grounded in assumptions, value choices, and the creative and imaginative judgment of the theorist. You may or may not share the values and views of the theorist, but your exposure to the theory and the views that it reveals can expand your own thinking about your experience, your profession, and the direction of your own work.

Our definition of theory is as follows:

Empiric theory: A creative and rigorous structuring of ideas that projects a tentative, purposeful, and systematic view of phenomena.

The word *creative* underscores the role of human imagination and vision in the development and expression of theory; it does not mean that "anything goes" or that theory is improvised. The creative processes required to develop theory are rigorous, systematic, and disciplined, thereby yielding a well-developed conception that bears the mark of the creator. In our view, theoretic statements are tentative and open to revision as new evidence and insights emerge. The statements are developed toward some purpose or within a specific context. Our definition does not require that a hypothesis be tested before the statements can be considered as theory. Ideas that the creator systematically develops on the basis of experience and observation can be considered as theory before formal testing occurs.

Given our definition, it is possible to contrast how empiric theory differs from related terms such as *science, philosophy, paradigm, theoretic framework,* and *model.* Like the word *theory,* these terms are highly abstract and have many different meanings for different people and within the discipline of nursing. Sometimes the meanings overlap, and sometimes they seem very different. When there are confusing overlaps and differences, you can resolve the confusion by clarifying commonly accepted disciplinary meanings and creating a reasonable definition that is appropriate for your purposes.

Your definitions cannot be arbitrary or simply based on your personal beliefs. As with our definition of *theory,* your definitions of any terms will reflect your beliefs. In addition, your definitions must be consistent with common threads of meaning that are generally accepted within the discipline and grounded in a logical rationale that is coherent to other members of the discipline. Definitions must also be suitable for the context in which they are created and the purpose that they serve. For example, if you are defining the word *self-esteem* for a research study, your definition might include the foundational meanings that are consistent with the tool that you are using to measure self-esteem. However, if you are defining *self-esteem* for a clinical project that is designed to assist women with the making of prenatal health choices, your definition may or may not reflect the underlying meanings of a specific measurement tool.

We have defined *theory* for the purpose of explaining to you, the reader, our view of what theory is, how to develop it, and how to evaluate it. Definitions of related terms help to make clearer the meaning of the central term (in this case, *theory*). Our definitions of several related terms for the context of this book are provided in Table 7-1. The definitions of related terms may not be universally accepted, but we believe that these are reasonable and reflect common meanings. In addition, no matter how rigorous the attempt to differentiate like terms by providing definitions, there will be elements of shared meaning among them.

The following sections address important processes for conceptualizing and structuring empiric theory. *Conceptualizing* involves creative processes of making meaning; it involves exploring a wide range of possible meanings for a concept and creating a meaning that is relevant to your purpose. The *structuring* processes involve placing concepts into a structure and then placing that structure into a larger context. Assumptions, or "taken for granted" truths, as well as your purpose for creating theory, are also important to consider when creating conceptual meaning and when structuring concepts into relationships.

CREATING CONCEPTUAL MEANING

Creating conceptual meaning is a theory-building approach that depends on thought processes. The process of creating conceptual meaning carefully examines the ideas, perceptions, and thoughts that are generated when word symbols are encountered. To say that words are *symbols* means that words stand for or represent some experience or

TABLE 7-1	Conceptual Definitions of Terms Related to the Concept of Theory
Term	**Definition**
Science	An approach to the generation of empiric knowledge that relies on accessible sensory experience to create knowledge and to form understanding. The term also refers to the results or products generated when the systematic methods of empirics are used.
Philosophy	A form of disciplined inquiry that discerns the nature of the world and of knowledge and knowing and that involves ways of discerning reality and principles of value. Philosophy relies on logic and reasoning rather than empiric evidence to create knowledge.
Fact	That which generally is held to be an empirically verifiable object, property, or event, which means that the phenomenon is experienced and named consistently and similarly by others in a given similar context.
Model	A symbolic representation of an empiric experience in the form of words, pictorial or graphic diagrams, mathematic notations, or physical material (e.g., a model airplane).
Theoretic or conceptual framework	A logical grouping of related concepts or theories that usually is created to draw together several different aspects that are relevant to a complex situation, such as a practice setting or an educational program.
Paradigm	A worldview or ideology. A paradigm implies standards or criteria for assigning value or worth to both the processes and the products of a discipline as well as for the methods of knowledge development within a discipline.

phenomenon. In similar cultures, the meaning associated with word symbols is both common and unique.

Think About It

In nursing, similar meanings for the word symbol "hypothermia" are shared among those who belong to the discipline. At the same time, a person's own subjective meaning may be unique and more real to the individual than any other possible interpretation of the word. For example, if I am in a room with a comfortable ambient air temperature and announce that I am cold (i.e., mildly hypothermic) when everyone else in the room is comfortable, my own perception or experience of being cold is the most real to me, although I recognize that I am the only one who feels cold. The everyday experience of feeling cold is quite different from what, as nurses, we associate with the term "hypothermia."

What other examples can you identify where common terms take on different meanings in a nursing context?

When you are creating conceptual meaning, you are giving meaning to the word symbols within the theory. During this process, use your mental capacity to recognize when your own perceptions are unique and to assess the extent to which your unique experience represents an oddity as well as the possibility of a new prospect for others to consider.

Conceptual meaning does not exist as an unexplored reality to be objectively discovered; it is created and deliberately formed from experience. The process of creating conceptual meaning brings dimensions of meaning to a conscious and communicable awareness. The perceptions or meanings that any language or word symbol calls forth are limited when it comes to expressing the fullness of the experience that is represented. For example, when you encounter the word *hope,* you have a sense of what that word represents. That sense may be quite rich and full, but it is still limited in relation to the full range of meanings possible, because personal experience is limited and never encompasses the full range of possible meanings. The process of creating conceptual meaning makes it possible to expand what we understand about a phenomenon that goes beyond the simple definition of its word symbol and our unique perception of its meaning.

Word symbols and language call to mind unique yet common meanings, and language systems shape and create perceptions and meaning (Allen & Cloyes, 2005; Crowe, 2005; Müller & Dzurec, 1993; White, 2004). If someone is called "clever," that person begins to form an awareness of self that may be affirming, but the word *clever* may not adequately express the person's rich inner experiences and instead may trivialize how the person experiences the world. If a word represents a desired value, the meaning that is understood when the word is encountered contributes positively to self-awareness.

Although the process of creating conceptual meaning provides a foundation for developing theory and is a logical starting point for theory development, it does not necessarily have to be accomplished first. It is a process that can be performed by the beginning or advanced scholar and by the novice or expert practitioner. Although this process is critical to all theory development, it is often overlooked (Norris, 1982). Most theorists provide definitions of terms that are used within a theory, but forming word definitions is not the same as creating conceptual meaning. Conceptual meaning conveys thoughts, feelings, and ideas that reflect the human experience to the fullest extent possible, which is not possible with a definition. A word definition provides an anchor from which to situate common mental associations with a term; conceptual meaning provides a mental picture of what the phenomenon is like and how it is perceived in human experience.

⊖ Image Collection – Conceptual Meaning Exercise

WHAT IS A CONCEPT?

We define the term *concept* as a complex mental formulation of experience. By "experience," we mean perceptions of the world, including objects, other people, visual images, color, movement, sounds, behavior, and interactions; in other words, we refer to the totality of what is perceived. Experience is considered empiric when it can be symbolically shared and verified by others with sensory evidence.

Figure 7-2 shows the three sources of experience interacting to form the meaning of the concept: (1) the word or other symbolic label; (2) the thing itself (object, property, or event); and (3) the feelings, values, and attitudes associated with the word and with the perception of the thing. As any one of these elements changes over time, the concept itself changes. Consider, for example, the concept of *mouse*. Until the 1980s, this word symbol was almost exclusively connected to a little critter that wreaks havoc in people's basements and prompts wild screams of terror. In a very short time frame, this word symbol came to signify not only that little critter but also a very different object: a device that is used to navigate on a computer. At first, this device was thought to be optional and mainly useful for the playing of games. However, it quickly became not optional but necessary (which is an attitude or feeling), and it is certainly not an object that elicits screams and screeches. Almost any word could have been chosen for this little object, but its originators selected the word *mouse,* which derives from the resemblance of early models that had a cord attached to the rear part of the device (suggesting a tail) to the common mouse.

Conceptual meaning is created by considering all three sources of experiences related to the concept: the word, the thing itself, and the associated feelings (see Figure 7-2). The same word may be used to represent more than one phenomenon. For example, the word *cup* may be used to represent several different kinds of objects or ideas. Each use of the word carries with it different perceptions. If the object is a fancy teacup, a very different mental image forms than if the object is the cup into which a golf ball falls on a putting green. The word *love,* which is a more abstract concept, can be used to describe a feeling toward a parent, a child, a pet, a car, a job, a friend, or an intimate partner, with each use implying a different but related feeling. When creating conceptual meaning, you examine the range of what is signified by a word symbol, find what is common

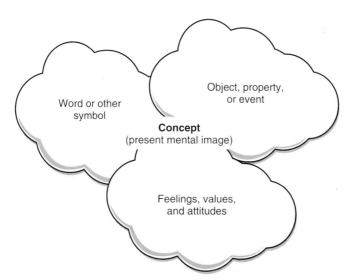

FIGURE 7-2: Sources of experience that form the meaning of a concept.

among all of the uses and what is different, and decide what elements of meaning are important for your purpose.

All concepts can be located on a continuum from the *empiric* (i.e., more directly experienced) to the *abstract* (i.e., more mentally constructed) (Jacox, 1974; Kaplan, 1964). In one sense, all concepts are both empiric and abstract. They are empiric because they are formed from perceptual encounters with the world as it is experienced, but they are abstract because they are mental images of that experience.

Some concepts are formed from very direct experiences that can be more readily verified by others. Others are formed from experiences that are commonly recognized but inferred indirectly. Figure 7-3 illustrates this continuum. Relatively empiric concepts are ideas that are formed from the direct observation of objects, properties, or events. As concepts become more abstract, they are inferred indirectly. The most abstract concepts are mental constructions that encompass a complex network of subconcepts.

The most concrete empiric concepts have direct forms of measurement. Concepts formed around objects such as a cup or properties such as temperature are examples of highly empiric concepts, because the object or property that represents the idea (i.e., the empiric indicator) can be directly experienced through the senses and confirmed by many different people. A relatively empiric property such as biologic sex can also be observed directly by noting the primary and secondary sexual characteristics that identify a person as male or female or—more precisely and especially if the sex is ambiguous—by identifying chromosomal patterns. Properties such as height and weight can be measured with standardized instruments.

As concepts become more abstract, their observational qualities (i.e., their empiric indicators) become less concrete and less directly measurable. The assessment of an

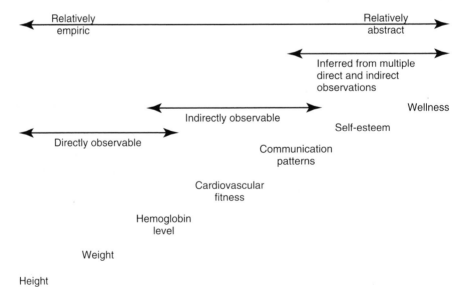

FIGURE 7-3: Illustration of the empiric-abstract continuum.

abstract concept depends increasingly on indirect means. Although an indirect assessment or observation is different from direct measurement, it is considered a reasonable indicator of the concept. An individual's hemoglobin level is representative of a concept that cannot be directly observed but that can be indirectly measured with the aid of laboratory instruments. This type of measurement depends on more complex and less direct forms of instrumentation.

Cardiovascular fitness is an example of a concept in the middle range on the empiric-abstract continuum. Concepts increase in complexity in this range, and several empiric indicators must be assessed. Because no actual object that can be called "cardiovascular fitness" exists, a definition is required if we are to know what it is. Although definitions for less empirically based concepts are thoughtfully formulated, these are arbitrary because many different definitions could be chosen. As concepts become increasingly abstract, definitions become more dependent on the theoretic meaning of the concept and the purpose for defining it.

Self-esteem is an example of a highly abstract concept for which there is no direct measure. The instruments or tools that are developed to assess self-esteem depend on theoretic definitions that serve a specific purpose and are built on many behaviors and personality characteristics that experts agree are associated with the concept. Ideas about these characteristics may be derived from a theory or from concept clarification. Each behavioral trait that is contained in the tool can be considered a partial indicator of self-esteem. When the composite behaviors and personal characteristics are built into an assessment tool, it is usually a more adequate indicator of the abstract concept than any one behavior alone. The composite score obtained from the tool is then considered to be a measurement that has been constructed as an empiric indicator.

Highly abstract concepts are sometimes called *constructs*. Constructs are the most complex type of concept on the empiric-abstract continuum. These concepts include ideas with a reality base so abstract that it is constructed from multiple sources of direct and indirect evidence. An example of a construct is *wellness*. Although the idea of wellness exists, it cannot be directly observed. Figure 7-3 illustrates the idea that highly abstract concepts are constructed from other concepts. All concepts shown on the continuum (as well as others) can be included in the concept of wellness.

Some abstract concepts have little meaning outside of the context of a theory. For example, Levine (1967) coined the word *trophicogenic* to mean "nurse-induced illness." Rogers (1970) discussed three principles of *homeodynamics,* a combination of the Latin root word *homeo,* meaning "similar to" or "like," and the common English term *dynamics,* which means "pattern of change or growth." The reader can infer the meaning of "change processes" for the term *homeodynamics,* which is consistent with Rogers' intent.

Abstract concepts may also acquire additional meanings through gradual transfer into common language usage. Freud's concept of *ego* is an example. The word *ego* once had no common meaning outside of Freud's theory, but now, with gradual changes in its meaning and broad usage outside the theory, almost everyone who speaks American English and many other English speakers around the world know the meaning of the phrase "a big ego."

A single phenomenon can also be represented by several different words. Each word conveys a slightly different meaning and often reflects nuances that relate to socially derived value meanings. For example, the words *luxury car, Model T,* and *Hot Wheels* all refer to one basic thing: an automobile. The use of any of these words to describe an automobile conveys the perspective or values of the person who is using the word, as well as the features of the object itself. As the words acquire contextual and value meanings, they shift further toward the abstract.

Feelings, values, and attitudes are inner processes that are associated with experiences and words. For example, the word *mother* carries feelings, values, and attitudes that form in human experience with an actual person. Varying experiences with a certain mother (the person) account for the range of feelings that people associate with the word *mother.* At the same time, the human meaning of the concept *mother* is formed from shared cultural and societal heritages. A concept such as *mother,* which can carry specific or highly complex meanings, changes in its level of abstraction, depending on the context of usage.

Many nursing concepts are highly abstract. Although theory and other common forms of empiric knowledge (e.g., models, frameworks, descriptions) incorporate and depend on highly empiric facts, nursing theory does not generally reflect factually based concepts.

Although it usually is not possible or necessary to identify precisely where concepts fit on the empiric-abstract continuum, it is important to understand that concepts vary in the degree they are connected to what is perceived as experience and the extent to which their meaning is mentally constructed. When you begin to study an abstract concept, it is natural to wonder why it is difficult to grasp the meaning of the term and understand all that is conveyed by the concept.

Think About It

Nurses often claim that they tend to be very "concrete"—that they do not relate to theoretic abstractions. At the same time, nurses regularly address experiences such as *grief, anxiety,* and *hopelessness,* all concepts that are highly abstract. These concepts come to be seen as more "concrete" because the behavioral manifestations that we associate with them have been commonly accepted. But are these behaviors reliable indicators of what we assume them to be? Could the behaviors you associate with *anxiety* actually be signals of some other experience?

METHODS FOR CREATING CONCEPTUAL MEANING

Creating conceptual meaning produces a tentative definition of the concept and a set of tentative criteria for determining whether the concept is meaningful in a particular situation. We use *tentative* because both the definition and the criteria can be revised. This does not mean, however, that "anything goes" or that any definition that suits the author will do. The use of *tentative* here means that the definition is open and can be changed as new insights and understandings come to light. This process is a deliberative, disciplined activity. The person who is creating meaning draws on many information sources, examines many possible dimensions of meaning, and presents ideas so that they can be tested and challenged in the light of the purposes for which the conceptual meaning is intended.

There are various methods for creating conceptual meaning, each of which has advantages and drawbacks (Beckwith, Dickinson, & Kendall, 2008). Norris (1982) describes several methods for concept clarification. Walker and Avant (2010) detail a method of concept analysis based on the work of Wilson (1963). Morse (1995) proposes methods of concept development and analysis that draw on qualitative and quantitative research approaches to validate meanings projected by analytic processes. Moscou (2008) describes a method of concept analysis based on research evidence. An "evolutionary" method of concept analysis proposed by Rodgers recognizes that conceptual meaning is dependent on context (Rodgers and Knafl, 2000). Morrow (2009) describes a creative process for selecting and conceptualizing meaning on the basis of the contemplation of a painting, then placing the meaning within a nursing framework. Bonis (2013) describes an approach to concept analysis that focuses on detecting differences in the conceptual understandings embedded in different disciplines, so that nurses can better judge the value of borrowing research instruments from other disciplines.

Our approaches to creating conceptual meaning are similar to some of the processes described by other authors, but our approach is based on the view that meanings are created for a particular purpose and do not remain static but rather change over time and in different contexts. Therefore, it is not possible to make a claim that a concept is "mature" or sufficiently developed. Meanings are not inherent in objects or in a reality that exists independently; rather, they are shaped and formed in relation to a particular purpose and a particular context. For example, consider again the example of the word *mouse* and the two very different conceptual meanings that it carries. The conceptual meanings you would bring with you to a pet store and those you would bring to a computer store intending to purchase a mouse are shaped by the purpose of your shopping trip and the type of store that you enter to achieve this purpose.

When creating meaning, a wide variety of sources and methods can be used. There is no recipe or specific method to follow, and the approach to creating meaning can shift according to the purpose for which your concept is intended or used. The following sections provide guidelines that you can select and adapt as needed.

Selecting a Concept

Selecting a concept is a process that involves great ambiguity. Concept selection is guided by your purpose and expresses values related to your purpose. If you are a student in a nursing class, your concept selection may be guided by expediency as well as interest. If you are a postdoctoral student, you may create conceptual meaning to resolve a dilemma that you encounter when moving through the research process.

Values that influence your selection of a concept include your beliefs and attitudes about the nature of nursing. We believe that concepts should justifiably relate to the practice of nursing. An example would be a concept that represents a human response to health or illness, such as fatigue. Characteristics of clients such as "hardiness" may also be selected, particularly if they are important determinants of health. Characteristics of nurses, care systems, or nurse-client-family interaction may also be chosen if they are related to nursing's purpose of creating health and well-being.

Often, many different disciplines share interest in the same concept. To claim that a concept is justifiably related to nursing does not mean that it is *only* a nursing concept. For example, *fatigue* is a concept of interest to nurses but also to physicians and clinical pharmacists. Fatigue becomes more of a nursing concept when a conceptual meaning is created for *fatigue* that is useful and important within a nursing context, such as when the meaning reflects what nurses have control over and what they do. Locating the concept of *fatigue* within a theory that conceptualizes fatigue as a human response to chemotherapy and developing criteria for fatigue that can be assessed and alleviated by oncology nurses makes it a nursing concept. Physicians might develop criteria for fatigue that index it in relation to the safety of continuing a regimen of treatment (i.e., their role), whereas clinical pharmacists might create criteria that would assist drug manufacturers with formulating pharmaceuticals that are more effective for alleviating fatigue.

Thus, when choosing concepts, the role and context of nursing is important to the choice. However, as you create conceptual meaning, it is more important to make choices that help ensure the meaning created is useful to nurses as they manage human responses and help persons to move toward health. The important question is not, "Is this a nursing concept?" but rather, "Is this concept of interest to nursing, and is the meaning created useful for nursing's purposes?"

Sociopolitical considerations will also influence your choice of a concept, often in ways that are subtle and difficult to perceive. For example, if you choose to examine the concept of *transition* for daughters who must place their mothers in nursing homes, you will eventually come to examine the consequences of women's caretaking within a society that devalues its elders and that disregards women's work when caring for aging parents by not considering it to be real work.

Some concepts are not appropriate as a focus for the process of creating conceptual meaning. Some are too empirically grounded, and others are too expansive to yield a useful outcome. Concepts that represent empirically knowable objects (e.g., antiembolic stockings) are usually not good choices, because they are highly empirically grounded and can be demonstrated by a display of the thing itself. You do not need to examine the concepts to understand their meanings, and having criteria for recognizing them will not help you clinically in any significant way. Broad concepts such as *caring* and *stress* pose another set of problems. Because these types of concepts are so vast, creating meaning can result only in a broad understanding that omits detail and that may be misleading. This is not to say that creating conceptual meaning for very narrow or broad concepts is never useful, and for some purposes, it may be justifiable. In our experience, the concepts that are most often amenable to the creation of conceptual meaning are those in the middle range. It often is helpful when choosing a concept to place it within the context of use to narrow its scope in relation to your purpose.

It often makes sense to choose a concept that is poorly understood or that tends to have competing or confusing meanings. However, most concepts carry a certain degree of ambiguity, and your meanings will alter as contexts for use change. Moreover, much of what is in the literature about concepts will be found to be inadequate or erroneous when you examine the concept in a new light. For example, much of the early information about fatigue was generated from research on airplane pilots and proved to be inadequate for understanding cancer fatigue. As a result, nurses began to generate knowledge about this particular type of fatigue. Remember that other disciplines do not have the same perspectives and motives for generating conceptual information as nursing does. Although knowledge of nursing concepts within other disciplines may be useful, these other circumstances need to be carefully examined. Other disciplines have a different perspective, and scholars in those disciplines are not likely to take into account perspectives that are common to nursing. Their work can inform nursing perspectives, but usually the conceptual meanings derived from other disciplines will not be adequate for nursing purposes.

With these guidelines in mind, you can select a word or phrase that communicates the idea that you want to convey. Despite your best efforts to make the perfect initial choice, that choice will probably change as you explore various meanings. Trying out alternative words becomes part of the process itself. For example, there is no adequate single term for the idea expressed by the phrase "the use of humans as objects." The term *objectification* is close, but it implies some experiences that do not involve the use of humans. The process of working with various terms related to this idea will help you to explore various meanings that are possible. Because the experience is not adequately expressed in common language, words may seem quite inadequate at first. You may select a common word for a concept and eventually assign a specific definition to the word to suit your particular purposes, or you may borrow a word from another language, combine two or more common words to specify a particular meaning, or make up a phrase or a word. Many significant concepts for nursing have not been adequately named. As nurses engage in processes for creating conceptual meaning, a more adequate language for nursing phenomena will be created.

Clarifying Your Purpose

To provide a sense of direction, you must know why you are creating conceptual meaning. One purpose is to set boundaries or limits so that you do not become hopelessly lost in the process. For example, your purpose might be to work with the concept *dependence* for a research project. Eventually, you will need a clear conceptualization of dependence as well as ideas about how to measure or assess it. Another purpose might be to differentiate between two closely related concepts, such as *sympathy* and *empathy*. In this case, your concern is to create definitions that differentiate on the basis of a thorough familiarity with the meanings that are possible.

Another reason for creating conceptual meaning is to examine the ways in which concepts are used in existing writings. For example, the concept of *intuition* frequently appears in nursing literature, with many different but related meanings. The meanings that are conveyed reflect different assumptions about the phenomenon. As you become aware of these meanings, you can explore the extent to which the meanings are consistent with your own purpose.

Other purposes behind creating conceptual meaning include generating research hypotheses, formulating nursing diagnoses, and developing computerized databases for clinical decision making. Creating conceptual meaning is also a valuable process for learning critical thinking skills (Kramer, 1993). When you keep your purpose as clear as possible, you have an anchor that provides a sense of direction when you seem to be lost.

Sources of Evidence

After selecting a concept, you proceed with the process of creating conceptual meaning by using several different sources to generate and refine criteria for the concept. You may involve others in the process to review and respond to your work as a way to generate new understanding and insights. The sources that you choose and the extent to which you use various sources depend on your purposes. Early during the process of gathering evidence for the concept, tentative criteria are proposed, and those criteria are refined in the light of additional information provided by continuing gathering of evidence. We recommend beginning the process of criteria formulation early so that useful information is not lost. *Criteria* are succinct statements that describe essential characteristics and features that distinguish the concept as a recognizable entity and that differentiate this entity from other related ideas.

Exemplar Case. An exemplar case is a description or depiction of a situation, experience, or event that satisfies the following statement: "If this is not *x*, then nothing is." The case can be drawn from nursing practice, literature, art, film, or any other source in which the concept is represented or symbolized. If the case is depicted as an object or in some form of media, many rich aspects of the phenomenon can be conveyed by displaying the media for others to experience. Regardless of the format used for presentation, the case is selected because it represents the concept to the best of your present understanding. For concrete concepts such as *cup*, an exemplar case is relatively easy. An ordinary teacup, for example, can be presented for others to see and hold. The people who examine the object can then verify, "If this is not a cup, then nothing is." To demonstrate the concept *red* (a property), a model case is more difficult. You can physically present to the group something that you perceive as being red in color and find out whether the group agrees that this is what its members would also perceive as being red. However, a more precise and consistent identification of red would result from measurement with the use of a spectrophotometer.

When you deal with highly abstract concepts, the task of constructing and selecting exemplar cases is even more difficult, and often these concepts can only be measured indirectly. Many such measurements depend on scales that rely on self-report. For example, the concepts of *anxiety* and *pain* are typically measured by self-report rating scales. Usually, exemplar cases of abstract concepts involve experiences and circumstances that are described in words. Exemplar cases may be created from your own experience, or you may find cases in the literature that have been constructed or described by others. For example, to demonstrate an abstract concept such as *sorrow,* a scenario from a novel or film or a rich description of an experience from your practice can be shared with others, who respond to the scenario as a representation of the phenomenon of sorrow.

If you create your own exemplar case, work with your ideas and revise your description until you are satisfied that the case fully represents your concept. For a concept such as *mothering,* your exemplar case might describe the following event: an infant cries, and an adult picks up the infant. The event is a start, but when you share your case with others, they might object, saying that this description represents only the physical act of picking up a crying child and does not necessarily demonstrate mothering. Your exemplar case develops until there is enough substance that people respond to the case by forming a mental image of mothering. As you build on the scenario of an adult picking up an infant to represent mothering, you could include various circumstances, behaviors, motives, attitudes, and feelings that surround the act of picking up the infant. You paint a picture or tell a story so that people can confirm that this is indeed mothering. As this and other exemplar cases are created, you can compare various meanings in the experience and define what is common and what is different about the various cases that you consider.

It often is useful alternatively to include and exclude various features of exemplar cases to reflect on how central each feature is to the meaning you are creating. In the exemplar case of mothering, the adult initially might be portrayed as female. Later, you might portray a male in the same case. In the absence of any evidence one way or the other, you might tentatively decide that the idea of mothering that you are creating will be deliberately limited to instances that involve women. Because your decision is tentative, you can change your construction for another purpose or circumstance. You can acknowledge that some men mother, but clarify that, for your purpose, your idea deliberately includes the experience of women.

While you are working with exemplar cases, pose the following question: What makes this an instance of this concept? The responses to this question form the basis for a tentative list of criteria. During the early stages, the criteria may be quite detailed, and they may be the essential characteristics associated with the concept, given the meanings that you deliberately decide to include. The criteria are designed to allow you to recognize the concept when it occurs and to differentiate this concept from related concepts. For example, in the case of mothering, you would want to be able to recognize mothering when it happens and distinguish mothering from related phenomena such as caring, nurturing, or helping.

Impressions regarding the criteria begin to form as you work with your exemplar case. You develop ideas about which features are essential for your purposes and why, as well as their qualitative characteristics. These ideas become the criteria for the concept. Sometimes exemplar cases are presented after clarification is complete. In these instances, the exemplar case is similar to a definitional form for the concept. Here we use exemplar cases as a way to create meaning rather than to represent it.

Definitions. Two sources that provide information about conceptual meaning are definitions and word usages of the concept you are exploring. Existing definitions are often circular and do not give a complete sense of meaning for the concept, but they do help to clarify common usages and ideas associated with the concept. Existing definitions often help to identify core elements of objects, perceptions, or feelings that can be represented by a word. They are also useful for tracing the origins of words, which provides clues about core meaning.

Dictionary definitions provide synonyms and antonyms and convey commonly accepted ways in which words are used. They are not designed to explain the full range of perceptions associated with a word, particularly a word that has a unique use within a discipline or that represents a relatively abstract concept. Existing theories, however, provide a source of definitions that may extend beyond the limits of common linguistic usage. Theoretic definitions and ways that concepts are used in the context of the theory convey meanings that pertain to the domain of the discipline from which the theory originated. For example, the term *mother* as defined in the dictionary refers to the social and biologic role of parenting and includes a few characteristics of the role, such as authority and affection. In the context of psychologic theories, however, the meanings that are conveyed with respect to the values, roles, functions, and characteristics of people who are mothers are almost endless and include parenting, physical care, guilt, responsibility, power, and powerlessness.

Visual Images. Visual images that already exist, such as photographs, cartoons, calendars, paintings, and drawings, are useful sources for creating conceptual meaning (Morrow, 2009). If you are choosing existing images, they may be explicitly labeled or named as the concept of interest, or you may judge them to reasonably represent it. If you can find images that others have explicitly labeled as an instance of the concept, such as a picture that the artist labels "Sorrow," the artist's linking of the visual image to the concept provides further validation of the meaning of the concept, enriches the range of meaning, and helps to minimize any bias inherent in your own views of the meaning of the concept. In some instances, you or others might deliberately create images that represent the concept that is being clarified rather than use existing sources.

Whether you personally create and examine an image or ask others to create images, the idea is to compare them for similarities and differences. For example, advertisements and photographs that document the concept *depression* provide information about conceptual meaning. Often, visual imagery will highlight some aspect of the concept that is significant. On other occasions, visual imagery may raise questions about the essential nature of the phenomena that are important to the refinement of criteria. Visual images that represent concepts well also highlight difficulties with expressing meaning linguistically. A photograph may express rich dimensions of the concept of *dignity,* yet the essence of dignity expressed by the photo is impossible to describe. This is an example of how aesthetic expressions of concepts contribute to empiric knowledge.

Popular and Classical Literature. A variety of literature resources can provide information about conceptual meaning. Literature reflects meanings that arise from the culture and provides rich sources of exemplar cases for concepts. Classical prose and poetry are often good sources of meaning for concepts used in nursing. For example, images of love and longing may be found in the poetic works of Emily Dickinson. Louisa May Alcott's classic *Little Women* provides information about the nature of intimacy and caring. The popular current literature is also a source of valuable data about conceptual meaning. Popular self-help books on topics such as overcoming negative thinking and codependency often can clarify commonly understood (or misunderstood) conceptual meanings. Fairy tales, myths, fables, and stories provide relevant insights, depending on the concept that you are exploring. Usages for words that are expressed in popular jargon and cartoons may highlight borderline meanings. For example, when a 5-year-old child jumps up and down and exclaims, "I'm so anxious for my birthday to be here!" the meaning of *anxious* is not the same meaning that concerns nurses. What the child's usage does convey is the physical agitation that accompanies the experience of anxiety within the context of nursing practice.

Music and Poetry. The imagery of music or poetry may be useful for the creation of conceptual meaning. You can find music or poetry by seeking out lyrics or titles that name the concept under consideration. The music itself or the metaphoric images in the title or lyrics may reasonably suggest the concept. Music and poetry can effectively convey meanings through rhythm, tones, lyrical or linguistic forms and metaphors, or musical moods that reflect experiences in life events with which nurses deal. For example, the Shaker folk tune "Simple Gifts" suggests criteria for concepts of authenticity, genuineness, centeredness, and community. The tune itself conveys a sense of inner happiness and peace; the lyrics reflect relationships between inner peace and the ability to build strong relationships. The popular Cole Porter song "Don't Fence Me In" conveys through its musical mood, rhythm, and lyrics what it feels like to be confined emotionally and projects a yearning to be free.

Professional Literature. The meanings of concepts can be explored from within the context of the professional literature. This literature often provides meanings that are pertinent to the practice of nursing. For example, philosophers as well as nurses have written about the concept of *presence* as a way of being with another. When the work of a scholar in another discipline coincides with your experience as a nurse, the scholar's work can augment your conceptual meaning. When you find contradictions with your experience as a nurse, this prompts you to clarify your own insights about the phenomenon.

Anecdotal Accounts and Opinions. Peers, coworkers, hospitalized individuals, other professional workers, and people who are not connected to nursing can provide valuable information about the meaning of a concept. It may be useful to seek others' opinions about the meaning of a concept, particularly if your direct experience with the concept is limited. Nurses who work with the concept daily may be able to shed light on nuances of meaning that will greatly affect how meaning is integrated into your theory. For example, a nurse who works with people whose lung function is severely compromised might observe that anxiety, although usually characterized by increased activity, evokes a different reaction in these patients. Rather than random activity, anxiety may be accompanied by a deliberate quieting of behavior to conserve energy. Asking others to share their ideas about a concept is an informal exploration that is different from standard research procedures that might investigate conceptual meaning. Rather, it is an exploration of the opinions and understandings of others to ground your meaning in everyday perception or to test your professional meanings in the light of everyday assumptions about a phenomenon.

Methods for Testing Tentative Criteria and the Exemplar Case

As you examine various sources of evidence, you will begin the process of testing the soundness of your conceptualization that has been created in the light of your purpose. You may find alternative meanings that are reasonable or plausible but not well suited to your purpose. For example, for someone who is interested in a cup to be used for the purpose of drinking liquids, a golfing green cup, although a plausible instance of the concept of *cup*, does not have the defining features required for drinking liquids. To stimulate your thinking about nuances of meaning, you can turn to a number of cases that challenge your conceptualization and consider alternative contexts.

Contrary Cases. Contrary cases are those cases that are certainly not instances of the concept. They may be similar in some respects, but they represent something that most observers would easily recognize as significantly different from the concept you are considering. For more concrete concepts, contrary cases are relatively easy. A saucer or a spoon can be presented, and most observers in Western cultures would agree that these things are not cups. A spoon may hold liquids that people sip, but it is not a cup; a saucer that a cup sits on is also clearly not a cup. A contrary case for the color red might be the color green. For the concept of *restlessness,* calmness could be presented as a contrary case.

As you consider contrary cases, ask the following: What makes this instance different from the concept that I have selected? By comparing the differences between exemplar and contrary cases, you will begin to revise, add to, or delete from the tentative criteria that are emerging. If your purpose includes designing an exemplar case for your concept, you also might use this information to refine the exemplar case. For example, one of the traits that distinguishes a cup from a saucer or a spoon is the shape of the cup. You may already discern that this feature is essential by looking only at the cup. When you see the spoon and saucer, however, the shape stands out in sharp contrast, and your description of essential features of the shape of the cup can be more complete and precise. As you compare the objects, you may also decide that the volume of liquid that a cup holds is an important distinguishing characteristic. Later, when you consider miniature teacups as cases, you might decide that volume is not an essential quality, especially if your other criteria are sufficient to distinguish which objects can be considered cups, which is your purpose.

Sometimes, when creating narrative contrary cases, the tendency is simply to reverse the situation depicted in the exemplar case. Usually, this does not add new information of significance for creating conceptual meaning. If you are having difficulty with constructing a negative case, ask another to suggest a contrary case or something that is definitely not what you are trying to describe. Sometimes you can locate a contrary case in the literature. Contrary cases that contribute to meaning often reveal important aspects of the exemplar case that are hidden in assumptions you may be making about the concept.

Related Cases. Related cases are instances that represent a different but similar concept. Related cases usually share several criteria with the concept of interest, but one or more criteria will be particularly associated with the model cases to distinguish them from the related cases. A different word is generally used to label the related instances. If you find that one word is typically used to refer to essentially different phenomena, you may need to select language for your concept that differentiates it from the related meanings. For example, if you were focusing on the concept of love between a parent and child, you may need to use the word label *parental love* to signify that you see essential differences between this experience of love and other related experiences of love.

In the case of a *cup,* you might consider a drinking glass. For the concept of *red,* you might consider a red-orange hue or magenta. For the concept of *mothering,* you could design a case of child tending, such as care provided by a nanny, that would be similar to the exemplar case. You might make a child care worker the adult or substitute an elderly person for the infant. Again, you consider differences and similarities between the exemplar case and the related cases and revise the tentative criteria to reflect your new insights.

Borderline Cases. A borderline case is usually an instance of metaphoric application or pseudo-application of the word. A borderline case is found when the same word is used in a different context. For example, if you are examining the concept of *fatigue* in chronic illness, a useful borderline case of the use of the term *fatigue* would be "military fatigue clothing." Poetry and music lyrics provide rich sources of metaphoric uses of words. In the evolution of language, the metaphoric meanings of words carry powerful messages that often persist as new usages emerge and thus illuminate the core meaning. The metaphoric meanings for the concept of *red* are excellent examples. *Red* as a word and as a color has become, in Western culture, a metaphoric symbol for communism, violence, passion, and anger. To give a "cup of cheer" is an exemplary borderline usage of the term *cup.* This highlights the feature of cups as being capable of holding something.

Slang terms and terms used to describe technologic operations or features are rich sources of borderline cases when they are first entering the language. After they become well accepted, they are no longer borderline; they move to more central conceptual meanings, and they may even become exemplary cases. *Slang* can develop from a quirky application of a word. The language that emerges to refer to new technology is also a rich source of borderline cases. During the early 1990s, the word *web* probably would have prompted a mental image of something that a spider creates, and a reference to the Internet would have been considered a borderline case. By the end of the 1990s, the word *web* (i.e., World Wide Web) was so fully associated with the Internet that it might have become a model case of *web.*

For the concept of *mothering,* a borderline case might be a computer motherboard, because this term and its related concept are not part of the typical computer user's conceptual realm and remain primarily technical. You might choose this borderline usage to help clarify features of the concept of *mother* that can be seen as foundational to the concept of mothering. These features could include the central importance of the mother in some cultures for defining the scope of relationships or structuring the energy of all relationships within the system. Ask what happens to your meaning if you perceive mothering as a process that structures and directs the nature of relationships in a system.

Paradoxic cases are variants of borderline cases that are useful to highlight the central meanings of concepts. Paradoxically, these cases embody elements of both exemplar and contrary cases. For example, when exploring the meaning of *dignity*, you might create a case in which actions that violate dignity occur to preserve a central feature of dignity. Your case might be the emergency cardiopulmonary resuscitation of a person in a public space to preserve the life of that person. Such a case is paradoxic in that it violates some criteria for dignity but highlights the importance of a central criterion for discerning the concept.

You will probably invent other varieties of cases during the process of creating conceptual meaning. How the cases are classified is not critical. Rather, their important function is to assist you with discerning the range of possible meaning important for creating a meaning that is useful for your purpose. Although creating conceptual meaning is a rigorous and thoughtful process, cases are somewhat arbitrary, and they are historically and culturally situated. What you call them is not essential to the process; what is important is the meaning that you derive from the conceptual exploration and the investigation.

Exploring Contexts and Values. Experience and the values that grow out of experience occur in social contexts that provide important cultural meanings that influence the mental representations of that experience. For example, consider the concept of *judgment* if you are a student taking an examination, a real estate agent assessing a home for sale, an official scoring a gymnastics meet, or a magistrate preparing to impose a sentence. When you explore the various meanings acquired by virtue of the context, you probably will become aware of meanings that you previously had not considered.

One way to imagine various contexts is to place your exemplar cases in different contexts and ask the following: What would happen in a different situation? You mentally imagine the practical outcomes of your conceptual meaning in its context. For example, if you place your exemplar case of the color red in the context of a magazine advertisement, what symbolic meaning is conveyed? What advertising results does the advertiser intend? If the color red is placed in the context of traffic signs and symbols, what meaning does the color now convey? What behavioral responses do you now expect? What about a woman who is wearing a red suit in a boardroom where everyone else is dressed in dark suits? As you consider various possible combinations of context, you will clarify how meanings are influenced by context.

Placing the concept in a subtly differing context also reveals values. The concept of *mothering* has a relatively positive connotation for most people. Most people agree that humans require "good" mothering to grow and develop adequately. However, people differ widely with regard to what they consider to be good mothering; these differences are often associated with the cultural context. For example, people probably would disagree about whether what happens in a schoolroom, in a hospital, or in counseling can be considered mothering. What is considered mothering reflects deeply embedded cultural values. When you consider your exemplar case being placed in several different social contexts, you create an avenue for perceiving important values and making deliberate choices about them.

Formulating Criteria for Concepts

We focus on criteria as an expression of conceptual meaning because they are a sensitive and succinct form for conveying essential conceptual meaning. Criteria are particularly useful as tools to initiate other processes of empiric theory development. Your exemplar case is itself a full expression of conceptual meaning, but the criteria make explicit the features and characteristics of the exemplar case that represent your conceptual meaning.

Criteria for the concept emerge gradually and continuously as you consider definitions, various cases, other sources, and varying contexts and values. As you develop the criteria, you will naturally refine them so that they reflect the meaning that you intend. Criteria often express both qualitative and quantitative aspects of meaning and should suggest a definition of the word. Because criteria are more complex than a limited word definition, they amplify the meaning and suggest direction for the processes of developing theory.

Consider This Example

To illustrate the function of criteria for a concept, consider how you might convey the idea of one U.S. dollar in coins to a person who is not familiar with American money. One way is to present all possible combinations of coins to the individual, who then memorizes the combinations to consistently collect the right coins together to yield the equivalent of a dollar. Another approach is to provide guidelines that enable the individual to recognize and compose the various combinations independently. An exemplar case might involve the use of three quarters, one dime, two nickels, and five pennies. Because many other combinations are possible, criteria are created from the exemplar case to cover all other possible combinations. The exemplar case is chosen deliberately to include all of the types of coins available so that, when examining the case, several characteristics of all possibilities emerge. One feature is that the units of the various coins add up to an equivalent of 100 pennies, which is the smallest coin value in the coin mix. However, this criterion alone may not be sufficient for someone who is not familiar with this monetary system and other criteria are created to ensure that all other possible combinations are recognized.

You might consider the weight of the possible coin combinations, the colors of the coins, their metallic makeup, or the exchange value of each coin. All these features may be used, but the criteria should convey as simply as possible the information that is needed by a novice to collect one U.S. dollar in coins. The fact is that any color combination or any number of coins up to 100 may be used as criteria. The metallic content of the coins might serve as an adequate criterion and may even be the most precise of all possible criteria. However, if your purpose is to assist a person from another country with understanding how to make a dollar's worth of change, you would not select the metallic content as a criterion, because it is impractical for that purpose.

For concrete objects, the criteria may be relatively simple. For the concept of a cup, examples of criteria might include the following:

- The object is cylindric or conic in shape.
- The object is capable of containing physical matter.
- The height normally is between 3 and 7 inches, and the widest diameter is 3 to 4 inches.
- When the object contains liquid, it can safely hold hot liquids.

Notice that this set of criteria is phrased so that a disposable foam cup or a golfing green cup can be included. This choice is guided by the purpose. If you needed to make sure that the golfing green cup was not included as a cup, you might revise the criteria to include "the object is capable of being held in the hand, regardless of what it contains." This criterion places a limit on the volume and weight of the cup and implies that it must be a portable object.

Developing criteria for more abstract concepts is a more complex process, and the criteria are thus often more abstract. Criteria for the concept of *mothering* might include the following:

- The mothering person must have visual contact with the person who receives the mothering in a manner that can be observed.
- The person who receives the mothering must be physically touched by the mothering person.
- Some positive feeling must be experienced by the mothering person and by the person who receives the mothering.
- There must be a reciprocal interaction between the mothering person and the person who receives mothering.
- Vocalization by the mothering person must occur.

These criteria do not limit the mothering person by gender, age, or species. With this description, the person doing the mothering could be an elderly man. The criteria also do not specify that the person who receives the mothering is an infant. If the purpose of applying the criteria is to distinguish between instances of mothering and fathering, these criteria would need to be revised to specify at least gender. If the purpose is to differentiate between mothering and neglect, they might be adequate.

The following question arises during the course of creating conceptual meaning: How do I know that the meaning that I have created is adequate? You can examine your conceptual meaning for adequacy in relation to the processes that are used to create meaning as well as the conceptual meaning that you have created. Fuller (1991) suggests examining the process and the product of conceptualization in terms of both validity and reliability. A conceptualization is *valid* if it is based on multiple examples that are fully representative of the range of meanings for the concept, if you used multiple interpretive stages during the clarification process, and if the essential structure (or pattern) of the concept can be understood from the criteria. The conceptualization is *reliable* if the concept can be consistently recognized on the basis of the criteria that you have created. The meaning that you create is also adequate if it reflects a reasonable and communicable understanding that is useful for your purposes. If your aims reflect valued nursing goals, if you have been careful when choosing and using resources, and if you understand why you have made the choices that you have, you will have created an adequate and useful meaning. Additional processes for theory development will provide a check on conceptual meaning and will contribute to further refinements in your conceptual meaning.

Conceptual Meaning and Problems of Theoretic Development

Problems associated with conceptual meaning often underlie other problems that are involved when developing theory. A major challenge with respect to structuring and confirming theoretic relationships is the selection of direct and indirect empiric indicators for a concept. When research reports give conflicting results, the differences are sometimes tied to the use of different definitions and empiric indicators for the concept. If you explore the conceptual meanings within research reports, you can often clarify the extent to which differing conceptual meanings account for the differing research findings. As you carry out the processes for creating conceptual meaning, you will be able to suggest a full range of possible empiric indicators for a concept that are pertinent to your specific purpose. You also will be able to identify the limits of empiric approaches when specifying indicators for a phenomenon.

For example, consider the concept of mothering and the sample criteria that we listed in the previous section. These criteria include characteristics that can be observed empirically: reciprocal interaction, visualization, touch, and vocalization. The criterion that states, "Some positive feeling must be experienced by the mothering person and by the person who receives the mothering," might be one of the most important distinguishing features of your intended meaning for mothering, but it does not easily lend itself to objective observation. Asking mothers to describe their feelings can assess this indirectly.

Conceptual meaning is fundamental if you must distinguish one concept from a closely related one. This is often the case when you are forming theoretic relationships or structuring and contextualizing theoretic statements. The processes of creating conceptual meaning make it possible to propose differentiating features of similar concepts that are useful to guide theorizing and related research activities. Consider the concepts of *tending* and *mothering*. Individuals tend to the needs of others in many different contexts, and mothers tend to their children. A question to be resolved might be the following: Is there a particular kind of tending that occurs as part of mothering? You can examine a related case of a nanny who is tending to children to determine whether any characteristic of tending is within your idea of mothering. As you explore various differentiating features of the central concept, your ideas will become clearer, and the structure of your theory or research study will improve. Creating conceptual meaning helps you make decisions about the qualitative dimensions of criteria, such as whether they always need to be evident or whether they may be expressed with different intensities. For example, you may decide that, for the concept of mothering, the expression of positive feeling must be present, but the degree to which it occurs may vary.

When creating conceptual meaning, the challenge is to evolve a useful and adequate meaning from a range of possibilities. The processes for creating conceptual meaning are in and of themselves useful. When you also create meanings that can be used in conjunction with other activities of theory development, you move toward refinements of meaning that are useful for research, and you ultimately practice confirmation and validation that can further refine the theory.

STRUCTURING AND CONTEXTUALIZING THEORY

Structuring and contextualizing theory involve forming systematic linkages between and among concepts. Many approaches can be used (Alligood & Tomey, 2010; Dubin, 1978; Grace & Perry, 2013; Newman, 1979; Reynolds, 1971). The choice of a particular approach depends on your purposes for developing theory, what you already know or assume to be true, and your underlying philosophic ideas about the nature of nursing knowledge. If you begin with an entirely new idea about something and with very little reported about such an idea in the existing literature, the form of the theory that you construct may be a categorization of the concepts into a relational taxonomy that essentially describes your ideas. If you begin with an idea that builds on other theorists' descriptions, you might develop a theoretic structure that provides explanations of the complex interrelationships among concepts. If you are structuring theory as an outcome of grounded research, the interrelationships between data clusters guide the theoretic structure that you create. Approaches to structuring and contextualizing theory are described in detail in the next sections and include the following:

- *Identifying and defining the concepts.* Concepts are important elements that convey the focus and meaning of the theory. Definitions of concepts can evolve from the processes of creating conceptual meaning, they can be thoughtfully borrowed from other theories, or they can be formulated from other sources. Definitions should indicate as clearly and concisely as possible the theoretic meaning of important concepts within the theory.
- *Identifying assumptions.* Assumptions are the basic underlying premises from which and within which theoretic reasoning proceeds.
- *Clarifying the context within which the theory is placed.* Contextual placement describes the circumstances within which the theoretic relationships are expected to be empirically relevant. Clear statements about context are particularly important if the theory is to be used in practice.
- *Designing relationship statements.* Projected relationships between and among the concepts of the theory, taken as a whole, provide the substance and form of the theory.

Identifying and Defining Concepts

Structuring theory requires that you identify the concepts that will form the basic fabric of the theory. The concepts can come from life experiences, clinical practice, basic or applied research, knowledge of the literature, and the formal processes of creating conceptual meaning that were just described. Often, theory emerges because of a conviction that existing knowledge and theories are not adequate to represent an experience.

Some concepts are better suited for theory development than others. Concepts that are extremely abstract carry broad meanings and refer to a wide range of experience. They usually are not suitable as a beginning point for theory development. For example, concepts such as *social structure, politics,* and *love* refer to such a broad range of experiences that defining them within the limits of empiric inquiry is extremely difficult. However, such concepts can be useful when considering the context within which the theory is placed.

If concepts are extremely narrow and concrete, they refer to only a narrow range of experience, and the level of abstraction may not be sufficient for theoretic purposes. For example, concepts such as *toothache* or *postappendectomy surgical pain* apply to relatively few instances of pain. *Chronic pain* and *acute pain* may be more suitable concepts from which to develop theory. What is considered a suitable level of abstraction for theory varies in the field of nursing. The recent trend toward middle-range, situation-specific theory and evidence-based practice provides a useful guideline for decisions about the level of abstraction required for theoretic concepts.

As the concepts are specified or begin to form, early ideas about the structure of their relationships begin to emerge. There are usually one or two primary or central concepts around which the theoretic relationships build. Thinking about possible relationships helps to clarify what concepts the theory needs to include. Previous research, existing theories, philosophies, and personal experience provide a background for forming theoretic relationships. Initially, you might simply note concepts that you think are related on the basis of your experience, what you find in the literature, or ongoing research.

Assumptions that stem from cultural history also influence conceptual structure. For example, an assumption that is inherent in most empiric theory is the concept of linear time, which in turn determines the relationship linkages that various concepts have with one another.

Antecedent, coincident or intervening, and consequent concepts imply prediction within a linear time frame. *Antecedent concepts* are those experiences that you identify as coming before other concepts. *Coincident concepts* are those that coexist in time. *Intervening concepts* are also coincident and have a particular influence on relationships among concepts that are specified in the theory. *Consequent concepts* are those that follow other concepts.

Some theories place antecedents in a causal relationship with those that follow. Other theories rest on a philosophic view that rejects the idea of causation. Instead, the ideas of influence or affect are used to explain relationships over time. If a primary concept within your developing theory is *anger,* you might propose that previous experiences cause the anger experience, or you might consider specific experiences as an antecedent that affects the anger experience in some way.

Consequents also can imply *causation.* For example, when a person experiences uncertainty, consequents of that experience can be thought of as resulting from uncertainty. Changes in mental functioning, in sleep and rest patterns, and in relationships with other people might be theoretic concepts that are structured to reflect phenomena caused by the uncertainty experience.

Intervening concepts can be used to shift from a view of causation to one of *influence*. Intervening concepts are those that influence the relationships between antecedent experiences, the event itself, and its consequents. For example, the central concept of fear might be viewed as being influenced by the antecedent experiences of childhood, and sleep patterns might be viewed as an intervening variable that influences the relationship between the childhood experience and present fear.

As initial ideas are formed about the relationships among concepts, the concepts themselves become clearer, and processes of creating conceptual meaning can be used to make the meanings explicit. Some concepts might be grouped together and assigned more abstract terms to compose a new concept. This occurs especially when theory is structured and conceptualized with inductive theory development processes such as grounded theory. For example, you might begin to see that self-identifiers of female caregivers such as *weak, fearful, inadequate, dependent*, and *unworthy* could be grouped to become components of the more abstract concept of *powerlessness*.

As the concepts of the theory are identified and conceptualized, theoretic definitions emerge. Theoretic definitions form the basis for and reflect empiric indicators and operational definitions for concepts needed for research, and they convey the general meaning of the concept. Empiric indicators are different from theoretic definitions in that they specify as exactly as possible how the concept is to be assessed in a specific study. For example, a theoretic definition for the concept of *mothering* might read as follows:

> *Mothering:* An interaction between a human adult and a child that conveys reciprocal feelings of attachment. The interaction is behaviorally expressed by reciprocal visual contact, touching, and vocalization.

This theoretic definition gives a general idea of the concept's empiric indicators, which are sometimes referred to as *operational definitions*. The first part of the definition provides a general meaning for the term, and the second part suggests behaviors associated with the concept that can be assessed. Empiric indicators would specify specific observational tools or measurements that would be used in a research study. For example, measurements of vocalizations would be clearly defined in terms of the characteristics consistent with the conceptual idea of vocalizations and consistent with the concept of mothering; the tools or instruments used to measure these vocalizations and the range of outcomes would also be specified.

Notice that the theoretic definition is consistent with the tentative criteria for the concept of *mothering,* but the definition serves a different purpose. The criteria are specific and useful as a foundation for the construction of theory and for the empiric study of the concept. The theoretic definition summarizes the insights that are formed when creating conceptual meaning and concisely conveys the essential meaning of the concept.

Identifying Assumptions as Part of Theory

Assumptions are underlying givens that are presumed to be true. In the context of empiric theory, they can be challenged philosophically, and they may be assessed empirically. Philosophic assumptions form the grounding for a theory. If they are challenged, the substance of the entire theory is also challenged on philosophic grounds. Assumptions that could be empirically assessed but that are not within the context of the theory also affect the value of the entire theory. For example, a theory intended to promote self-care in older female dementia caregivers may assume such caregivers desire to be self-caring. Although this assumption could be empirically assessed, for purposes of the theory, it is assumed to be true, which seems reasonable. If the guidelines inherent in the theory are used when caregivers have little or no desire to be self-caring, the theory will not be helpful, and another approach will be required.

Stated assumptions are easy to recognize, but many assumptions are implied or not stated and thus may be difficult to recognize. An example of an underlying assumption that is usually not stated is that humans are separate from but interact with their environment. For theories that involve human experience, this statement can be taken as being reasonably true. However, many commonly accepted truths about human existence gain new significance within a theoretic context, and they need to be stated even if they seem self-evident. For example, if a theory includes the concept of death, certain underlying assumptions about the nature of life and death would influence the essential ideas of the theory, and these assumptions need to be stated. A theory of grief that is based on a view of death as a transition to another form of life will be very different from a theory of grief that views death as the end of life.

Rogers (1970) explicitly stated her assumption that humans are unified wholes who possess their own integrity and who manifest characteristics that are more than and different from the sum of their parts. On the surface, this statement seems perfectly reasonable and sensible, but it is significant because it is an assumption that is not common to all nursing theory and conceptual models. As an assumption, it does not require empiric evidence, but it is fundamental to the relationship statements that Rogers proposed. In theory, the relationships, not the assumptions, are empirically validated and confirmed.

Assumptions influence all aspects of structuring and contextualizing theory. If the assumption of wholism is used as a basis for a theory of mothering, interrelated concepts must be consistent with a wholistic view of human experience. Patterns of behavior that reflect the whole would be reflected in the theoretic concepts; these might include patterns of movement and communication. By contrast, if humans are assumed to be biologic and social organisms, the concepts of a mothering theory might include physical responses and cultural mores.

Clarifying the Context

Theoretic relationships must be placed within a context if the theory is to be useful for practice. If a theory of mothering is meant to apply only to the interactions of women and children in Western cultures, these limits on the applicability of the theory must be considered and stated. As the theory is extended, it might be useful for other cultures and for other types of intimate relationships, such as adult-child, adult-adult, and adult-animal interactions.

Contexts that are very broad or very narrow reflect the range of applicability of a theory. A theory that is structured for many cultures may not be useful for any culture. Conversely, a theory that is structured within the context of a single institution (e.g., one specific hospital) may not be useful for other settings. Historically, as nursing incorporated an emphasis on middle-range theory, the context for which theories were developed narrowed. Broad frameworks that addressed phenomena such as adaptation or conservation were still considered theory and were useful in many nursing situations. Middle-range theories tended to focus on phenomena that did not emerge in all nursing situations but that were commonly recognized in nursing, such as uncertainty and hopelessness. Situation-specific theory narrowed context even further to particular situations of uncertainty or hopelessness (Im & Meleis, 1999). Thus, a middle-range theory of hopelessness or uncertainty would need to be adapted and developed for use across different contexts. For example, a middle-range theory of uncertainty would be made situation specific if it addressed factors significant to the experience of uncertainty, such as the ethnicity or age of the clients.

Designing Relationship Statements

Relationship statements structurally interrelate the concepts of the theory. The statements range from those that simply relate two concepts, to relatively complex statements that account for interactions among multiple concepts. Theories usually contain several levels of relationship statements, which comprise a reasonably complete explanation of how the concepts of the theory interact. The relationships begin to take form as the concepts are identified and emerge, but the process of designing the relationship statements requires specific attention to the substance, direction, strength, and quality of the interactions that occur among concepts.

Consider a relationship statement that might be formulated about the concept of mothering. A theorist might propose that, as an adult's visual contact with an infant increases, the infant's visual contact with the adult will also increase. This relationship statement speculates that one event (increased adult visual contact) precedes a second event (increased infant visual contact). This relationship also describes a substantive interaction (visual contact) as a component of mothering. It implies direction (an increase) as part of the interaction.

A more complex relational statement addresses further dimensions of quality, contexts, and circumstances that are proposed. Such a statement might take the following form:

Under the conditions of *C1* through *Cn,* if *x* occurs, then *y* will occur.

A way to illustrate the concept of mothering might take the following form:

When an adult mothering figure and an infant are in close proximity (C1),
and
when the adult has a negative feeling toward the infant (C2),
and
when the frequency of physical contact is limited (C3),
then,

if the adult's frequency of visual contact decreases,
the infant's frequency of visual contact will also decrease.

A relationship may also be designed to introduce new concepts to the potential theory. Initially, such a relationship might read as follows:

If the infant's frequency of visual contact is not sufficient to satisfy the mother, the adult's frequency of visual contact will increase in a conscious effort to engage the infant in interaction.

This relationship introduces the concept of *awareness* as well as the subjective value of "sufficient to satisfy." The idea of awareness and a value of sufficiency are not objectively identifiable or empirically observable. As the theory is developed further, possible empiric indicators for satisfaction might be created, or this dimension of the theory might be viewed as something to be subjectively assessed. In this way, the theory not only stimulates the creation of new empiric knowledge, but also opens possibilities for exploring and integrating other ways of knowing.

Although empiric theory is primarily designed to propose and create empiric relationships, its development requires attention to ethical, aesthetic, personal, and emancipatory knowing. The researcher needs to consider ethical questions that involve inappropriately disturbing the mother-infant relationship and the aesthetics of creating measurement approaches that do not create distress for either party. Researchers who are assessing a subjective variable such as "sufficient to satisfy" might bring their own experience-based biases about mothering to the research project; this reflects the personal knowing dimension. Emancipatory knowing is used as researchers ponder whether social practices have created expectations for mothers that demand or expect mother-infant bonding, thereby creating the possibility that mothers will not exhibit authentic expressions of satisfaction.

A *hypothesis* is a type of propositional statement that is a single statement of a proposed relationship between two or more variables. Hypotheses can take several forms and still provide a basis for developing theory. A neutral hypothesis asserts that one variable *(x)* is related to a second variable *(y)* or that *x* changes in relation to *y* without indicating the direction of change. A directional hypothesis indicates the direction of association between variables by stating that, as *x* increases or decreases, *y* also increases or decreases.

A confirmed hypothesis is a relationship statement for which there is research support. It can be either directional or neutral. Hypothesis testing requires that certain controls and procedures be adhered to and that statistical methods be applied during the confirmation process. The traditional form of expressing hypotheses requires statements that conform to rules of logic. The logic may be either deductive or inductive.

⊖ Image Collection – Deduction/Induction Examples

Comparison of Deduction and Induction

Deductive logic is reasoning that moves from the general to the particular. Inductive logic is reasoning that moves from the particular to the general. With inductive logic, particular instances are observed to be consistently part of a larger whole or set, and the set of particular instances is merged with that larger whole. This larger set can then be considered in relation to still another set of events or phenomena in another system of logic.

With deductive logic, the premises used as starting points embody two variables that can be categorized in relation to each other as broad or specific. With deductive logic, the movement is from premises that embody broad and specific variables to a conclusion in which the variables are more specific.

Like most other words, *deduction* and *induction* have common meanings that are related to but different from their meanings within systems of logic. People often state that they deduce hypotheses from theory, or that they deductively develop theory. These deductions are not the result of applying rules of logic; rather, they arise out of careful thought without specifically making use of a system of logic. When used in this way, the term *deduction* implies that a more general theory was a source of specific hypotheses or relational statements. With induction, people induce hypotheses and relationships by observing or experiencing an empiric reality and reaching some conclusion.

These related meanings of *induction* and *deduction* should be noted, because the terms may refer to systems of logic and to rules and conventions for the ordering of reasoning. At other times, the terms may refer to a general approach to thinking that is short of the rules of logic but similar in form.

Think About It

To deepen your appreciation of conceptualizing and structuring as empiric theory development processes, consider the following related to the content of this chapter:
1. Identify a situation or phenomenon (a concept) in nursing that you believe has not been named or clarified. Consider why this may be the case. Is this an important concept to address?
2. Locate a research study that embodies a broad concept such as uncertainty or hopelessness. How was the concept measured or assessed? Did the assessment adequately represent the fullness of the concept?
3. Examine a standardized tool for the assessment or measurement of a broad concept, and consider the groups and individuals for whom the measurement tool might not be appropriate and why.

REFLECTION AND DISCUSSION – SUPPLEMENT ⊖

References

Allen, D., & Cloyes, K. G. (2005). The language of "experience" in nursing research. *Nursing Inquiry, 12,* 98–105.

Alligood, M. R., & Tomey, A. M. (2010). *Nursing theorists and their work* (6th ed.). St. Louis, MO: Mosby-Elsevier.

Beckwith, S., Dickinson, A., & Kendall, S. (2008). The "con" of concept analysis. A discussion paper which explores and critiques the ontological focus, reliability and antecedents of concept analysis frameworks. *International Journal of Nursing Studies, 45*, 1831–1841.

Bonis, S. A. (2013). Concept analysis: Method to enhance interdisciplinary conceptual understanding. *ANS Advances in Nursing Science, 36*(2), 80–93.

Crowe, M. (2005). Discourse analysis: Toward an understanding of its place in nursing. *Journal of Advanced Nursing, 51*, 55–63.

Dickoff, J., & James, P. (1968). A theory of theories: a position paper. *Nursing Research, 17*, 197–203.

Dubin, R. (1978). *Theory building* (Rev. ed.). New York, NY: Free Press.

Ellis, R. (1968). Characteristics of significant theories. *Nursing Research, 17*, 217–222.

Fuller, J. (1991). *A conceptualization of presence as a nursing phenomenon.* Salt Lake City: University of Utah.

Grace, P. J., & Perry, D. J. (2013). Philosophic inquiry and the goals of nursing: A critical approach for disciplinary knowledge development and action. *ANS Advances in Nursing Science, 36*(2), 64–79.

Im, E. O., & Meleis, A. I. (1999). Situation-specific theories: Philosophical roots, properties, and approach. *ANS Advances in Nursing Science, 22*(2), 11–24.

Jacox, A. (1974). Theory construction in nursing: An overview. *Nursing Research, 23*, 4–13.

Kaplan, A. (1964). *The conduct of inquiry.* New York, NY: Crowell.

Kramer, M. (1993). Concept clarification and critical thinking: Integrated processes. *Journal of Nursing Education, 32*(9), 1–10.

Levine, M. E. (1967). The four conservation principles of nursing. *Nursing Forum, 6*(1), 93–98.

McKay, R. P. (1969). Theories, models and systems for nursing. *Nursing Research, 18*, 393–399.

Morrow, M. R. (2009). Being judicious: A creative conceptualization. *Nursing Science Quarterly, 22*(2), 103–107.

Morse, J. M. (1995). Exploring the theoretical basis of nursing using advanced techniques of concept analysis. *ANS Advances in Nursing Science, 17*(3), 31–46.

Moscou, S. (2008). The conceptualization and operationalization of race and ethnicity by health services researchers. *Nursing Inquiry, 15*, 94–105.

Müller, M. E., & Dzurec, L. C. (1993). The power of the name. *ANS Advances in Nursing Science, 15*(3), 15–22.

Newman, M. A. (1979). *Theory development in nursing.* Philadelphia, PA: Davis.

Norris, C. M. (1982). *Concept clarification in nursing.* Rockville, MD: Aspen Systems.

Reynolds, P. D. (1971). *A primer in theory construction.* Indianapolis, IN: Bobbs-Merrill.

Rodgers, B. L., & Knafl, K. (2000). *Concept development in nursing: Foundations, techniques and applications.* St. Louis, MO: Mosby-Elsevier.

Rogers, M. E. (1970). *An introduction to the theoretical basis of nursing.* Philadelphia, PA: Davis.

Walker, L. O., & Avant, K. C. (2010). *Strategies for theory construction in nursing* (4th ed.). Upper Saddle River, NJ: Prentice-Hall.

Watson, J. (1985). *Nursing: Human science and human care—A theory of nursing.* Norwalk, CT: Appleton-Century-Crofts.

White, R. (2004). Discourse analysis and social constructionism. *Nurse Researcher, 12*(2), 7–16.

Wilson, J. (1963). *Thinking with concepts.* London, England: Cambridge University Press.

Wright, M. (1966). Research and research. *Nursing Research, 15*, 244–245.

Description and Critical Reflection of Empiric Theory

We converse with one another of knowledge, research, assumptions and so forth, overconfident that we understand.

Norma Koltoff (1967, p. 122)

After theories are developed, the researcher can ask, "What is this?" and "How does it work?" These questions stimulate the development of empiric theory and serve as an organizing framework for deliberately examining it. The processes of describing and critically reflecting theory address these questions and lead to a clearer understanding of the nature of a theory. This is important if you are going to use a theory in research processes or practice.

The opening quote from Koltoff supports the imperative to examine carefully the meaning of a theory when it is used to guide nursing practice and knowledge development. When you read a particular theory that has the potential to guide your research or practice, it is reasonable to believe that you understand what it means. To a certain extent, you likely do grasp much of its meaning, but the possibility exists that you are inserting meanings, making assumptions, or creating purposes for its use that might not be consistent with the theory.

Suppose you are working in oncology and have an interest in comfort theory as a way to help people who are going through chemotherapy. As you read theory that addresses the nature of comfort, what enhances comfort, and the projected outcomes of comfort for the persons you care for, it is important to understand clearly what the theorist means by the term *comfort*. For example, knowing what the theorist means and understanding the theorist's underlying assumptions about comfort are important for judging whether the theory will be useful in your practice. If comfort as described by the theorist is not even possible for persons receiving chemotherapy, the theory may not be useful to you. If the theorist assumes that comfort can be achieved but, in your situation, individuals are destined to remain uncomfortable, the theory again may not be useful.

The processes of description and critical reflection can be used to scrutinize theory to determine not only if it is useful for your purposes but also if it can be modified to be useful. Just because a theory might not totally fit your situation does not mean that it cannot be used to guide care. The critical issue, however, is knowing how the theory does and does not reflect your situation so that decisions about its use can be deliberatively made. In our example, if the definition of *comfort* proposed in a theory is not exactly appropriate for your situation but the assumptions and the other features of the theory are, you may rightfully decide that the theory could be used to promote comfort in a way that is appropriate for persons receiving chemotherapy.

Description and critical reflection are also basic to understanding the degree to which theory might be used as a component of evidence-informed practice. Indeed, the use of *evidence-informed practice* as an alternate term for *evidence-based practice* invites the use of well-developed theory. We believe that theory can and should serve to inform clinical practice decisions and activities. Theory that has been developed in conjunction with empiric generalizable research, carefully formulated through analytic thought, and subsequently critiqued in relation to a clinical purpose may be most valuable in guiding clinical outcomes in a desired direction. Well-constructed theory has the advantage of being generalizable across similar situations within the domain to which it applies. Theory, as a more general guide than isolated research findings, underscores the importance of considering context of care and allows for individualization of care practices to the unique situation of the patient or client (Thorne & Sawatzky, 2014). Theory that has been developed over time in conjunction with an ongoing research program or *informed by* meta-analyses may be the strongest form of evidence to support care decisions, because such theory represents and reconciles shared knowledge within a practice domain.

When you are serious about using a theory as a basis for clinical practice or for guiding research, it is critically important to examine the theory carefully and not assume that you understand the nature of the theory. Without careful examination, care decisions guided by the theory will be less than effective, and research outcomes that are grounded in or that extend the theory will likely be flawed. In addition, if not carefully examined and understood in relation to the purpose of its use, a theory remains underdeveloped with regard to its usefulness for the discipline of nursing. It is through the processes of description and critical reflection that disciplinary theory is both evaluated and refined.

The definition of empiric theory that we use in this text, as stated here, points to the elements of a theory that can form the basis for describing what the theory is all about. Our definition is as follows:

Theory: A creative and rigorous structuring of ideas that projects a tentative, purposeful, and systematic view of phenomena.

The descriptive components that this definition suggests include the following:

- *Purpose:* If a theory is purposeful, a purpose can be found. The purpose of a theory may not be stated explicitly, but it should be identifiable.
- *Concepts:* If a theory represents a structuring of ideas, the ideas will be in the form of concepts that are expressed through language.
- *Definitions:* If the concepts of a theory are integrated systematically, their meanings will be conveyed by definitions. Definitions vary with regard to precision and completeness, but conceptual meaning should be identifiable and consistent in a theory.
- *Relationships and structure:* If the concepts are related and structured into a systematic whole, the overall whole of the theory is identifiable by examining the network of interrelationships among concepts.

- *Assumptions:* If a theory is tentative, assumptions form the underlying taken-for-granted truths on which the theory was developed, thus leaving open possible theoretic interpretations that can come from different sets of assumptions.

WHAT IS THIS? THE DESCRIPTION OF THEORY

Describing a theory is a process of posing questions about the components of the theory as suggested by the previous definition, then responding to the questions with your own reading or interpretation of the theory. Some elements will seem clear, some will depend on tentative interpretations, and some will remain unclear. Despite ambiguities, the process of describing theory creates a description that can then form the basis for critical reflection. This chapter focuses on theory as a form of empiric knowledge to be described and reflected on critically. You should note, however, that many of the questions we propose to describe and reflect theory could be used in relation to other forms of empiric knowledge as well.

What Is the Purpose of This Theory?

The general purpose of a theory is important because it specifies the context and situations in which the theory is useful. Purpose can be approached initially by asking, "Why was this theory formulated?" The responses to this question provide information that pertains to theoretic purposes.

Some purposes are specific to the clinical practice of nursing. In these theories, the concepts of the theory include nursing actions and behaviors that contribute to the purpose. Pain alleviation and restored self-care ability are examples of purpose that require clinical practice and suggest that nursing actions are part of the theory. Note that these purpose statements have a value orientation of alleviation and restoration. These ideas imply change toward a certain goal rather than just change for the sake of change. Such value connotations are important to notice when describing the purpose of a theory.

Some purposes may not require the direct clinical practice of nursing but are useful for understanding phenomena that occur in the context of nursing practice. These purposes can contribute to the achievement of practice purposes, or they may not be directly relevant to practice goals. For example, consider a theory with the central purpose of explaining the variables that affect blood flow velocity in the skin. Clinical practice is not necessary to explain blood flow velocity, but a theory with this purpose might be linked to a theoretic explanation of how blood flow velocity influences the incidence of decubitus ulcers or the extent of peripheral neuropathy in people with diabetes. A theory that explains skin blood flow velocity and the factors that affect it might have the potential to help practitioners prevent skin breakdown and peripheral neuropathy.

Theoretic purposes that do not require direct clinical nursing actions but that are of concern to nursing also may involve professional issues in nursing. For example, the purpose of an empiric theory might be to describe the features of organizations that empower nurses. This valued and necessary purpose is not directly related to the specific nursing actions of giving care, but it is certainly useful for changing practice.

It is important to clarify whether purposes are embedded in the theoretic structure or they are reasonable extensions of the theory. For example, consider a theory of mother-infant attachment that links together the following concepts: (1) the birth or adoption experience, (2) maternal support systems, (3) the degree of bonding, and (4) healthy infant development. The linkages are formed in a way that suggests that maternal attachment is influenced by the nature of the birth or adoption experience, which determines the extent of maternal support and bonding; it goes on to suggest that these features, if positive, encourage healthy infant development. In this example, healthy infant development is an example of a clinical outcome or purpose that is structured within the theory.

Suppose the theorist stated that the purpose of the theory was quality of life of the family unit, but the theorist did not explain how the concepts within the theory inter-relate to create a certain quality of life. Quality of life as a purpose would constitute an extension of the theory because the concept is not located within the structure of the theory. Purposes that are embedded within the structure of the theory are usually explicit. Purposes that are reasonable extensions of the theory are important for under-standing the clinical usefulness of the theory, although they are not clearly linked to the central concepts within the theory. Often, purposes that are extensions of theory are linked to the concepts and structures of the theory by implicit assumptions. Purposes outside the context of the theory also suggest directions for the further development of the theory. In the example just cited, research or logical reasoning would be indicated that links healthy infant development with quality-of-life indicators.

Purposes within a theory may be found for different individuals or groups of indi-viduals who might use or benefit from the use of the theory. For example, if a theory is developed to address the clinical goal of alleviating pain, the theory can be examined for purposes that are appropriate for the individual nurse, the physician, the person receiv-ing care, and the person's family. Consider a theory that is developed with a clinical purpose of alleviating fatigue associated with cancer therapy. The theoretic purpose for the nurse might be distinctly different from that implied for the person receiving nursing care. The nurse's purpose might be to design a plan of care that minimizes stressors asso-ciated with care provision. The purpose for the person receiving care might be to rest and to provide responses that indicate the effectiveness of the system for minimizing fatigue. Taken together, these two purposes might be viewed as an overall purpose of creating a nurse-patient interactive process that minimizes patient fatigue.

In addition to whether or not purposes can be found for various individuals who use or who are affected by the theory, you can ask questions related to the scope of the theory's pur-pose. For example, does the overall purpose focus on an individual, a family, a group, or soci-ety in general? An organized society or an expanded collective consciousness is an example of a broad purpose that can be applied to relatively unbounded groups of people. Purposes such as environmental health or political activism may apply to whole communities or may be linked to definable groups within those communities. When there are multiple pur-poses within a theory, the scope of those purposes may vary. You may find narrower-scope purposes for individuals and families and broader-scope purposes for a community. When multiple purposes within a theory are found, if clarity is not compromised, you should be able to order purposes in a hierarchy that flows toward one central purpose.

The following question often arises: "How are purposes to be separated from the concepts of the theory?" Purposes that are part of the matrix of the theory are also concepts of the theory. One approach to identifying which concept is also the central purpose is to describe or designate the concept toward which theoretic reasoning flows. This is related to the structure of the theory. Ask the following: "What is the end point of this theory?" and "When is this theory no longer useful?" Responses to these questions provide clues about purpose and help to clarify the context in which the theory can be used. In the theoretic framework of Hall (1966), for example, the theory would cease to be valuable when the client has achieved self-actualization, which may be deemed the overall purpose. This purpose of self-actualization within the structure of Hall's theoretic framework represents the end point of theoretic reasoning. Within the context of Hall's theory, self-actualization is a purpose that requires nursing practice. Outside the context of Hall's theory, self-actualization is a purpose shared with other professions.

> **Think About It**
>
> Reflect on a purpose that guides your practice of nursing. Do you frequently seek to alleviate pain, or calm someone's anxiety, or help families deal with the uncertainty of living with a chronic illness? What theoretic ideas inform your practice around this purpose? Can you identify a theory that has been developed in the literature that addresses your purpose? Think about the challenges you face in your practice, and whether or not the theoretic ideas you identify might give you some guidance.

What Are the Concepts of This Theory?

Concepts are identified by searching out words or groups of words that represent objects, properties, or events within the theory. You can begin to describe concepts by listing key ideas and tentatively identifying how they seem to interrelate. As you begin to discern relationships, your perception of the key concepts of the theory will become clearer. One initial difficulty that is faced when identifying concepts is determining which concepts are integral to the theory and which are part of some supporting narrative. There is no easy way to deal with this difficulty. By beginning to identify concepts and then deriving interrelationships, decisions can be made about which concepts are central to the theory.

As you identify important theoretic concepts, ask questions about the nature of the concepts and their organization. Is there a major concept with subconcepts organized under it? Are there several major concepts with subconcepts organized under them? Are the concepts singular entities? Are some concepts singular entities and others organized with subconcepts? What are the relationships and interrelationships between and among concepts? Are some concepts mentioned that do not seem to fit the emerging structure? What is the relative scope of the various concepts? After the concepts are identified and such questions addressed, the relationships and structure will begin to emerge.

Other questions deal with the number of concepts. How many concepts are there? How many might be considered major concepts? How many are minor concepts? Do not become stuck trying to distinguish between major and minor. Rather, notice whether one or a few concepts really stand out as important while others seem less important, and consider why this is the case. As you consider the organization and number of concepts, address qualitative features of the concepts as well. Do the concepts represent abstractions of objects, properties, or events? Is it possible to identify what they represent? Are the concepts more empirically grounded, or are they more abstract? Which type of concept—more empiric or more abstract—seems to prevail? Are the concepts fairly discrete in meaning, or do several have similar meanings? When similar meanings for concepts exist, do they all seem to express a single idea, or do they differ? How are they different? Concepts that are alike may represent either one central idea that is fairly clear or several different images. For example, the concepts of *rehabilitation, restoration,* and *recovery,* which share common meanings, may appear in the same theory with similar meanings or with different meanings.

Ask questions about how concrete or abstract the concepts of the theory are. The nature of the concepts in a theory helps you to identify how general the theory is or to determine the range of situations in which the theory can be applied. Theories that focus on very broad, abstract concepts (e.g., caring) can be applicable to a very wide range of situations; these theories are sometimes labeled as "grand" theories. When the concepts tend to be descriptive of more specific situations, they can be labeled as "middle-range" theories. The labels or categories are not important in themselves; what is important to note is the potential for the concepts to be useful in practice, under what circumstances, and for what purposes.

The nature of the concepts also provides an indication of the potential for the further development of the theory. If the concepts are so abstract that they cannot be defined sufficiently for empiric investigation, then the potential for development as an empiric theory is limited.

When you are addressing the question of a theory's concepts, the concepts within it must be examined carefully for quantity, character, emerging relationships, and structure. The description of concepts is crucial because the quantity and character of those concepts form an understanding of the purpose of the theory, the structure and nature of theoretic relationships, the definitions, and the assumptions.

What Are the Definitions in This Theory?

A definition is an explicit meaning that is conveyed for a concept. Definitions exist to clarify the nature of the abstraction constructed by the theorist in a way that others can comprehend. Definitions suggest how word representations of an idea (concept) are expressed in experience.

It is often difficult to determine from a listing of key words the concepts that are basic to the theoretic structure and that comprise definitions and assumptions. Carefully reading the theory and relying on your own judgment should provide this information.

Concepts may be defined in a list of definitions or in narrative form in the text, but not labeled as definitions. It is not always easy to recognize narratives as definitions, because narratives are not labeled and may contain information that is not directly pertinent to the definition of the concept.

Concept definitions can also be implied by how the theorist uses the conceptual terms in the context. For example, if a theorist uses the concept of *wholism* but this term is not explicitly defined, you can examine the use of the term and infer the meaning or definition. If the theorist identifies and describes various dimensions of wholistic health, the definition of *wholism* might be akin to "the sum of the parts." If the theorist does not use parts or dimensions when speaking of wholistic health, the theorist may be using a definition that is more closely associated with wholism as being more than the sum of the parts.

Because concepts may have both *explicit* and *implicit* definitions, ask the following: how are concepts defined: explicitly, implicitly, or both? Are implied definitions consistent with explicit definitions? Can common language meanings be taken as the meaning intended? Would a common-language approach lead to differing interpretations of the meanings of the concepts?

Another way to describe definitions is to characterize the extent to which the definitions are *general* or *specific*. Both explicit and implicit meanings may be general or specific. Assess how general or specific the definitions are. How clearly does the definition suggest an associated empiric experience? Is the definition specific about what a phenomenon is, or does it suggest what its use is? Does it provide possibilities for empiric indicators that represent the phenomenon?

For the abstract concepts that are found in many nursing theories, specific definitions are difficult to formulate. Attempting prematurely to create specific meanings for abstract concepts may interfere with exploring a wide range of possibilities that lead to the discovery of richer or alternative meanings. Definitions that specify general features can conjure specific mental images of the actual experience. An early definition that is broad and nonspecific encourages the exploration of many possible meanings. General meanings are preferred in broad-scope theories or theories that are not likely to be empirically tested. Most definitions have both specific and general features. It is important to attend to how definitions are both specific and general.

After the definitions are identified, ask the following: Are similar definitions used for different concepts? Are differing definitions used for the same concept? Are some concepts defined differently than common convention would define them? Are definitions expanded as the narrative proceeds? Is it difficult to judge whether definitions are provided at all? Can definitions fit other terms within or outside of the structure of the theory?

What Are the Relationships in This Theory?

Relationships are the linkages among and between concepts. The nature of relationships in theory may take several forms. Often the relationship statements that are uncovered may be peripheral to the core of the theory.

As concepts are identified, ideas about relationships between and among them begin to form. Suppose you uncover the following relationship statement: "The individual is composed of three dimensions and is an integral part of the environment." This statement suggests that the individual is related to an environment and that there are three interrelated subcomponents of the individual.

When a tentative identification of the relationships is made, ask the following: Are there concepts that stand alone and that are unrelated to others? Are there concepts that are interrelated with other concepts in several ways and others that are related in only one or two ways? Are there concepts to which several other concepts relate but that, in turn, are not related to other concepts?

The ways in which the relationships emerge provide clues regarding the theoretic purposes and the assumptions on which the theory is based. Some concepts may be linked to the theory by assumptions, which may explain why the concept seems to fit within the matrix of the theory but why a theoretic relationship that contains the concept is not explicitly stated. The theoretic purpose may be represented by the linear relationships of several concepts that converge on one specific concept that, in turn, is not linked to any other concepts; in other words, the linkages end with a specific concept. As linkages between concepts are identified, you can address the nature and character of the relationships. If a relationship is unclear, ask yourself what relationships might be possible, and ask about their associated characters; your ideas can provide clues for the further development of the theory.

Examine the *nature* of the relationships. Are the relationships basically descriptive, or do they explain something about the phenomenon of interest? Do they create meaning without explaining it? Do they impart understanding? Is there evidence that some relationships are predictive? Relationships within theory that create meaning and impart understanding often link multiple concepts in a loose structure. In other forms of description, concepts are interrelated without elaboration on how and why conceptual relationships are arranged. Concepts that are interrelated often explain how empiric events occur and may provide some detail about how and why concepts interrelate. Prediction implies "if-then" statements about the occurrence of empiric phenomena. When empirically based predictions of human behavior are shown to be valid, they are usually based on explanation.

The statement, "Individuals are composed of three dimensions," is mainly descriptive. It implies that one concept—the individual—is composed of three parts called *dimensions*. If this sentence was expanded to, "The individual is composed of three dimensions that overlap and share common core areas," the statement becomes more explanatory. It proposes that each dimension has a shared area with another dimension, and that there is an area shared by all three. If the phrase "an interrelated whole" were to be added, the "how" of the relationship becomes even clearer because the dimensions must overlap to integrate the "parts" of the individual.

Predictions are fairly easy to detect. Sentences that translate into "if-then" statements are predictive. It is not possible to make such a statement from the sentence, "The individual is composed of three dimensions," unless it would be the following, which is implied: "If there are not three dimensions, then it is not an individual." The statement, "The individual is an interrelated whole composed of three dimensions that overlap and share common areas," implies that disturbances in one sphere would be reflected in other spheres. However, this prediction is implied and not explicit.

Suppose the statement read as follows: "Because the individual is an interrelated whole that is composed of three dimensions that overlap and share common areas, a disturbance in one dimension is reflected by disturbances in other dimensions." This statement is clearly predictive. The distinctions among *description, explanation,* and *prediction* are not always clear. Generally, the term *description* means that the statement projects what something is or the features of its character, whereas *explanation* suggests how or why it is. *Prediction* is used to project circumstances that create or alter a phenomenon. Our use of the terms *descriptive, explanatory,* and *predictive* when describing the nature of theoretic relationships refers only to the form of the theory. For the purposes of describing a theory, research findings are not required to confirm the nature of relationship statements as descriptive, explanatory, or predictive.

What Is the Structure of This Theory?

The structure of a theory gives overall form to the conceptual relationships within it. The structure emerges from the relationships of the theory. Consider these two concepts within a theory: the *individual* and the *environment.* In one theory, the individual is part of the environment; in another theory, the individual is separate from the environment. In both theories, there is an identifiable relationship between the individual and the environment, but the structure of the relationship differs.

Although your responses to questions about the relationships of the concepts of a theory usually suggest the theory's form, in some cases they do not. Many theories do not contain a single discernible structure in which all concepts will fit into a coherent, unified network. There may be several, perhaps competing structures that cannot be reconciled. Determining the structure of the theory will be difficult if the network of relationships is unclear or extremely complex. Figure 8-1 illustrates a sample of four structural forms and the ideas that these suggest. Some theories may reflect one or more of these structures, whereas others will not. Individual concepts within theories may be structured in these forms. Structural forms are powerful devices for shaping our perceptions. As you describe a theory, do not expect that it will fit into one of these four structures. The theory may fit, but many more structures are possible. Conversely, during the process of theory development, these are only examples of various structures that might evolve during the process of relationship structuring.

Consider how you might structure the following relationship statement: "Individuals are composed of component parts." This statement only suggests a structure in which parts are perceptible, and any image on Figure 8-1 could easily represent it, except the image that suggests polarity. Suppose each of these structures represents the broad theory of health. The triangular drawing suggests that health is composed of a series of related subconcepts that vary in breadth or simplicity. It also suggests foundational concepts on which other subconcepts are built. The base level might be genetic integrity, which could be followed by organ or system health, and finally by the health of communities or societies. A theory that deals with how genetic health forms the basis for individual, collective, and societal health might be structured in this way.

The overlapping circles in Figure 8-1 depict discrete components that have common areas between and among them. Health might be viewed as having biophysiologic, psychoemotional, and sociocultural aspects. If a person is biologically well but

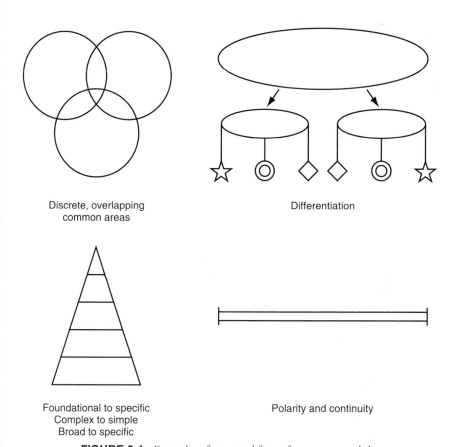

Discrete, overlapping
common areas

Differentiation

Foundational to specific
Complex to simple
Broad to specific

Polarity and continuity

FIGURE 8-1: Examples of structural forms for concepts and theory.

psychoemotionally unwell, the diagram suggests that the psychoemotional illness will affect biophysiologic wellness. Psychoemotional ill health could result in biophysiologic consequences. Basically, the overlapping circles illustrate that health is composed of separate components, but that sharing occurs between any two components as well as among all three. The structure, as illustrated, suggests equality with regard to importance, overlap, and sharing among the three subunits.

Applying this idea to the horizontal line drawing on the figure shows health being represented as a continuum in a linear relationship with illness. When health is placed on a continuum with illness at the opposite end, health and illness are conceptualized as a continuous variable, and degrees of health and illness are possible. The extremes of a continuum also suggest that health is the absence of illness and that illness is the absence of health. If health is viewed as a concept that is continuous with illness, health and illness can be represented by a continuum. However, if health and illness are not considered as continuous concepts, they do not fit this structural form.

The fourth structural form conveys the idea of differentiation by dividing major concepts into subconcepts. For this structural form, health might be differentiated into its mental and physical components. Physical health could be further divided into bodily or anatomic health and functional or physiologic health, with some comparable divisions such as emotional and spiritual for mental health. Differentiation can proceed indefinitely. Some concepts lend themselves to differentiation more easily than others. *Needs* is a concept that can be easily differentiated, whereas the concept of *wholism* cannot.

Conceptually unrelated or distinctly different concepts cannot be structured as a continuum. A relationship between gender and social practices could not be represented on a continuum. Gender and social practices could be structured as overlapping circles, as two conceptual entities that influence one another, or in a structure in which social practices shape gender. As you study the examples of structure, note how different concepts fit some structures more easily than others, and how some concepts such as *wholistic health* cannot be represented well by any structure. In fact, none of these structures for representing health may make sense to you, because the structures may be inconsistent with your personal ideas about the nature of health.

As relationships are explored, the overall theoretic structure and the structures of individual components begin to emerge. To address questions of structure, begin by asking the following questions: What are the most central relationships? What are the direction, strength, and quality of those relationships? Can I draw a model that shows the structure of the theory? What is the order of appearance of relationships within the narrative? Do relationships appear to move toward or away from the theoretic purpose? Do relationships coalesce the concepts or differentiate them? Does the theorist diagram the structure?

After the structures of the major or central relationships are identified, other aspects of structure can be described: How are other structures united with the central or core relationships? Can all the relationships be structured? Do the structures take multiple forms? Are competing or partial structures suggested? Does the theorist provide diagrams that illustrate aspects of structure?

After you have linked together concepts and purposes in relationships, it becomes possible to describe the entire structural form of the theory. Notice how the relationships move as the theory unfolds. A theory that defies structuring can sometimes be approached by simply outlining the order in which the concepts are presented. Outlining can provide insight about how ideas are organized. Some recognizable structure is essential to theory because structure flows from relationships.

What Are the Assumptions in This Theory?

Assumptions are those basic givens or accepted truths that are fundamental to theoretic reasoning. To uncover assumptions, a central question can be asked: "What is the author taking as an accepted truth?" This question can be asked after the purposes are determined, the concepts are structured by relational statements, and the definitions are described.

Sometimes the theorist states assumptions explicitly. If so, ask the following: "What are the explicit givens?" and "What do they assume?" Statements that are explicitly labeled as *assumptions* may not be the same as the assumptions that are basic to the theory. The extent to which explicitly labeled assumptions are assumptions and not something else must be examined. It is often difficult to separate assumptions that are implicit or integrated into the narrative of the theory from relationship statements, but they can be identified. As with explicit assumptions, ask the following: "What are the implicit givens?" and "What do they assume?"

Explore your ideas about the assumptions of the theory further. What individual, environmental, nursing, and health-related assumptions are made? Are the assumptions competing or compatible? Are there several assumptions about one phenomenon and few about another? Are the assumptions made at the outset, between and within relationships, or in relation to the purposes of the theory?

Assumptions may take the form of factual assertions, or they may reflect value positions. *Factual assumptions* are those that are knowable or potentially knowable through perceptual experience. *Value assumptions* assert or imply what is right, good, or ought to be. Often, an empirically knowable assumption (e.g., "It is assumed for the purposes of this theory that people want information") contains important underlying value assumptions. The assumption that people want information (which could be empirically verified) may further imply that information is good, which cannot be verified empirically. The value assumption that "it is good to have information" leads to further questions about what sort of information is good. It is important to examine factual assumptions by asking, "What value does this factual assumption reflect?" It is also important to examine all the other components of theory. What does this concept, definition, relationship, structure, or purpose assume?

After you discern the assumptions, the values that are held by the theorist can be explored. What does the theorist assume to be valuable, good, right, wrong, or worthwhile? Are there value-laden terms and phrases in the definitions of the concepts and in the supporting narrative of the theory? Who is assumed to be responsible for the experiences or circumstances depicted in the theory? Who benefits from the circumstances or experiences of this theory? These questions often give clues to values that form fundamental assumptions. For example, the Freudian theoretic notion of *penis envy* implies that penises are body parts that are so valued as to be enviable, and that a person who does not have a penis will experience this value-laden emotion. A useful approach to uncovering hidden values is to imagine possibilities other than those presented in the theory. If these alternative possibilities are plausible but unconventional, you have uncovered important value assumptions. Imagining the idea of *womb envy*, which is not a part of Freudian thinking but is a plausible alternative possibility, indicates that you have uncovered an important androcentric assumption from which the theory builds.

Describing or discerning assumptions are often grounded in beliefs so taken for granted that they are difficult to recognize. Sometimes it is not possible to agree personally with and accept a theory because it is so unusual or strange. Uneasiness or discomfort with a theory may be a clue to assumptions that are unlike your own beliefs or values. After assumptions are recognized, the theory that contains them can be understood on its own terms.

Forming a Complete Description

In summary, we propose the following six questions for describing a theory:
1. *What is the purpose of this theory?* This question addresses why the theory was formulated and reflects the contexts and situations to which the theory can be applied.

2. *What are the concepts of this theory?* This question identifies the ideas that are structured and related within the theory.
3. *How are the concepts defined within this theory?* This question clarifies the meanings of concepts within the theory. It questions what empiric experience is represented by the ideas within the theory.
4. *What is the nature of the relationships within this theory?* This question addresses how concepts are linked together. It focuses on the various forms that relationship statements can take and how they give structure to the theory.
5. *What is the structure of the theory?* This question addresses the overall form of the conceptual interrelationships. It discerns whether the theory contains partial structures or has one basic form.
6. *On what assumptions does the theory build?* This question addresses the basic truths that are believed to underlie theoretic reasoning. It questions whether those assumptions reflect philosophic values or factual assertions.

A general approach to describing theory is to read the work and then begin to consider the descriptive questions. All the questions are not necessarily answerable for a single theory. However, as you answer the questions that apply to the theory under consideration, concepts will be tentatively identified, and the purpose of the theory will emerge. As definitions become evident, you will begin to see relationships. From the nature of the relationships, you will be able to address questions regarding the structure of the theory. Responses to the questions about assumptions provide a level of awareness of meanings that will help you form an understanding of the theory. After an initial description of the components, each component can be reexamined and revised.

For any theory, it is often not easy to describe theoretic purposes and assumptions. Concepts and their definitions may be more readily identifiable, especially if they are fairly explicit. Discerning relationships and structure is often problematic when describing theory, but these traits, too, will be present.

Forming a complete description of a theory requires the systematic and critical examination of the work. When approached seriously, every word, phrase, and sentence must be examined and reexamined for meaning. Ideas that emerge in response to the descriptive questions often lead to uncertainty and the revision of earlier ideas. After a time, the description does begin to take shape, and fewer changes occur. There will always be some tentativeness in your descriptions, because your description requires your own interpretive insights with respect to the theorist's ideas, and these insights change. If you are not able to reach a tentative resolution with respect to the fundamental nature of a theory after reasonable study and thought, the best course of action is to propose your ideas for the revision and further development of the theory. Your continuing uncertainty indicates that further theoretic development must occur.

Despite uncertainty and tentativeness, it is important to rely on your own judgment about the nature of a theory and not to assume that published descriptions and analyses are more accurate or authoritative than yours. When you complete a description and critical reflection with care and precision, your conclusions should be trusted to be an accurate understanding of the theory.

⊖ Image Collection – Theory Guide

HOW DOES IT WORK? THE CRITICAL REFLECTION OF THEORY

After a theory is described, critical questions can be addressed to develop information about how well developed a theory is or how adequate it is in relation to its purposes. Note that describing and critically reflecting theory are fundamentally different processes. Description can be compared with a more objective process of setting forth facts about the theory by asking, "What is this?" By contrast, critical reflection involves ascertaining how well a theory works in relation to some purpose. In this section, we identify questions that can be used as part of critical reflection. As you question the worth of a theory, you will form insights that will help you to know how that theory might be used and further developed.

As you study and read different nursing theories, you may think, "This does not seem right," "Maybe I could change my practice along this line," or "This is really exciting." When these types of thoughts occur, you are comparing the theory with some personal and perhaps unrecognized ideas about what is important for theory. Each person's ideas of the adequacy of a theory are influenced by a personal perspective of what is valuable or good. For research, you might agree, "This could be helpful." For practice, you might think, "Maybe I could use this." For idea stimulation, you might think, "This really gives me some exciting new ideas." In these instances, you have formed an impression of the value of the theory from your personal values about practice, research, and critical thinking. Your values are important components that are integrated into a more formal critical reflection process.

Critical reflection contributes to understanding how well the theory relates to practice, research, or educational activities. Members of a discipline form ideas about what questions to ask and what responses are generally accepted if a theory is to be seen as valuable for the discipline. Just as there are many ways to describe theory, there are many critical questions that can be asked about the functional value of theory, and there are many responses to these questions. When these questions are asked, members of a discipline can consider what responses they tend to value and why. The questions that we pose are consistent with generally accepted methods for evaluating theories that have been described in the nursing literature (Alligood & Tomey, 2010; Barnum, 1998; Ellis, 1968; Fawcett, 2005; Hardy, 1974). However, our approach differs from accepted methods in that normative criteria are not implied. Normative criteria represent a standard or ideal and imply a "good" or "bad" judgment on the basis of the criteria. In our view, the judgment of the worth of a theory is relative to your purpose and how the theory can contribute to what you envision for nursing practice.

The questions for critical reflection are as follows:
- How clear is this theory?
- How simple is this theory?
- How general is this theory?
- How accessible is this theory?
- How important is this theory?

Because these are not normative criteria, there are no correct answers to these questions, and the questions do not imply the responses. For example, "How clear is this?" does not necessarily mean that a theory should be perfectly clear or that clearer is necessarily better. Rather, when you address this question, you are using it as a tool to examine whether the level of clarity of the theory is adequate for the theory's purpose. As you engage in discussions about the questions, you can form a consensus with your colleagues regarding where to go next with the theory. These insights can best be formed in discussions among people with diverse perspectives. For example, although a theory that challenges assumptions about practice is somewhat unclear, it may be an important theory for changing nursing practice and providing new concepts. The lack of perfect clarity allows for imagining new possibilities, which may be part of the theory's strength.

Although each of the five critical reflection questions is fundamentally different, the questions are interrelated. For example, one question addresses accessibility, and another addresses generality. If seen as general or broad in scope, a theory may be less accessible (i.e., less related to perceptual experience) than a narrower (i.e., less general) theory.

Responses to the questions used to create a description affect your responses to the critical reflection questions. For example, to decide how clear, accessible, or general a theory is, you need to describe the purpose of the theory, what concepts are included, and how those concepts are structured. As your description of the theory is formed, you can begin the process of critical reflection. The ideas that you develop from this process contribute to your own critical insights and to substantive discussion that gives direction for further theory development. The issues to consider as you address each of the questions for critically reflecting theory are described in the following sections.

How Clear Is This Theory?

When determining how clear a theory is, you will be considering semantic clarity, semantic consistency, structural clarity, and structural consistency. *Clarity,* in general, refers to how well the theory can be understood and how consistently the ideas are conceptualized. *Semantic clarity* and *semantic consistency* primarily refer to understanding the intended theoretic meaning of the concepts. *Structural clarity* and *structural consistency* reflect an understanding of the intended connections between concepts within the theory as well as the whole of the theory.

To help understand the subset criteria of clarity, consider a diagram or figure representing a theory in a professional journal article. The figure contains a series of boxes with concepts named within those boxes and with lines or arrows connecting the boxes to complete the figure. *Semantics* concerns meaning. *Semantic clarity* refers to how clearly the concepts within the boxes are implicitly or explicitly defined, usually within the narrative explanation of the theory. *Semantic consistency,* on the other hand, examines if the meaning proposed for those concepts is used the same way throughout the explanation or description provided with the figure.

As you begin to read the article describing the theory, a concept's meaning when first encountered may be quite clear, but when you reach the conclusion the writer seems to be using the concept in a way that refers to something a bit different although both meanings, when considered individually, may seem pretty clear. This divergence of meanings sets up semantic inconsistency. On the other hand, the meaning of concepts may be unclear, although the reason for this unclarity and the unclarity itself is consistent. This is an example of *semantic unclarity* with semantic consistency. This distinction may seem trivial but is important. When you detect *unclarity* in a theory with regard to conceptual meaning, making this distinction means you will have a sense of whether the unclarity occurred because the concept was poorly defined or because the concept took on different meanings throughout the theory, or both. If the source of unclarity is understood, it can be corrected or recognized as problematic in relation to intended uses.

Structural clarity addresses the conceptual linkages within the theory, whereas *structural consistency* refers to the extent to which linkages remain stable throughout the description of the theory and without contradictions. In the example of the figure or diagram of the theory, structural clarity would address whether or not the connecting lines or arrows between the boxes (relationships among and between concepts) support a coherent understanding of the entire theory. Structural clarity also means that individual relationships between concepts are clear, particularly within the narrative portion of the theory. Structural consistency addresses whether the linkages between concepts are similarly presented throughout the theory, and it can be assessed by examining the narrative of the theory in relation to the figure. If the theory narrative proposes that two important concepts are interrelated, but this is not obvious in the figure, structural clarity is lacking. If it appears from the figure that two concepts are linked, but you find the narrative seems to link those concepts differently, you have found structural inconsistency.

In summary and most importantly, *semantics* involves conceptual meaning, *structure* involves conceptual linkages, and these are subcriteria within *clarity*. Understanding the conceptual meaning or linkages is a tool for deciding if and how you might use the theory, and what would be needed to use it appropriately for your purposes.

Semantic Clarity. The definitions of concepts in the theory are important aspects of semantic clarity. Definitions help to establish empiric meaning for concepts within the theory. If concepts are not defined or are not completely defined, the empiric indicators for the idea become less clear. When concepts are clearly defined, empiric indicators can be more easily identified. Clarity implies in part that when different nurses read the theory, a similar empiric image comes to mind when the word for the concept is used. If there are no definitions or if only a few of the concepts are defined, clarity is limited.

The types of definitions that are used within theory affect semantic clarity. Definitions that reflect both specific and general traits enhance clarity, whereas a general or a specific definition alone often limits clarity. Specific definitions usually lend clarity, because they provide clear and accurate guidance for the intended empiric indicators for a concept. General definitions contribute a contextual sense of meaning for concepts and lend a richness of meaning that is not possible with specific definitions. Considering the extent to which each type of definition contributes to clarity of meaning can help you to form your own ideas about the adequacy of the theory for your purpose.

Clarity may be obscured by the borrowing of terms from other disciplines or the use of common-language terms that carry broad general meanings. Words such as *stress* and *coping* have general common-language meanings, and they also have specific theoretic meanings in other disciplines. If words with multiple meanings are used in a theory and not defined, a person's everyday meaning of the term is often assumed rather than the meaning within the theory; therefore, clarity is lost. Clarity is enhanced when the concept's definition is consistent with common meanings of the term in the profession.

Clarity is affected when words that have no common meaning are used, or when the theorist invents or coins words to represent some idea. Coined words can help to convey a meaning for which there is no word, but they also can detract from clarity, especially when a more familiar word or phrase would suffice. It would be possible to generate an entire theory about quizzendroids, plankerods, and ziots. The theory could be logical and consistent, but it would be unclear because the words are invented and do not signify recognizable objects, properties, or events. Although exaggerated, this example demonstrates the effects on clarity when vague or strange words are used, when words are not defined, or when words with many possible meanings are used and not defined.

Semantic clarity can also be affected by excessive verbiage. Normally, the use of varying words to represent similar meanings is a writing skill that can be used to avoid the overuse of a single term. In a theory, however, if several similar concepts are used interchangeably when one would suffice, there is excessive verbiage, and the clarity of the theory's presentation is reduced rather than improved. In a theory, varying the word for an important concept interjects subtly different meanings. For example, interchanging the words *restoration, rehabilitation,* and *recovery* for the same concept affects clarity, because each word has a slightly different meaning and suggests different contexts of use.

Clarity is also affected when excessive narrative is included. Semantic clarity may be decreased by excessive examples; however, the judicious use of examples usually aids clarity. Diagrams can enhance or obscure clarity. To enhance clarity, diagrams should be self-explanatory and simple in expression, because overly complex illustrations discourage comprehension. In general, the alternative mode of providing information in the form of diagrams helps to clarify the ideas in the theory.

An economy of words, the provision of key definitions, and the wise use of examples and diagrams lend clarity. Absolute semantic clarity can never be achieved, nor is it necessarily desirable. Because of the limitations of language, no matter how clearly the theorist represents theoretic meaning, it will not be perceived uniformly by all readers.

Semantic Consistency. Semantic consistency is a second feature to consider with respect to the question of clarity. A theory that implicitly or explicitly defines concepts inconsistently gives competing messages with regard to meaning. Semantic consistency means that the concepts of the theory are used in ways that are consistent with their definition. Sometimes a definition is explicitly stated, but somewhere within the theory, another meaning is implied. When key words are not explicitly defined, their implied meanings may be inconsistent from one instance of use to the next. Occasionally, words are explicitly defined but in different ways. Inconsistencies that occur when terms are defined explicitly are fairly easy to uncover, but other types of inconsistencies may be more covert.

The consistent use of basic assumptions is also important to the achievement of consistency. The theory's purpose, the definitions of concepts, and the relationships need to be consistent with the stated and unstated assumptions of the theory. Examples and diagrams can also be considered in the light of the assumptions of the theory. For example, suppose a basic theoretic assumption is the unity of the individual and the environment and that both change simultaneously and irreversibly through time and space. This assumption is consistent with a definition of health as expanding consciousness, but it is inconsistent with a theoretic conceptualization of health as a state of adaptation. Adaptation typically implies conforming or adjusting to environmental stimuli to fit within the environment. The concept of *adaptation* tends to suggest the assumption that events external to the person are primary determinants of health, and that the person and the environment are separate entities. The unity of the individual and the environment is a concept that can be used to convey an assumption that humans and the environment are interconnected and that they change simultaneously. Simultaneous change negates the idea of conforming or adjusting to stimuli as health; rather, it implies incorporating change, becoming a different person, and increasing options and awareness of choice.

For clarity, the purposes of the theory must be consistent with all other components. A purpose of health that is achieved by deliberate nursing actions may be at odds with the basic assumption that health is deterministic. As you become aware of inconsistencies, you will uncover other meanings that are conveyed in the definitions and the other components of the theory.

When reflecting on consistency, examine your descriptions for each component of the theory, and consider where there are consistencies and inconsistencies within and among the descriptive elements of the theory. Definitions must be examined for consistency with one another and in relation to assumptions. Structure is sometimes inconsistent with relationships. If a theory is extremely inconsistent, it is difficult to continue the process of critical reflection regarding the theory. Some semantic inconsistencies within theory are more common early during the theory's development and leave room for new possibilities for further development. However, inconsistencies at the basic roots of a theory (e.g., between assumptions and goals) have implications that will affect the entire theory and that must be addressed.

Structural Clarity. Structural clarity is closely linked to semantic clarity. Structural clarity refers to how identifiable and apparent the connections and reasoning are within theory. The descriptive elements of structure and relationships provide important information for addressing this dimension of clarity.

In a theory with structural clarity, you can readily identify and recognize the underlying conceptual network. With structural clarity, concepts are interconnected and organized into a coherent whole. If you cannot discern the structure of the theory, you begin to search for those structural elements that are related and for gaps that occur in the flow of the theory. If all major relationships are included within a single structure, clarity is enhanced. Clarity is lost when significant relationships are not contained within a coherent structure. Pieces of relationships, rudiments of structure, or concepts that stand alone are evidence that parts have not yet been integrated into the whole during development of the theory.

Structural Consistency. Structural consistency refers to the consistent use of structural form within a theory. Often a theory, especially a more middle-range theory, is built around one predominant structural form, such as a form that differentiates concepts, structures concepts linearly, or structures concepts in a hierarchy. Sometimes, one structural form provides an overall general profile for major relationships within theory, and more minor components of the theory take a different structural form. Whatever structure or structures are used to link together concepts and relationships, their consistent use throughout the theory serves as a structural map that enhances clarity. A theorist may begin with a structural movement that is linear. If this structure is reflected in the linkages among elements of the theory, you will observe a high level of structural consistency. A shift in reasoning to a structure that integrates concepts (e.g., Venn diagram of overlapping circles) may be confusing, or the structure might function well within a structural scheme that is linear.

In summary, "How clear is this theory?" can be asked as a means of exploring the ways in which a theory is or is not clear and comprehensible and what its level of clarity means for the development and use of the theory. The ideas of semantic and structural consistency and clarity can be used to guide the discussion of issues of clarity, because inconsistencies provide double messages that confound clarity. A very general (broad-scope) theory may be quite ambiguous but still useful for the stimulation of new ideas. For example, a middle-range theory of hopelessness may have aspects that are vague but that may still be important to help nurses understand the experience. However, the ambiguity of that same theory may affect its usefulness for guiding research. Becoming aware of the ways in which clarity is obscured in the light of your purpose makes it possible to design ways to develop further the theory's clarity. The degree to which a theory must be clear depends on how the nurse intends to use it.

How Simple Is This Theory?

Simplicity means that the number of elements within each descriptive category—particularly concepts and their interrelationships—are minimal. *Complexity* implies many theoretic relationships between and among numerous concepts. The following example illustrates theoretic simplicity. Suppose that a theory contained three major concepts: A, B, and C. A theory that interrelates these as discrete concepts would be quite simple, because only three interrelationships would be possible: A and B, A and C, and B and C. Adding subconcepts 1 and 2 to A, B, and C (e.g., A1, A2) would leave the theorist with three major concepts and six subconcepts for a total of nine concepts. A theorist who is working with nine concepts has significantly greater theoretic complexity than a theorist working with only three concepts. Adding even one or two concepts to a theory greatly increases the potential for theoretic interrelationships and, subsequently, complexity.

The desirability of simplicity or complexity can vary with the stage of theory development. In grounded theory or phenomenologic descriptions, there may be considerable complexity as the theory begins to emerge. As the theory develops, however, relationships and concepts coalesce, and the theory becomes simpler.

Regardless of the approach to theory development, some concepts created early during the process eventually may be deleted or changed. In the previous example, suppose concepts A, A1, and A2 came to be seen as unimportant in relation to the theory's purpose. The theoretic complexity added by A and its subconcepts could be removed, and only the simpler relationships between B and C and their subconcepts would remain.

Theories reflect varying degrees of simplicity. In nursing, some situations suggest the need for relatively simple and broad theories that can be used as general guides for practice. Other situations suggest simple but more empirically accessible theories to guide research. Still other situations suggest the need for theories that are relatively complex because of the value that such theories have for enhancing the understanding of extremely complex practice situations.

How General Is This Theory?

The *generality* of a theory refers to its breadth of scope and purpose; a general theory can be applied to a broad array of situations. The term *parsimony* is sometimes used as a synonym to describe the trait of theoretic simplicity, but the concept of parsimony also includes the idea of generality. A *parsimonious theory* is conceptually simple (i.e., it contains few structural elements), but it accounts for a broad range of empiric experiences.

The scope of concepts and purposes within the theory provides clues with regard to its generality. A theory that contains broad concepts will encompass more empiric indicators than a theory that contains very narrow concepts. The concepts of *humans* and *universe* could be interpreted as organizing almost every empiric indicator possible. A comprehensive theory that involves these two concepts would be highly general. A theory that interrelates the individual and the physical environment is less general, but still fairly broad in scope. The concept of the *individual* implies that the theory is concerned with a single person. The use of *physical* as a modifier for *environment* conveys the notion of part of the environment only. Information about individuals in communities could not be understood within this theory. A theory that addresses the characteristics of acutely ill people in the intensive care unit environment is even less general, and the scope of concepts subsequently narrows.

Questions that address the generality of a theory include the following: To whom or what does this theory apply, and when does it apply? Does the purpose pertain to all health care professionals? Does it apply to people in general? Does the purpose apply to specific specialties of nursing and only at given times? The more limited the scope of application of the theory, the less general is the theory.

Whether generality is viewed as desirable depends on your purpose for the theory. General theory is quite useful for generating ideas or hypotheses. Nursing theories that address broad concepts (e.g., individuals, society, health, environment) have a high degree of generality and are useful for organizing ideas about universal health behaviors. Theories that address a specific human experience (e.g., pain) are less general and, because of their relative specificity, are useful for guiding practice in a clinical setting.

⊖ Image Collection – Scope of a Theory

How Accessible Is This Theory?

Accessibility addresses the extent to which empiric indicators for the concepts can be identified and to what extent the purposes of the theory can be attained. If a theory is to be used for explaining some aspect of practice, its theoretic concepts must be linked to the empiric indicators that are available in practice. *Empiric indicators* are perceptually accessible experiences that can be used in practice to assess the phenomena described by the theory and can help determine whether the purposes of the theory are realized in a way that the theory suggests.

Only selected dimensions of highly abstract concepts may be empirically accessible. If the concepts of a theory do not reflect empiric dimensions, or if the empiric dimensions are obscure, the concepts may be ideas that cannot be explored or understood empirically.

Consider the example of a theory about rehabilitation and interaction. The theoretic definitions of the concepts are clues to the accessibility of the theory. Without definition, the words *rehabilitation* and *interaction* can assume many dimensions of meaning. If the concepts are defined, the ways in which they are to be empirically accessed is clearer. If the definitions point to the measurements or observable behaviors that can be associated with rehabilitation and the specific types of interactions that promote rehabilitation, then the theory can be judged to be relatively accessible in a clinical context.

Increasing the complexity of a theory often increases its empiric accessibility. As subconceptual categories are clarified, empiric indicators become more precise. Suppose that the concepts of *rehabilitation* and *interaction* are related within the same theory. The theory is judged to have a high degree of generality and simplicity because the concepts are broad and few in number. Designating five subconcepts for each concept would increase the theory's complexity. Those five subconcepts are likely to have more precise empiric bases than are the broader concepts. With empirically accessible subconcepts, the empiric accessibility of the theory increases. If a concept does not have an empiric basis at the outset, specifying subconcepts for larger wholes does not increase empiric accessibility.

Research testing requires the empiric accessibility of concepts. It also confirms those concepts that are clinically relevant and accessible. For example, if *rehabilitation* is defined in a research project as "able to complete activities of daily living independently," you have established a clear link between the idea of rehabilitation and a reasonable clinical observation. If the research supports the hypothesis derived from the theory, it also provides evidence of empiric accessibility for the concept of rehabilitation.

The empiric accessibility of the concepts contained within a theory is basic to validating theoretic relationships and making use of the theory in practice. Although grounded approaches to generating theory assume empiric accessibility, the extent to which empiric accessibility is important can vary. Considering the theory's purpose will help you to make judgments about how empirically accessible a theory should be. Theory that provides a conceptual perspective for clinical practice may not require much empiric accessibility. If a theory is to be used to guide research, empiric accessibility is important. If a theory will be used to shape nursing practice, concepts need to be empirically accessible in the clinical area. If concepts are not empirically grounded, creating conceptual meaning may provide direction for the empiric indicators that are needed for research.

How Important Is This Theory?

In nursing, the importance of a theory is closely tied to the idea of its clinical significance or its practical value. An important theory is forward looking; is usable in practice, education, and research; and is valuable for creating a desired future. The central question to be answered is, "Does this theory create understanding that is important to nursing?" Some nursing theories guide research and practice; some generate radically new ideas about health and caring; and some differentiate the focus of nursing from other service professions.

If a theory contains concepts, definitions, purposes, and assumptions that are grounded in practice, it will have practical value for enhancing theory-based research that can become research evidence that is integrated into evidence-informed clinical decisions. A theory that has limited empiric accessibility may not have practical value for research, but it can stimulate ideas and spark political action that improves practice.

One approach to addressing the question of importance is to reflect on the theory's basic theoretic assumptions. If the underlying assumptions are unsound, the importance of the theory is minimal. For example, if a theory is based on a view of the individual as *parts,* its importance for wholistic nursing is minimal. If a theory is based on an assumption of *wholism* and it moves the understanding of wholism to a new dimension, it likely is to be highly important to nursing.

Theories that have extremely broad purposes may be essentially unattainable and therefore have limited value for the creation of clinical outcomes. This same theory may be important for generating ideas and challenging practice.

The importance of theory depends on the professional and personal values of the person who is addressing the question. Asking, "Do I like this theory?" and "Why do I like it or not like it?" will help you to identify the values that you hold for yourself, your practice, the profession, and the theory. Contributing your ideas about what is important for nursing through careful deliberation and discussion with nurse colleagues will help clarify the direction that a theory should take to achieve important professional purposes.

Forming a Complete Critical Reflection

In summary, the five questions to consider when critically reflecting on the description of a theory are as follows:

1. *Is this theory clear?* This question addresses the clarity and consistency of the presentation. Clarity and consistency may be both semantic and structural.
2. *Is this theory simple?* This question addresses the number of structural components and relationships within the theory. Complexity implies numerous relational components within the theory; simplicity implies fewer relational components.
3. *Is this theory general?* This question addresses the scope of experiences covered by the theory. Generality infers a wide scope of phenomena; specificity narrows the range of events included in the theory. Generality in combination with simplicity yields parsimony.
4. *Is this theory accessible?* This question addresses the extent to which concepts within the theory are grounded in empirically identifiable phenomena.
5. *Is this theory important?* This question addresses the extent to which a theory leads to valued nursing goals in practice, research, and education.

When Are Thorough Description and Critical Reflection Important?

As you might expect, there is no easy answer to the previous question, except to say, "You will know." When you are serious about appropriately using theory and begin the work of understanding any given theory, you will soon understand why considering it carefully is important. The use of any theory for any purpose should not be done unknowingly. Deciding to what extent theory ought to be examined in relation to its intended use comes with an understanding of and practice with the processes of description and critical reflection.

We believe that completing at least one guided and thorough description and critical reflection, even as an exercise, is important for appreciating the complexity of developing and using theory for shaping practice outcomes. It also underscores the problems of attempting to use theory without a good general understanding of it. Misuse of theory for shaping practice outcomes can range from harmful to worthless. The analytic skills developed in this process also transfer to other areas and may mitigate tendencies to think understanding is present when it is not.

For knowledge developers, including researchers and theoreticians, once the process of description and critical reflection is well understood, it becomes much easier to make decisions about which parts of the process take precedence over others. Although it is always important to have a good general understanding of the theory, the *purpose* that you intend the theory to serve should guide your decisions about how much detail is important and where the focus of examination and understanding should be. If a single conceptual relationship is the focus of research, looking at clarity of conceptual meaning and relational structure of the concepts becomes centrally important to choose assessment measures and methods that are consistent with that part of theory. Even when a single conceptual measurement is the focus of the researcher, it is also important to establish that the whole of the theory is important, and that the generality of the theory fits the context of use.

Think About It

To deepen your appreciation of description and critical reflection, consider the following related to the content of this chapter:
1. Create several structural forms for the concept of your choice. What does each suggest about the concept?
2. Name a concept of interest to nursing that defies definition, and think about why it is so difficult to define.
3. Identify a theory that you find likable or workable. What is it about the theory that you like? Which particular components of the theory have contributed to your feelings?

REFLECTION AND DISCUSSION – SUPPLEMENT ⊖

References

Alligood, M. R., & Tomey, A. M. (2010). *Nursing theorists and their work* (6th ed.). St. Louis, MO: Elsevier.

Barnum, B. J. S. (1998). *Nursing theory* (5th ed.). Boston, MA: Lippincott-Raven.

Ellis, R. (1968). Characteristics of significant theories. *Nursing Research, 17,* 217–222.

Fawcett, J. (2005). Criteria for evaluation of theory. *Nursing Science Quarterly, 18*(2), 131–135.

Hall, L. E. (1966). Another view of nursing care and quality. In K. M. Straub & K. S. Parker (Eds.), *Continuity in patient care: The role of nursing.* Washington, DC: Catholic University Press.

Hardy, M. E. (1974). Theories: Components, development, evaluation. *Nursing Research, 23,* 100–107.

Koltoff, N. (1967). The use of the laboratory. *Nursing Research, 16,* 122.

Thorne, S. E., & Sawatzky, R. (2014). Particularizing the general: Sustaining theoretical integrity in the context of an evidence-based practice agenda. *ANS Advances in Nursing Science, 37*(1), 1–10.

⊖ http://evolve.elsevier.com/Chinn/knowledge/

Research extends knowledge through application of scientific methods—not with absolute certainty—but with minimal misinformation. Skepticism, alert self-criticism, constant testing of hypotheses by empirical research and awareness of limitations of science make research a most dependable source of information.

Laurie M. Gunter (1964, p. 231)

The opening quote by Gunter affirms both the significance of research as an application of the scientific method and its limitations. Gunter assumes that research—to produce the most dependable information—must be carefully performed, but even then, the information that research provides is limited. Misinformation, according to Gunter, arises when research methods are not carefully accomplished (for her, by the constant testing of hypotheses) but also when researchers do not have an attitude that involves questioning their motives, goals, and biases. Also, recognizing the inherent limitations of even the best research, Gunter cites three factors that create limitations in research: (1) shoddy methodologies, (2) problematic personal characteristics of researchers, and (3) the inherent nature of scientific research.

In previous chapters, we address the limitations of science and empirics as forms of knowledge. Although scientific research and empiric knowledge are most certainly important, empirics is limited to knowledge about abstracted generalities. In other words, empiric knowledge informs us about what we could usually expect to happen in a given situation. It is this feature of scientific empiric knowledge—its focus on the general—that makes empirics and research that leads to empiric knowledge both limited and powerful. Knowledge that is generated from scientific research is powerful precisely because it does relate to the usual or the general; it is limited because nursing is also concerned with the specific and unique needs in individual circumstances. Nursing relies on understanding the general principles of scientific evidence as well as knowledge derived from other sources of knowing that inform the unique instances of clinical practice (Thorne & Sawatzky, 2014).

This chapter focuses on the methodologic features of empiric research that will result in strong, reliable, and valid empiric evidence to inform nursing practice. Researchers have a responsibility to provide this type of evidence. Practitioners have a responsibility to assess the strength of the research evidence, use the evidence to inform their practice, and determine the extent to which a unique situation in their practice demands other forms of knowledge to guide their practice.

In this chapter, we describe research methods for confirming and validating empiric phenomena. Figure 9-1 shows the empiric quadrant of our model for nursing knowledge development, which highlights the role of confirming and validating theories, formal descriptions, and other forms of empiric knowledge. These processes authenticate what is expressed in the formal knowledge of the discipline, which in turn supports scientific competence in practice. The confirmation and validation of empiric knowledge also draw on practice-based methods, as detailed in Chapter 10. The research and practice-based methods, taken together, provide a strong foundation that strengthens nursing practice in relation to the general principles provided by empiric knowledge.

We use both confirmation and validation to characterize authentication processes within the empiric pattern. Their meanings are similar, yet there are important differences. *Confirmation* is the term reserved for the authentication of more qualitative and naturalistic forms of empiric research findings, whereas the term *validation* is used to refer to authentication processes for more quantitative, measurable forms of empiric research findings. Qualitative and naturalistic inquiry processes may result in knowledge that can already be considered confirmed, depending on the inquiry method used as well as the nature of the findings. Alternatively, additional clinical confirmation may be needed for some qualitative and naturalistic research findings. For the purposes of this text, confirmation and validation can be considered to be similar processes.

The development of empiric knowledge depends on systematic methods of inquiry. Research can be used as a means of testing empiric knowledge and as a method of generating the concepts and relationships for the empiric knowledge structures being

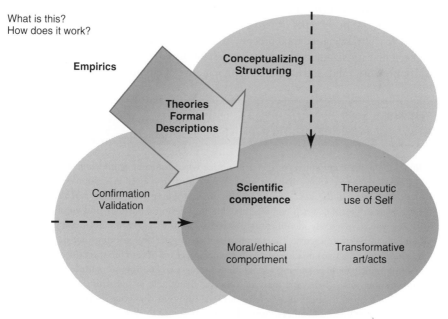

FIGURE 9-1: Empiric knowing and knowledge: confirmation and validation.

developed. Sound empiric knowledge development requires that the researcher make deliberate choices that link the underlying philosophies of science and nursing with research methods, theory, and practice.

Of all the processes of empiric knowledge development, research-related activities are more visible to the casual observer than the cognitively based theoretic processes. The concept of *research* is often associated with the image of a laboratory where experiments are conducted or some other activity occurs that involves making measurements and describing facts. In actuality, creating empiric knowledge is more related to abstract theoretic processes than to uncovering isolated facts that can be reported in great detail and with numbers. Factual knowledge is useful, but facts alone are not sufficient for the development of useful empiric knowledge. To develop empiric knowledge that is valuable for practice, facts and observations must be interpreted or made meaningful in relation to one another. It is theory that helps to place facts and isolated observations into meaningful interrelationships (Box 9-1).

We first distinguish between theory-linked and isolated research, then review the processes required to refine concepts and theoretic relationships using empiric research methods. We also describe the approaches that help ensure any given research project fulfills sound standards of theoretic adequacy. We use the term *theory* in a way that is consistent with our broad definition to include a wide range of empirically grounded knowledge structures.

THEORY-LINKED RESEARCH AND ISOLATED RESEARCH

Research, as with theorizing, can be conducted in a variety of ways and with many motivations. There are many types of research, and each research text presents a somewhat different way of viewing the total process. The traits that are common to each approach reflect certain basic standards that have been established to obtain results that are considered confirmable, valid, and accurately representative of empiric phenomena.

BOX 9-1	Exploring Connections between Abstract Ideas and Empiric Observations

Think about the common traits that you notice when someone is grieving. The "facts" include all the observations that you might notice, such as a facial expression with a furrowed brow, tears in the eyes, sobbing vocalizations, wringing of the hands, and a slumped and downcast posture. When naming these kinds of gestures, postures, and vocalizations as *grief,* you have already identified an abstract concept that provides an initial concept from which to create theory. The various theories of grief and grieving that have been developed over the years provide you with mental images of how to interpret the behaviors that you notice, perhaps causing you to identify stages of grieving, or cultural traits that give meaning to the behaviors that you observe. Being able to translate the things you observe in relation to larger and more meaningful ideas enriches your ability to reach out to grieving persons and families in ways that give substance to your practice.

Any of the accepted research methods described in textbooks can be used with a theo-retic link. The major trait that distinguishes theory-linked research from research that is not linked to theory (i.e., isolated research) is that theory-linked research is designed to develop, extend, examine, or validate a theory. This quality sets the stage for research studies to contribute to the larger knowledge of the discipline. By contrast, isolated research is not linked to the processes of theory development.

From a research point of view, both theory-linked research and isolated research can be of excellent quality. Both types of research can ultimately contribute to knowledge, although isolated research is much more limited with regard to the contribution that it can make to a discipline. Because theory-linked research is conceived and conducted to develop, extend, examine, or validate theory, the findings of research have signifi-cance at an abstract level of understanding. The research findings are not only useful in relation to the research problem or question, but also valuable for development of the theory or for speculation about other situations in which the theory might be tested or applied.

In isolated research, the research problem is not linked to theory in any deliber-ate way. Rather, the investigator formulates questions or hypotheses and uses accepted methods to refute or support the hypotheses or to answer the questions. When theory is used as a loose guide to spark ideas for research questions, we would consider the research to be isolated. Isolated research can be useful to solve a problem (e.g., to deter-mine the major sources of infection on a unit) or to provide initial evidence on which to build theory-linked research (e.g., to confirm the traits of a concept or phenomenon). The results of isolated research can provide new insights that prompt the researcher or someone reading a report of the research to speculate about the larger implications of the research, which in turn can lead to the development of a theory that has broader meaning for the discipline.

For research to be theory linked, the researcher must intend to develop, extend, examine, or validate theory, and deliberate linkages to the theory must be made during the process of research development. Questions or hypotheses may come from the prac-tical circumstances that surround the investigator's work, the imagination, an idea that occurred as the investigator read other research results, or any number of other sources. These same factors can also provide direction throughout the ongoing process of the development of theory-linked research.

All research is confined to a particular place and time in history. Because theories are constructions of the mind, they can transcend to a certain extent the limitations of time and space. The cultural and historical circumstances of the theorist influence the mental construction of the theory, but because it is an abstraction, the theory can be generalized beyond the limits of particular circumstances.

Theory-linked research has advantages that overcome the limitations of the specific place and time in which the research occurs. Theory-linked research hypotheses that are developed from abstract statements within a theory represent a translation of the theory's statements to the circumstances of the specific study. *Theory-generating* research studies culminate with a linkage to theory by organizing study data into a more abstract theo-retic structure. Theory-linked research findings can be generalized only within limits, just like those reported in isolated research. However, the study findings in theory-linked research can be retranslated into theoretic terms and implications that are discussed in relation to the theory.

CHALLENGES RELATED TO THEORY-LINKED RESEARCH

Although theory-linked research has definite advantages over isolated research with regard to its ability to contribute to the development of knowledge, certain hazards and challenges are unique to this type of research.

Inappropriate Use of Theories

It is possible to use a theory inappropriately in conducting research. For example, if a theory is designed to explain animal behavior, it may not be appropriate as a basis for explaining or understanding human behavior without sufficient conceptual examination. Theory and theoretic concepts that are used inappropriately lead to erroneous conclusions. For example, as pertains to client teaching, behavioral learning works well for some types of learning and poorly for others. Operant conditioning might be useful for learning rote information and skills or in other situations where behavioral tasks are important to master. If cognitive understanding of complex ideas and phenomena is the goal, the theory of operant conditioning would be inappropriate, resulting in failure to change behavior in a desirable way (Shuell, 2013).

In a U.S. National Institute of Justice report, Jackson and Hafemeister (2013) caution against the use of theories borrowed from other disciplines to guide research related to elder abuse. For example, *caregiver stress theory* has been a staple underpinning for explaining elder abuse. Originally developed in relation to parent-child abuse, use of the theory to explain elder abuse raises questions about the similarity of parent-child relationships to those of elderly parents and adult children. *Social exchange theory*, also often used to explain elder abuse, was originally intended to account for violence within ongoing adult relationships, such as a long-term partnership; when one partner experiences an imbalance in costs and benefits from the relationship, violence is used to restore balance. Assuming that the relationship between adult children and elderly parents is one of mutual exchange of costs and benefits is a questionable way to account for the occurrence of elder abuse. Jackson and Hafemeister suggest that theories of elder abuse need to be multidimensional, rather than monolithic as historically has been the case.

Theories as Barriers

Theories can obscure a researcher's ability to notice certain features of data or events. The mindset provided by the theory, whether appropriate or not, may preclude the recognition of other possibilities. When the focus is on expected outcomes, unless something startling or drastically different occurs, some elements may not be noticed. For example, you can view a child's behavior and, because of a certain theory, assume that what you observe is problem-solving ability. At the same time, you might fail to notice other details about the child's behavior that are not brought to your attention by the theory. These other behaviors might include less obvious and therefore easily overlooked actions, such as attention patterns, facial expressions, or eye motion. It is possible that qualities of these behaviors relate to problem-solving ability, but the mental set that you acquire from the theory focuses your attention on limited behaviors, and something potentially important to understanding the child's experience is overlooked. If you are conducting a grounded-theory study with the purpose of uncovering the parental processes of attributing blame when teenage children join gangs, your background knowledge of the socialization patterns of adolescents will influence how you interpret and understand the data obtained from interviewing the parents.

Paradoxically, although a theory may be useful and appropriate for understanding certain phenomena, it may limit your thinking about the range of possibilities for interpreting and understanding a situation or experience. Overcoming this difficulty requires that you constantly question what you read, think, and observe. Theory is not intended to represent phenomena and events exactly; it is intended to be an approximation and a tool that can be used to see possibilities. The purpose for using research to develop theory is to discover to what extent a theory can be regarded as sound and how it functions to reveal new possibilities.

Ethical Considerations

Theories as mental constructions may relate ideas that cannot or should not be tested out of respect for human and animal rights and dignity. For example, given the threat of nuclear disasters, you might imagine that it would be useful to predict events in a large population of people who experience significant exposure to radiation, and that this knowledge might help to prepare for such circumstances. However, it is not ethical to subject humans or animals to such an experience to confirm or validate theory. It also is not feasible to test imagined theoretic ideas that claim to predict the consequences of exposure to radiation. Ethical considerations may also be much subtler and need to be examined. For example, certain approaches to the study of cultures outside of the mainstream (e.g., hearing-impaired persons, ethnic minority groups, gays or lesbians) undermine those cultures and provide avenues for further discrimination. In addition, ethical considerations may curtail a study when interim findings suggest that its continuation is likely to harm participants.

Occasionally, historical circumstances provide evidence that is used to develop useful theory, but further development is limited by concern for human and animal welfare. Theories of mother-infant attachment and separation grew out of the experiences of wartime children who were separated from their mothers for extended periods. Researchers studied the effects of exposure to toxins among rescue personnel and canines after the collapse of the World Trade Center on September 11, 2001. The evidence that grows out of historical events can demonstrate the effects, but research that replicates similar circumstances is ethically indefensible.

REFINING CONCEPTS AND THEORETIC RELATIONSHIPS

A particular type of theory-linked research is research that is designed specifically to refine concepts and theoretic relationships. These types of investigations are crucial early during the stages of a theory's development, but they can be used at any point throughout the process. Refining concepts and theoretic relationships involves a focus on the correspondence of the ideas of the theory with perceptible sensory experience (Dubin, 1978; Glaser & Strauss, 1967; Newman, 1979; Reynolds, 1971/2006). Because empiric concepts and theories are abstractions of what can be observed or perceived during an experience, a translation is made from the theoretic to the empiric (i.e., deductive approach) and from the empiric to the theoretic (i.e., inductive approach).

To function as viable structural elements of theory, concepts must adequately represent experience. Both quantitative and qualitative descriptive approaches are typically used to obtain empiric evidence that the concepts, as created within the theoretic structure, have adequate empiric indicators. The evidence from the investigations may suggest the use of processes of creating conceptual meaning to better represent the experience. Investigations designed to develop and refine empiric indicators and operational definitions of concepts are crucial for adequate research to refine and validate theoretic relationships.

Theoretic relationships, which connect two or more concepts in a specific structure, are directly influenced by the nature of the empiric indicators for the concepts that are being related. The activities of refining concepts and theoretic relationships involve qualitative and quantitative approaches. Replication requires repeating the confirmation or validation activities in other contexts. Theoretic relationships cannot be proved, but it is possible to show empiric support for proposed relationships. If the evidence does not support theoretic relationships, the ideas of the theory cannot be sustained. Alternative theoretic explanations are then considered on the basis of the empiric evidence.

Refining concepts and theoretic relationships draws on one or more of the following subcomponents: (1) identifying empiric indicators for the concepts, (2) empirically grounding emerging relationships, and (3) validating relationships with the use of empiric methods.

Identifying Empiric Indicators

Empiric indicators and operational definitions are used to represent concepts as variables in empiric research, and these are empirically formed for concepts as an outcome of some inductive research approaches. Formally structured theory can propose empiric indicators, but until those indicators are put into operation in research, they remain speculative. Making use of the ideas in actual research makes it possible to refine the theory.

Consider the following abstract relationship statement:

> As the adult's eye contact increases, the infant's eye contact will increase.

Imagine that a research project is designed to obtain empiric evidence about the designation of eye contact as an empiric indicator of mothering. Details such as length of gaze and frequency of eye contact could be specified for the relatively abstract concept of *eye contact.* To use these indicators, the researcher would create a method for observing and timing the length of gaze and the frequency of eye contact.

Part of the process for identifying empiric indicators, especially when primarily deductive processes are used, is to state operational definitions. *Operational definitions* specify the standards or criteria to be used when making the observations. For example, an operational definition of the term *gaze* might be "a steady, direct, visual focusing on an object that lasts at least 3 seconds." This definition indicates what gaze is (the empiric indicator for visual contact), the characteristics that must be present to call a behavior a *gaze* (direct visual focusing on an object), and a standard time parameter that distinguishes a gaze from other related behaviors, such as a glance or a look.

It is difficult to identify empiric indicators for concepts that are more abstract than the concept of *eye contact.* Many concepts related to nursing, such as *anxiety, body image,* and *self-esteem,* are highly abstract and cannot be directly measured. Tests and tools have been constructed to provide an indirect estimate of traits such as these. The inability to measure them directly does not mean they are nonexistent or cannot be assessed. The empiric challenge is to refine ideas about and evidence for empiric indicators so that the strength of the relationships can be explored.

The difficulties of finding adequate empiric indicators for abstract concepts can be compared with trying to describe the taste of a tomato. After biting into a tomato, the person knows how a tomato tastes. After smelling a purulent wound, the nurse recognizes that smell as being associated with a wound that is infected and not healing well. The descriptions of these specific tastes and smells are inadequate for comparison with the actual taste or smell experiences.

Many of the concepts that are important for nursing are highly abstract, and even the actual experiences are not clearly perceived. Subsequently, the problem of finding adequate empiric indicators becomes complex and difficult. For example, *anxiety* is an abstract concept that can be theoretically defined. However, when we explore the experience of anxiety, we find that although people recognize what we mean by the term *anxiety,* the actual experiences of anxiety are elusive to describe, much like trying to describe the taste of a tomato. Nevertheless, if the concept is important for nursing, empiric knowledge development depends on diligent efforts to make visible, as accurately as possible, the link between the abstract concept and the contextualized human experience. These examples underscore the value of creating conceptual meaning for adequate theory in nursing.

One approach that can be used to derive empiric measures for abstract nursing concepts is to use multiple empiric indicators to form useful research definitions. For example, anxiety might be measured with a self-report tool. The tool can be constructed to include many sensations that are generally indicative of anxiety. An operational definition of the concept of *anxiety* then becomes "what is assessed with the use of the tool." Anxiety may also be assessed empirically by observing a person's behavior and appropriate physiologic indicators of neuroendocrine function. In this case, operational definitions would include specific ways to measure the behaviors observed and the specific range of laboratory test results associated with anxiety. All these empiric indicators are possible.

It is important to recognize that the empiric indicators identified for concepts must consider the theory that is to be validated. For example, if the concept of *caring* in the context of Madeleine Leininger's theory needs to be empirically assessed, it would be counterproductive to use a tool to assess caring that was developed for use with Jean Watson's theory. In addition, dictionary definitions are generally not a good source of empiric indicators for concepts. In other words, when concepts are operationalized, they must be defined and measured together with the meaning of the theory in which they are embedded; not just any approach to measurement will do.

When inductive research processes form the basis for refining empiric indicators, the indicators are directly or indirectly observed and then used to form concepts. Knowing the empiric indicators that are used to generate the concepts would assist with the deductive testing and the extension of the theory into other contexts.

Think About It

In your nursing practice, which behaviors do you associate with pain, with anxiety, with fear, and with stress? How do you know that the behaviors you associate with these phenomena are "true" indicators of what another person is actually experiencing?

Empirically Grounding Emerging Relationships

The process of empirically grounding emerging relationships involves connecting experiences with representations of those experiences. When an abstract theoretic relationship is taken as the starting point, the investigator designs a study in which the hypothetic relationship, when framed in terms of the empiric indicators for the concepts, can be studied. Several investigations may be required to confirm that the relationship proposed is accurate. When the investigations provide sufficient empiric evidence that conclusions can be drawn about the relationship, the investigator can return to the theoretic ideas and refine the theoretic statements to reflect what has been supported empirically. These conclusions are often presented as examples that accompany citations of the empiric investigations within the narrative explanations of the theory.

An investigator can begin by exploring a selected empiric situation as a starting point, with the goal of finding the concepts and relationships that accurately represent a situation that is not yet clearly understood but that is recognized as important to the discipline of nursing. The investigator selects a social context in which the phenomenon under consideration is likely to occur and observes the interactions and circumstances of that context. From the observations, the investigator derives relationship statements that are grounded in the available empiric evidence. A variety of inductive approaches can be used to ground emerging relationships (Denzin & Lincoln, 2011; Glaser & Strauss, 1967; Lincoln & Guba, 1985; Creswell, 2012).

Validating Relationships Using Empiric Methods

Validating theoretic relationships requires creating a design that tests the descriptive and explanatory powers of a designated relationship. Designs may be proposed after a theory is structured (i.e., deduction). When the purpose of the research design is to use inductive methods to generate theoretic relationships, the relationships are considered to be confirmed and ready for replication and additional confirmation in other settings.

A key to the *deductive* validation of theoretic relationships is to use a design that ensures that the proposed relationship is actually the one that occurs and thus accounts for the study findings. For example, if a study concludes that a mother's gaze prompts an infant's gaze in return, the researcher needs to consider ways to be sure that it is actually the mother's gaze that accounts for the infant's behavior. Typically, the researcher designs the study so that other factors that could influence the behavior of the infants in the study (e.g., sensory experiences such as noise, touch, or visual distractions that might affect the process of visual interaction) are accounted for or held constant.

The purpose of deductively validating any relationship statement is to provide empiric evidence that the relationships proposed in the theory are adequate within a specific situation. With each approach to design that is used, the research question or hypothesis is revised to suit the type of design that has been selected. Empiric evidence based on many different research design approaches provides a strong basis for judging the adequacy of the theory. If theoretic statements are deductively tested and are not supported by empiric evidence, one or more of the following four possibilities can account for the disparity between the theory and the empiric findings:

- *The meaning of the concepts is not adequately created.* The process of creating conceptual meaning can be used to determine whether the definitions and meanings of the concepts under study are clear and whether they are well differentiated from related concepts. If they are not, theoretic revisions can be made, which may result in new approaches to empiric study.
- *The relationship statement is not adequately structured.* The processes of theory structuring and contextualizing can be used to examine the logic or form of the statements. Given the benefit of the empiric evidence, new insights into the form and structure of the theory may emerge. The theorist can revise the theoretic relationship statements on the basis of these insights.
- *The empiric indicators for the concept are not adequate.* The empiric evidence might point to new possibilities for empiric indicators or suggest revisions of the existing indicators. This process is particularly important when the empiric indicators represent highly abstract concepts and are constructed out of speculative ideas about how the concepts can be observed empirically.
- *The definitions are inadequate or inconsistent.* Typically, conflicting research results are attributed to faulty definitions and the related measurement problems of empiric research. This is a possibility, but accurate assessment depends on adequately conceived concepts, sound theoretic statements, and adequate empiric indicators. If these are all in place, it is then reasonable to consider problems with measurement or with assessment of the concept.

When *inductive* methods are used to refine concepts and theoretic relationships, the relationships may be considered valid and confirmed if sound research procedures and processes are used to generate them. When relationships are deduced from inductively generated theory, they can be explored in similar settings or extended into new contexts. When this occurs, problems with faulty concepts, relational statements, empiric indicators, and operational definitions will become evident.

DESIGNING THEORETICALLY SOUND EMPIRIC RESEARCH

Investigations that are linked to theory can be either theory generating or theory validating. In the following sections, we explain these two approaches and provide guidelines that you can use as a frame of reference for designing investigations when planning a study or to assess the theoretic adequacy of a completed investigation.

Theory-Generating Research

Research that generates theory is designed to clarify and describe relationships without imposing preconceived notions of what the relationships mean. This approach is usually thought of as inductive. It is impossible to observe or interpret events or phenomena in the world without some preconceived idea of what they mean. Preexisting ideas are inherent in the experience of being socialized in a human culture, and the process of learning the theories of a discipline conveys meanings. A researcher who designs a study to generate theory observes with as open a mind as possible in an effort to see things in a new way (Box 9-2).

BOX 9-2	The Challenge of Preconceived Ideas

Suppose that a graduate nursing student named Carson is completing his master's thesis by addressing what motivates elders to purchase nutritional supplements. Carson has noticed recently that the advertising of nutritional supplements has been intentionally directed at older individuals. His knowledge of gerontologic nursing suggests that much of this advertising promotes supplements that have limited if any benefit. Carson has just completed a course in nursing theory and decides to use a theory-generating approach for his thesis research. He might begin by observing the shopping behavior of elderly persons in stores selling a variety of nutritional supplements, including those that are heavily advertised. Carson would probably have some belief, on the basis of theories of marketing and vulnerability, that elderly adults who feel vulnerable to the effects of aging demonstrate purchasing behaviors that are linked with television advertising. Carson's perceptions during the observation would not be really pure but would in fact be influenced by theoretic notions about marketing and the vulnerability of elders. However, if Carson intends to be open to previously unaccounted-for variables or features of shopping behavior that are potentially useful but that have not been described, his preconceived ideas must be recognized and set as far aside as possible.

One approach to theory-generating research that has been used in nursing is *grounded theory* (Charmaz, 2014; Glaser & Strauss, 1967; Strauss & Corbin, 2008). This form of field methodology requires the simultaneous processes of collecting, coding, and categorizing empiric observations and forming concepts and relationships on the basis of the data obtained. Grounded-theory methodologies also make use of deductive approaches to examine developing propositions of theory, although it is initially an inductive method.

Other forms of theory-generating research include *field observations,* as used in anthropology, and *participant observation,* as used in sociology. The investigator attempts to minimize any intrusion or effect on events observed and seeks to view and describe things occurring as they would if the observer were not present. The investigator attends to clues about how one event affects another and explains the things that are observed by developing theoretic relationship statements about those observations (Coffey & Atkinson, 1996; Eaves, 2001; Strauss & Corbin, 2008).

Because many phenomena cannot be observed directly, theory-generating research sometimes must make use of indirect ways of gathering data. Phenomenology is one example of this approach. As a research method, *phenomenology* is designed to describe or interpret the subjective, lived experiences of people and to comprehend the meanings that people give to these experiences (Benner, 1994). These experiences cannot be observed; they are directly accessible only to the person who has the experience. Indirect ways of observing include interviewing or questioning individuals about what they feel or remember or noting how they respond to certain situations. Feelings, thoughts, memories, dreams, and private human experiences can be known only through how people choose to relate them.

Different inductive methodologies produce different types of knowledge and different forms of descriptive statements or theories. Grounded-theory methods generate a structure of relationships and core variables that the researcher has observed. Phenomenology results in interpretive narratives that describe meaning as fully as possible. Phenomenology as a research method is not intended to generate formal theory, but the processes that are used are rigorous and systematic. We believe that the products of phenomenologic inquiry fall within our broad definition of theory. Regardless of how the products generated by phenomenologic inquiry methods are classified, the insights that they yield can contribute to conceptual clarity and theoretic thinking. Whatever the approach, inductive investigators whose purpose is to contribute empiric knowledge to the discipline address issues of soundness by systematically organizing and describing their research results.

Theory-Validating Research

After a theory is constructed by whatever means, it is possible to use research methods for validation. The methods are designed to ascertain how accurately the theory depicts empiric phenomena and their relationships. Theoretic statements can be translated into questions and hypotheses so long as the abstractions of the theory can be directly or indirectly represented with empiric indicators. A single study is usually based on one or two relational statements from among several that might possibly be extracted from a theory. No one study can test the entirety of a theory. Some theories contain relationship statements that can be tested and other relationship statements that cannot be tested by research because empiric indicators cannot be identified.

Although a theory may have been incompletely tested, it is regarded as relatively sound if several research studies conducted over time in different settings demonstrate a degree of confidence in the theory. If some statements are supported by research but others are unsupported or refuted by research, the research provides a basis for revising the theory or developing a new theory.

Theory-validating research is usually considered a deductive approach. The research starts with an abstract relational statement that is derived from a theory. From the theoretic statement, hypotheses or research questions are created for a specific research situation.

Research questions may also be used in theory-validating research. This type of research typically makes use of descriptive and correlational designs. The concepts in the research questions are empirically represented, and observations are made. The data are collated and described in such a way that the questions are addressed and the implications related to the development of the theory are stated.

Because hypotheses must contain a relationship between at least two variables, the research design is usually an experimental, quasi-experimental, or correlational approach (Polit & Beck, 2011). In theory-validating research, the investigator deliberately changes or controls conditions so that the study clearly focuses on the nature of the relationship between the variables selected for study. Several descriptive and relationship-validating studies are usually needed to validate and extend a theory, because only a limited number from among all possible relationships can be included in one study. A single study can contribute appreciably to the validation process if it is theoretically sound.

In the following sections, we examine the general research process and identify how both theory-generating research and theory-validating research can be designed and therefore evaluated to achieve the most value from the research effort.

DEVELOPING SOUND THEORETIC RESEARCH

The research process can be examined for theoretic soundness at each stage. The following descriptions of each stage can serve as a guide for developing or evaluating the theoretic soundness of a research study.

The Clinical Problem, Research Purpose, Research Problem, and Hypotheses

In *theory-linked* research, the clinical problem statements, research purposes, and hypotheses are designed to show the relationships between the chosen theory base and the particular study being conducted. In *theory-validating* research, each of these statements should be explicitly formulated, because each guides the process as it moves from the broad, general intent to the empiric specifics of the study. In descriptive and exploratory theory-validating research, hypotheses may not be stated or labeled as such, and research problems (questions) are developed. Although they are not necessarily stated in relationship form, the questions imply underlying relationships that are of significance to the developing theory.

In *theory-generating* research, only the clinical and research problems are required; the other statements may or may not be developed explicitly during the course of the research process. The statements are not necessarily explicitly stated in published reports of completed research, but in well-reported studies, the statements appropriate to each approach can be inferred from the text of the published article.

In *theory-validating* research, statements of purpose, problems, and hypotheses or questions are formulated before the data-gathering activity is conducted. In *theory-generating* research, the purpose and problem statements are formulated in advance; if relationships are stated, they are derived from the data. The clinical problem is a question that reflects the general experiential concern that generated or influenced the study and that suggests the study context. The clinical problem clearly reflects the experiential questions that are fundamental to developing empiric knowledge: "What is this?" and "How does it work?"

The research purpose indicates whether the study is theory generating or theory validating in nature and whether the study focuses on description, explanation, or prediction. If the study is *theory generating,* the purpose further states the empiric observations to be made. If the study is *theory validating,* the purpose states the theoretic frame of reference for the study.

For both *theory-generating* and *theory-validating* research, the research problem is less general than the statement of purpose and directs the more specific, circumstantial focus of the study. The research problem is phrased in the form of a question that implies how the purpose of the study is to be achieved. The problem reflects the variables or events to be studied and implies that empiric possibilities for abstract concepts to be developed are embodied in existing theoretic relationships.

In *theory-validating* research, hypotheses may or may not be stated. When stated, hypotheses indicate the circumstantial restrictions of the study, reflect the study design, and suggest the methods for data analysis. If the analysis of research data does not depend on statistics for drawing conclusions, hypotheses might not be stated; rather, research questions are used to guide data analysis.

In *theory-generating* research, hypotheses also may or may not be stated. Problem statements or research questions may be appropriate for guiding a study that is intended to generate theory, and hypotheses are formulated at the conclusion of the study, if at all. When formulated, hypotheses provide specific directions for future research.

Background of the Study and Literature Review

In all research, the literature review is used to survey research findings that are pertinent to the study being conducted. In theory-linked research, the literature review also includes a summary evaluation of the theoretic background for the study.

For *theory-generating* research, the background for the study includes a review of previous work that is pertinent to the area of concern. The author's thinking and experience are important to consider as background for the study. The literature review is comprehensive and continues throughout the data-gathering and analysis phases. As the ideas and concepts emerge from the data, the researcher uses the data to guide explorations of the existing literature. The empiric observations remain the primary source for analysis and interpretation. In some instances, however, the literature provides a basis for refining and delineating central concepts and the relationships among them.

In *theory-validating* research, previous studies based on the theory form a substantial portion of the literature review. The review also contains a critique of previous research that is based on alternative theories and on concepts or variables related to the study's central purpose. The review traces how the study has been conceived and summarizes the theoretic ideas being tested. It clarifies how and why specific relationships within the theory are being tested.

The Research Methodology

The following concerns with regard to research method must carefully be considered when theory-linked research is undertaken: the means of obtaining the data, the selection of the sample for study, the research design, the analysis of the data, and the conclusions.

The Means of Obtaining Data. How the data are collected or recorded must be consistent with the purpose of the research design. For *theory-generating* research, the study is usually descriptive in nature and requires observing either directly or indirectly and then recording empiric events that the investigator does not alter during the course of study. *Theory-validating* research also draws on these means of obtaining data. Because theory-validating research often relies on some type of experimental or correlational analysis, the tools and assessments that are used tend to be those that yield quantitative measures of the variables.

Direct observation requires that the observer be physically present. Data are recorded by some means, such as note taking, audio taping, or videotaping. Examples include watching and making notations about behavior during the process of mother-infant interactions, about interactions between nurses and patients within an intensive care unit, and about the behavior of a person who is experiencing a crisis (e.g., pain).

Indirect observation includes interviews; questionnaires and standardized tools that elicit feelings, thoughts, or memories; and self-reports of experiences that are not directly observed. Tools and assessments designed to elicit reports about selected phenomena must be carefully examined to ensure that they can provide the evidence needed to achieve the purposes of the study. In *theory-generating* research, tools that are developed with a particular theoretic bias introduce a perspective that may not be desirable. In *theory-validating* research, the means of obtaining data must be carefully considered in relation to the theoretic adequacy of the tools and the assessment approaches. For both types of research, the problems of reliability and validity of both direct and indirect observations are considered. Tools that are designed to yield a numeric score are assessed for reliability and validity with statistical methods. Interview approaches designed to produce narrative descriptions are examined carefully to ascertain how well the approach will function to elicit the types of responses needed. The research report should include a discussion of the level of development of the tools used, what theoretic perspective underlies any tools used, and available evidence related to the reliability and validity of tools.

Selection of the Sample. The selection of the sample is essentially what limits the research to a particular time and place. Selection is a part of the research that links the abstractions of the theory with empiric phenomena. The individuals who are chosen for the sample are purposely selected because they can contribute information and insight related to the phenomenon being studied.

In *theory-validating* research, sample selection requires the investigator to take the position that, if the theory is empirically accurate, it will be supported by what happens with the specific persons selected for study, or that, if the theory is not empirically accurate, the responses of the sample studied will refute the theory. Because most theory-validating research relies on the statistical analysis of quantitative data, sample selection is guided by the requirements of the statistical analysis. Both the population to whom the theoretic relationship applies and the sample being tested must be specified. Drawing conclusions about the strength of the theoretic relationship depends on the assumption that the statistical requirements for sampling from the identified population have been met.

Research Design. The design of the research outlines the procedure and contingencies that are used for answering the research questions or for testing the hypotheses. In *theory-generating* research, the design must be consistent with the generating orientation of the research. This often involves observation of a particular type of phenomenon of interest in a given group. Stern (1980) described the design of grounded theory as a matrix in which several research processes are in operation at once. The investigator examines the data that have been obtained and begins to code, categorize, conceptualize, and write impressions about the meaning of the data.

Sometimes research designs typically used in *theory-validating* research are needed for *theory-generating* research. This is the case when a sequence of ordinarily occurring events is an area of concern. For example, suppose something happens to create a sequence of events, such as the birth of a child or the death of a loved one. The research interest might be to describe the usual responses of individuals over a period of time, both before and after such an event, to generate theory regarding how people live through these situations. In these instances, comparative assessments over time are needed. The investigator does not, as in classic experimental designs, impose the changes as a part of the design, but rather waits for the changes to occur. The investigator then describes the nature of the outcomes that occur before and after the event to develop the theory.

Theory-generating research may also require comparison groups typical of experimental designs to determine whether a phenomenon occurs only under certain circumstances.

For example, suppose that an investigator wanted to determine whether body image formation is appreciably affected by chronic illness. The phenomenon could be studied by comparing body image formation in a group of people who have a chronic illness with body image formation in a group of people who do not have chronic illness. The comparison would determine whether aspects of the phenomenon of body image formation are unique to people with chronic illness. This information would contribute to the development of a theory related to body image formation.

In some forms of *theory-validating* research, the researcher deliberately alters circumstances in some way to test the relationships that are expressed in the hypotheses. The design usually includes some interventions or investigator-created circumstances that are consistent with the theoretic basis for the study.

Analysis of the Data and Conclusions. The analysis of data in theory-linked research must be consistent with the purposes of the research and the research design. For *theory-generating* research, the analysis of data involves narrative, descriptive, and other relatively qualitative types of analysis. Depending on the type of observation used, a quantitative, numeric, or statistical analysis of the data can also be presented. However, it is accompanied by a theoretic analysis that includes the full range of observations and the ways in which the observations occurred.

With a grounded-theory approach, the analysis of the data involves coding and categorizing the observations. During participant observation, the analysis may report sample observations that typify the characteristic events or the sequence of events that were observed. Whatever the form of data presentation, the investigator proposes concepts that have been generated from the data and, if possible, provides a description of the theoretic propositions that emerge from the data. The extent to which concepts and theoretic propositions are formulated depends on how well the evidence supports making conceptual and theoretic formulations and on the extent to which previous studies support such conceptual and theoretic development.

In *theory-validating* research, the analysis of the data should present sufficient quantitative and qualitative evidence to support or reject the hypotheses or to address the research questions. The conclusions of the study should include an interpretive analysis of the findings in relation to the theory being tested. The analysis of data focuses on the specific study findings, whereas the conclusions focus on the theoretic significance of the study.

Generalizability and Usefulness of the Study

In theory-linked research, one of the important considerations for a single study is how it contributes to theory development. In most instances, a single study raises more questions than it answers, and the questions raised must be presented to provide a basis for future study. *Theory-generating* research should result in relationship statements that can be studied and used to further develop the theory. *Theory-validating* research may result in evidence that suggests a revision or an extension of the theory being tested, or it may suggest an entirely new avenue for the development of a theory.

Theory-generating research can be useful for practice because of its grounding in the experience for which the theory is designed. Theory-generating research also often provides a basis for further theory-related work that is based on new insights and new questions. *Theory-validating* research can also have immediate practice application. If the research design is valid and if the findings are generalizable and consistent with related research findings, the investigator can conclude that certain approaches in the realm of practice may be useful. However, immediate use in practice cannot always be expected. The primary value of theory-validating research is to stimulate further study and theory development that will add to the empiric knowledge on which practice can be based.

Think About It

1. Identify a study that you consider to be isolated from theory. How is its value limited because a deliberate linkage to theory is absent?
2. Locate a research study in which hypotheses were not confirmed or in which expected findings were not supported. Do you believe that conceptual definitions and empiric indicators (i.e., operational definitions) for concepts contributed to the errors in measurement that accounted for the findings? Why or why not?
3. Choose a substantive concept of interest to nursing. Create an operational definition for the concept. Does the definition leave out any ideas of importance? Is it possible to create an operational definition for the concept that fully contains the concept?

REFLECTION AND DISCUSSION – SUPPLEMENT ⊖

References

Benner, P. A. (1994). *Interpretive phenomenology: Embodiment, caring and ethics in health and illness*. Thousand Oaks, CA: Sage.

Coffey, A., & Atkinson, P. (1996). *Making sense of qualitative data*. Thousand Oaks, CA: Sage.

Charmaz, K. (2014). *Constructing grounded theory*. Thousand Oaks, CA: Sage.

Creswell, J. W. (2012). *Qualitative inquiry and research design by John W Creswell*. Thousand Oaks, CA: Sage.

Denzin, N. K., & Lincoln, Y. S. (2011). *The Sage handbook of qualitative research*. Thousand Oaks, CA: Sage.

Dubin, R. (1978). *Theory building* (Rev. ed.). New York, NY: Free Press.

Eaves, Y. D. (2001). A synthesis technique for grounded theory data analysis. *Journal of Advanced Nursing, 35*, 654–663.

Glaser, B., & Strauss, A. (1967). *The discovery of grounded theory*. Chicago, IL: Aldine.

Gunter, L. M. (1964). Research techniques applied to nursing. *Nursing Research, 13*, 230–232.

Jackson, S., & Hafemeister, T. L. (2013). Understanding elder abuse: New directions for developing theories of elder abuse occurring in domestic settings. *National Institute of Justice*. https://ncjrs.gov/pdffiles1/nij/241731.pdf.

Lincoln, Y. S., & Guba, E. G. (1985). *Naturalistic inquiry*. Newbury Park, CA: Sage.

Newman, M. A. (1979). *Theory development in nursing*. Philadelphia, PA: Davis.

Polit, D. F., & Beck, C. T. (2011). *Essentials of nursing research: Appraising evidence for nursing practice* (9th ed.). Philadelphia, PA: Lippincott, Williams & Wilkins.

Reynolds, P. D. (2006). *A primer in theory construction.* Needham, MA. (Original work published in 1971). Allyn & Bacon.

Shuell, T. (2013). Conceptions of learning: Evolving theories of learning. Retrieved January 15, 2014, from http://www.education.com/reference/article/theories-of-learning/.

Stern, P. N. (1980). Grounded theory methodology: Its uses and processes. *Image—The Journal of Nursing Scholarship, 12*(1), 20–23.

Strauss, A., & Corbin, J. (2008). *Basics of qualitative research* (3rd ed.). Thousand Oaks, CA: Sage.

Thorne, S. E., & Sawatzky, R. (2014). Particularizing the general: sustaining theoretical integrity in the context of an evidence-based practice agenda. *ANS Advances in Nursing Science, 37*(1), 1–10.

Confirmation and Validation of Empiric Knowledge in Practice

⊖ http://evolve.elsevier.com/Chinn/knowledge/

> *Practice is goal directed. Clinical testing of theory is therefore essential. Choose your theory—it does not hold in all circumstances. The professional must not be just a simple user of theory, but a developer, a tester and expander of theory. Not for the purpose of scholarship, but for intelligent practice.*
>
> **Rosemary Ellis (1969, p. 1435)**

In this quote, Ellis reaffirms that the reason for testing, confirming, and validating theory in practice is that practitioners hold visions and goals for the individuals they care for as well as for the profession in general. Although this statement almost seems trite, how often are theories deliberately examined in relation to practice? There are many things that can interfere with the deliberate confirmation and validation of theory in practice, but current trends in practice and education have the potential to strengthen significantly the confirmation and validation of theory in practice. These trends include the focuses on evidence-based practice and translational research as well as growing emphasis on the development of research approaches that specifically address the challenges of practice and the increasing number of nurses obtaining doctorate of nursing practice degrees.

The current focus on evidence as a basis for practice is important, but we raise a caution that it is not enough to be a user of evidence or of theory as Ellis states. Rather, practitioners, especially those with advanced degrees, are expected to be developers, testers, and expanders of theory. This can occur as empiric evidence is used, evaluated, and integrated into theoretic structures that have potential for use in relation to visions and goals across the settings in which nurses practice. This chapter addresses the deliberative confirmation and validation of empiric knowledge in practice settings so that the goals of nursing can continue to be approached and met.

To underscore Ellis's contribution, the development of empiric knowledge (e.g., theories, formal descriptions for a practice discipline) requires deliberative confirmation and validation in the practice setting to assess the value of theoretic knowledge for moving toward significant nursing goals. The use of the word *deliberative* means that confirmation and validation processes must be reasoned, thoughtful, and carefully designed.

The practice-based deliberative confirmation and validation of empiric knowledge contributes to the development of scientific competence among nurses, which in turn enhances the quality of nursing care. It involves assessing the extent to which empiric knowledge is useful for guiding practice. Practice-based approaches to the deliberative confirmation and validation of empiric knowledge further contribute to empiric knowledge development as outcomes are shared within the discipline. Research methods are required, and practice-based research findings contribute valuable information to the development of empiric knowledge and theory.

The confirmation and validation of empiric knowledge in practice require the use of clinical settings to substantiate, modify, and propose evidence to guide the development of practice-relevant research and theory; to refine conceptual meaning; and to assess and evaluate the soundness of theoretic relationships.

By *practice,* we mean the experiences that a nurse encounters during the process of caring for people. Some experiences are those of the client, whereas others are those of the nurse; some are interactive, and some are environmental. These experiences occur in many settings, but when occurring in the context of the provision of nursing care, these are considered part of nursing practice.

This chapter addresses specific ways in which practicing nurses contribute to empiric knowledge development processes and empiric knowledge development processes contribute to practice. We suggest ways that evidence can inform practice and how confirmation and validation of empiric knowledge (including theory) in practice provides direction for the further development of theoretically grounded practice approaches. We discuss important dimensions of refining conceptual meaning that can be accomplished only in the context of practice. We propose guidelines for confirming and validating theoretic relationships in practice, as well as methodologic guidelines for confirming and validating theoretic relationships and outcomes in practice.

THEORY-INFORMED PRACTICE AND EVIDENCE-INFORMED PRACTICE

The confirmation and validation of empiric knowledge in practice settings are important processes that can substantiate or refute current evidence and provide direction for the modification of evidence on which practice can be based. We maintain in Chapter 9 that the linking of theory with research is important. We believe that best practices in nursing are informed by evidence that is not only grounded in sound, research-linked theory, but also takes into account a philosophic perspective consistent with a wholistic view of nursing knowledge. A strong, viable link among theory, research, and practice is vital to quality nursing care as well as to the ongoing development of the knowledge of the discipline.

The current professional trend to embrace evidence-based practice as a standard for professional nursing has the potential to influence significantly how empiric knowledge and theory are used and developed. However, a view of "evidence" that is narrowly defined as the "gold standard" of clinical trials leaves a substantial gap in the foundation that is needed for nursing (Porter, 2010; Thorne & Sawatzky, 2014). Some models of evidence acknowledge the value of such factors as expert opinion, peer-reviewed standards, and evidence-based theories, although a bias for traditional research seems to prevail (Armola et al., 2009; Fineout-Overholt, Mazurek-Melnyk, & Schultz, 2005; Melnyk & Fineout-Overholt, 2010).

The tension that exists in nursing regarding empiric evidence relates to the essential premise of empiric knowledge as that which is generalizable, while nurses are compelled to attend to the particular and unique aspects of a situation. Thorne and Sawatzky (2014) propose that "evidence" should be understood as scientific empiric knowledge that holds value for practice. As they explain, however, nurses must attend to, but not privilege, empiric forms of knowledge. Rather, nurses need to rely on critical reflection that yields best judgments to guide practice in a particular situation that is informed by all sources of knowledge. Best practices in nursing require that nurses remain attuned to knowledge that comes from all sources, responding appropriately to a specific situation.

Another perspective on evidence is reflected in proposals for practice-based evidence rather than evidence-based practice. *Practice-based evidence* is an approach that acknowledges the importance of the environment of practice for the determination of practice protocols. Practice-based evidence values knowledge generated from practice over knowledge that conforms to hierarchies of evidence and is created apart from the context of practice. Although some recommendations for generating empiric evidence are reasonable in terms of practice, many are not. For example, evidence may support providing multiple individualized sessions to teach families how best to communicate with a family member who has had a stroke. Such recommendations make sense but likely are not practical in a busy health care setting. Thus, practice-based evidence is not decontextualized, universal knowledge; in fact, it is quite the opposite and is focused on remaining in tune with the demands of the situation (Fox, 2003; Horn & Gassaway, 2007; Porter, 2010; Simons, Kushner, Jones, & James, 2003). Leeman and Sandelowski (2012) suggest an approach for qualitative inquiry that helps to ensure that practice-based evidence is generated through qualitative methods and can be implemented within the context of care.

A comprehensive range of situational factors provides a model to guide evidence-informed practice. As proposed by DiCenso, Guyatt, and Ciliska (2005, pp. 4-5), nursing practice should integrate best research evidence, health care resources, patient preferences and actions, clinical settings and circumstances, and the clinician's judgment with regard to clinical decision making. The model of practice proposed by Melnyk and Fineout-Overholt (2010) also acknowledges the need to incorporate clinical expertise, patient preferences and values, research evidence, and theories that are based on empiric research. In this model, nursing care is provided within the context of caring and guides clinical decision making to provide quality patient outcomes. These conceptualizations of practice include much more than the use of research in practice and integrate knowledge that arises from aesthetic, personal, ethical, and emancipatory patterns of knowing.

Nursing's focus on practice that requires the use of the best research evidence has the potential to promote the linking of theory, research, and practice. Furthermore, this emphasis will yield empiric theory that is increasingly more suitable for practice. Our use of the term *evidence-informed practice* reflects our belief that empiric evidence is an important dimension that informs practice, along with other sources of knowledge derived from other patterns of knowing. Evidence-informed practice requires meaningful connections among theory, research, and practice. For researchers, a significant challenge related to evidence-informed practice is the development of knowledge based on questions that are clinically important and will generate evidence that is useful for practice.

As clinicians strive to locate the best research evidence appropriate for informing nursing care, then attempt to use that knowledge given the limitations of the practice environment, the extent to which research evidence is available and usable will become more obvious. The difficulties and benefits of various methodologic approaches with regard to generating empiric research evidence will be revealed. As clinicians discover well-conceived research evidence that requires, for example, the use of assessment tools that are impractical clinically, researchers will begin to understand the importance of considering how research is conducted. The importance of structuring clinically important concepts into meaningful theoretic relationships and then assessing those relationships in ways that allow clinicians to make use of findings in practice will become clearer.

Evidence-informed practice also has the potential to illuminate areas in which even well-conceived and well-developed evidence cannot be easily used because of a lack of resources, patient or client considerations, and other contextual factors. Research evidence may be appropriate for practice, and concepts in relationship may have been operationalized and assessed in a way that makes them well suited for use in practice. However, features of context (e.g., nurse/patient ratios, insurance reimbursement patterns, institutional security policies) may make it difficult to use that best evidence in practice. These situations illustrate the need for emancipatory knowledge to create a care context that will allow and encourage the use of best evidence, as well as the need for researchers to consider such features of context during the research process.

The emergence of the doctorate of nursing practice (DNP) as the basic educational credential for advanced nursing practice is well under way. This trend has significant potential to strengthen the linkages among theory, research, and practice in a way that supports evidence-informed practice. The DNP was conceptualized as a path to prepare nurses to contribute to the development of nursing knowledge by implementing the science developed by nurse researchers and to develop and integrate nursing practices on the basis of theory (American Association of Colleges of Nursing, 2006). When these practitioners begin to implement research findings and theory-based nursing practices in the face of expectations for evidence-informed practice, the nature of the evidence that is needed and subsequent implications for research and empiric knowledge development should become increasingly evident. Although the effect of the DNP on nursing practice remains to be seen, these practitioners have the potential to have a marked effect on how research, theory, and practice are linked to facilitate evidence-based practice.

In summary, an emphasis on evidence in practice, as current literature suggests, is much broader than just the application of research in practice. Evidence-informed practice can strengthen the linkages between theory and practice. It also requires communication among nurses in a variety of roles. Specifically, embracing evidence-informed practice that arises from strong links among theory, research, and practice has potential to do the following:

- Increase collaboration between researchers and practitioners.
- Improve research utilization skills of practitioners.
- Make visible challenges inherent in integrating context of care, patient/client factors and research evidence.

- Close the theory-research-practice "gap" by facilitating a focus on knowledge that is usable within the context of care.
- Increase the dependence of researchers on knowledge provided by clinicians.
- Create inquiry methods appropriate for use in practice.
- Illuminate contextual factors that affect best care provision.
- Promote research in undeveloped areas in nursing such as health care disparities and social inequities.
- Increase collaboration between the academic and professional sides of nursing in health science centers.
- Promote the development of centers of research and practice excellence that model best practices.
- Promote the development of empirically validated and practice-validated theory.
- Emphasize the importance of ethical, aesthetic, personal, and emancipatory knowing for evidence-based practice.

When evidence is developed with the use of research processes that are sensitive to the context and goals of practice, the transformation of practice is possible. The processes described next for confirming and validating empiric theory and knowledge are significant approaches to the development of evidence for best nursing practices.

Think About It

For a nursing situation you have recently encountered, consider the various sources of knowledge required to provide the best nursing care possible. What empiric evidence did you draw on? Was empiric evidence alone sufficient? Or did you also draw on ethical reasoning, your personal knowing of the uniqueness of the situation, or your understanding of the meaning of the situation for those involved in the situation and those receiving your care? In reflecting on this situation, would you do things differently based on considering all sources of knowledge that could be important in this instance?

REFINING CONCEPTUAL MEANING

Nursing concepts come from the experience of practicing nursing. Practicing nurses who reflect on the nature of their experiences and who systematically communicate their reflections make significant contributions to confirming and validating empiric knowledge. Researchers who are primarily involved in knowledge development benefit from the ideas of nurses who practice clinically. Everyone does not participate equally in all the processes required for the development of empiric knowledge. Some researchers do engage in practice, and some practicing nurses do conduct research. Many nurses who do engage in both practice and research find the experiences rewarding and beneficial. Regardless, each person participates in the collective endeavor to develop nursing knowledge.

Empiric concepts are formed from nursing practice by observing, naming, and making sense of what happens. The processes described in Chapter 7 for creating conceptual meaning can be used for systematically documenting reflections on your experiences, from which you can derive a tentative conclusion about the experience that you might want to study. If you are practicing in a clinical setting, your thinking will be grounded in nursing practice, and you have a rich resource from which to explore conceptual meanings. After you have tentatively described your phenomenon of interest, you can turn to activities for the refinement of conceptual meaning. Four practice-dependent activities are required to refine conceptual meaning: identifying empiric indicators, differentiating similar concepts, identifying new concepts, and identifying conceptual and diagnostic criteria.

Identifying Empiric Indicators

Practice provides essential evidence that is used to select empiric indicators for abstract concepts. The experiences of practice can challenge existing theoretic conceptualizations and can reveal hunches that have not yet been linked to a particular concept or theory. The basic question is, "What have I experienced that can be linked to the abstract concept *x*?"

Anxiety is a good example of such an experience. Suppose that a wide range of behaviors observed in practice are described in a theory as manifestations of the concept of *anxiety.* These behaviors might include the wringing of the hands, being silent and refusing to talk, talking excessively, laughing, crying, sweating, eating compulsively, not eating, or lacking an appetite. Tools have been constructed that assess the concept of *anxiety* with the use of these empiric indicators. In your practice, you might observe that these ideas do not always fit and in fact may sometimes contradict one another. When you work with individuals who are anxious, you notice that they tend to behave in ways that are not consistent with the theoretic concept. Some behaviors are almost never observed, whereas others that are commonly experienced are not taken into account by the theory. Because *anxiety* as an abstract idea does convey something that you know exists, it might be helpful if you could better identify anxiety, understand how it works, and determine how people experience anxiety differently. As you draw on your experience, new ideas begin to emerge from the behaviors that you have noticed.

Differentiating Similar Concepts

Concepts that are similar yet different might share certain empiric indicators, and differentiating them may be difficult. If knowing the difference between concepts is important in practice, then practice can provide the empiric information and conceptual insights required to distinguish them. This purpose becomes critical when you realize that errors can be made when assigning meaning to a person's experience. For example, you might have been taught that certain behaviors are manifestations of anxiety on the basis of a popular theory of anxiety. You have integrated research evidence, theory, and your experience to make expert clinical judgments about how to help anxious people reduce their anxiety and improve their function, but your approach does not seem to be as effective as you think it should be. One problem might be that the behaviors are not indicative of anxiety but rather associated with fear. Your challenge is to begin to conceptualize anxiety more clearly, to understand what else might be happening, and to begin to find ways to differentiate between the experiences of anxiety and fear. As you question and challenge the conceptualization and the conclusions that you draw from

BOX 10-1	*How New Concepts Can Arise from Practice: A Clinical Example*

Suppose you begin to notice that something about how people learn during the postoperative period does not seem to be described in any of the literature you have read. Most learning theories have been developed and tested in classroom or laboratory settings where learners are healthy students. In nursing situations, however, the learner is often experiencing a health condition or an illness. The patterns of behavior that are the focus of learning in a nursing context may not have been addressed adequately during the development of concepts and theories of learning in the classroom. As you reflect on your experience, you see meanings that are different from the meanings of learning in existing learning theories. As you discuss your ideas with other nurses, you find that they have made similar observations. From this awareness, you can build a new conceptualization that, once named, can be incorporated into theory and used in practice.

it, you will form a basis for restructuring the concepts and form new or revised concepts that better represent nursing experience.

Identifying New Concepts

Creating conceptual meaning is a process that can lead to the identification of new concepts. Model, borderline, related, and contrary cases that come from practice reflect the richness and complexity of practice. As you reflect deliberatively on these situations, your insights can lead to new ideas that contribute to the formation of new concepts. See the example in Box 10-1.

Identifying Conceptual and Diagnostic Criteria

Although the criteria for nursing diagnoses are not the same as the criteria for a concept in theory development, nursing diagnostic criteria can be partially derived from criteria for a concept, and vice versa. Nursing diagnostic criteria take into account generally accepted standards for practice as well as the knowledge and application of many areas of theory pertinent to the diagnosis. For example, consider the nursing diagnosis "Parenting, impaired," as defined by inappropriate or non-nurturing parenting behaviors and a lack of parental attachment behavior (Carpenito-Moyet, 2012).

In practice, the purpose is to accurately identify this problem to provide effective nursing care. The diagnosis of "Parenting, impaired" implies knowledge of how certain factors affect non-nurturing parental behavior and parent-infant attachment. The observation of non-nurturing parental behaviors and of a lack of parent-infant attachment implies knowledge of human attachment theory and also suggests a focus for nursing actions. When the criteria for nursing diagnoses are derived in part from a concept that is not yet well developed, the process of creating conceptual meaning can be used to form tentative diagnostic criteria that can be tested for empiric accuracy or validity.

The criteria for the nursing diagnosis of "Parenting, impaired" could include conceptual criteria for parenting. The diagnostic criteria also must address value qualifiers, such as the terms *impaired* and *non-nurturing,* which convey the value that the practitioner assigns to a situation during the process of making clinical decisions. When the parent under consideration is the mother, the diagnostic criteria for "Parenting, impaired" may include the following:

- Visual contact between the mother and the infant is minimal or absent.
- Physical touching of the infant by the mother is limited to necessary touch.
- There is minimal or no vocalization directed by the mother to the infant.
- The mother's verbal expressions focus on herself (e.g., concerns about her own body image or her relationships with peers) rather than on the infant.
- The care of the infant is easily or passively given to another caretaker.

The diagnostic criteria just listed reflect but do not include all the conceptual criteria for mothering that were used as an example in Chapter 7, which were as follows:

- Visual contact must be observed to be directed from the mothering person to the person who receives mothering.
- The mothering person must physically touch the person who receives mothering.
- Some positive feeling must be experienced by the mothering person and by the person who receives mothering.
- There must be a reciprocal interaction between the mothering person and the person who receives mothering.
- Vocalization by the mothering person must occur.

Notice that the diagnostic criteria specify an altered interaction, whereas the conceptual criteria point to observations that signify "mothering." The diagnostic criteria focus on those aspects that are relatively accessible for being empirically observed and assessed in practice. The conceptual idea of "some positive feeling" could potentially be operationalized and measured or otherwise assessed. However, the many challenges of attempting to do so may not warrant the pursuit of this line of development, particularly when more readily accessible indicators (e.g., visual contact, touch) are suggested and may be adequate for most purposes.

The diagnostic criteria may be adequate for creating standard approaches to practice, as well as for use during the formal testing of the theoretic concept. Criteria for a nursing diagnosis may be adequate for some research projects, as well as useful for determining how research should proceed. If the purpose of creating conceptual meaning is to form criteria that are useful for nursing diagnosis, then traits that are present in practice need to be emphasized.

VALIDATING THEORETIC RELATIONSHIPS AND OUTCOMES IN PRACTICE

The essence of the theory-practice relationship is to deliberatively validate theory. Theory that addresses the goals of practice provides a way of systematically developing substantial empiric knowledge within the discipline. Theory is not a quick-and-easy answer to a problem but rather provides knowledge and understanding ultimately to enhance the practice of nursing.

Deliberatively validating theory involves employing research methods to demonstrate how a theory or another form of empiric knowledge affects nursing practice. It involves processes that place a selected theory or a formalized description within the context of practice to ensure that it serves the goals of the profession. Confirmation and validation provide evidence of the theory's usefulness for developing nurses' scientific competence and for ensuring quality care.

A first step is to ascertain whether the theory can be used in practice. Some theories that hold promise may not be sufficiently developed to justify their use in practice, whereas others might be poorly suited to a particular practice area. The guidelines suggested in the following section can be used to make this decision. After you decide to use a theory in practice, you can then design research methods to demonstrate how well the theory contributes to your practice goals through the confirmation and validation of theory.

How to Determine Whether a Theory Should Be Confirmed and Validated in Practice

Theory should serve to improve nursing practice. This goal is usually achieved by the use of theory or portions of theory to guide practice and by taking the necessary steps to evaluate the effectiveness of the theory-guided practices. Because theory can be used prematurely or inappropriately, it is important to consider how sound judgments are made regarding the confirmation and validation of theory in practice. The following questions point to the dimensions that you need to consider when making a decision to confirm and validate a theory in practice.

Are the Theory Goals and the Practice Goals Congruent? To answer this question, examine the goals of the theory and compare them with the outcomes or goals that you see as being valuable for nursing practice. The existing standards of practice can be used as one basis for clarifying the values on which your practice is based and the overall goals that your practice should be reflecting.

Another basis for the identification of practice goals is your own view of nursing as well as the view of your nurse colleagues. If a theoretic goal could lead to a situation that is not congruent with your idea of optimal health, you may not want to use the theory. This judgment may not be easy because of conflicting or difficult philosophic assumptions about nursing, health, the individual, the environment, and society. For example, confirmation and validation of a theory may be undertaken to determine whether the theoretic goal is consistent with the goal of optimal health. If the theoretic goal is *independence* and you are uncertain whether this concept is consistent with your idea of optimal health for the population you work with, you could design a trial that uses the theory in practice, observe the outcomes, and then evaluate the congruence of the outcomes in the light of your view of optimal health.

Is the Intended Context of the Theory Congruent with the Practice Situation? This question addresses how well suited the theory is for your situation given the general ideas about context that are stated or implied by the theory. For example, a theory of pain alleviation may explain the processes involved in alleviating pain in any instance in which it occurs. As you become familiar with the theory, you realize that it was developed with reference to mature adults, and you work with children. You and your colleagues would need to explore how well the ideas of the theory might transfer to your own situation before you make a decision to use the theory.

Is There or Might There Be Similarity Between the Theory Variables and the Practice Variables? This question compares the important theoretic variables, which are expressed as concepts in the theory, with the variables that are recognized to be directly influencing the practice situation. In some instances, important practice variables may not be included in the theoretic relationship statements. For example, a learning theory may not consider the health status of the learner, and the learner is assumed to be a healthy individual. If practice variables are not accounted for in the theory, or if substantial differences exist between the theoretic variables and the practice variables, the theory should be used with caution, if at all. If the theory appears to have value and satisfies the considerations of most people who will be involved in the confirmation and validation process, it might be used with systematic observation of the effect on outcomes, with consideration of the differing variables occurring in practice. Given your observations, you may have a basis to propose a revision of the theory to include important practice variables.

Are the Explanations of the Theory Sufficient to Be Used as a Basis for Nursing Action? Responses to this question must be based on expert judgment about the particular nursing actions that are implied within the theory. As an expert nurse, you may find it difficult to describe the basis on which you would judge a theory to be sufficient or not sufficient. One specific approach to consider when forming your ideas is to examine the correspondence between theoretic and practice variables. If variables in the nursing situation are similar to those suggested in the theory, you can then consider the nature of the relationships between the concepts of the theory. Examine the extent to which the explanation makes sense in the light of your practice. You may feel guarded about using the theory in practice, but you can see that the perspective of the theory is reasonable. In this case, the theory is probably sufficient as a basis for nursing action, but your tentativeness about it leads you to be cautious as you proceed to use it and to plan careful documentation of the relationships that you observe in practice.

An example of a theoretic explanation that is sufficient for application in practice is the theory of parent-child interaction, which has undergone extensive development and refinement through the work of Dr. Kathryn Barnard (Barnard, 1981, 1996; Barnard, Eyres, Lobo, & Snyder, 1983). The Barnard theory has been refined through a program of theory development and research that has spanned several years and that still is active.

In the Barnard model, the following three-way conceptual relationship is central to the theory. In Barnard's theory, (1) the child, (2) the caregiver or parent, and (3) specific environmental factors interact. The interaction of these three elements determines how a parent or caregiver and a child will relate interpersonally. For example, features of the child (fussy? docile?), features of the caregiver or parent (oversolicitous? nonattentive?), and features of the environment (child care classes available? other individuals available for care relief?) create interpersonal interaction patterns. A fussy child who is being cared for by an oversolicitous parent in an environment in which alternative sources of care support are not available will create a certain type of parent-child interaction. Alternatively, other combinations of factors within these three broad concepts will create different qualities of parent-child interactions. The practice value of Barnard's model comes from research describing which factors and combinations of factors interfere with normal infant development.

Normal infant development is a goal in which nurses have much interest. The theoretic relationships justify the importance of assessing caregiver/parent-child interactions and providing early intervention when interactions are problematic. Checklist scales have been developed that a nurse can use to observe and assess parent-child interaction during activities of feeding or when caregivers or parents teach the child a developmentally appropriate skill. The Barnard theory and accompanying assessment tools have been used extensively to benefit families and children. This theory can be used widely because research was employed to identify, confirm, and validate the factors that were significant in creating problematic parent/caregiver-child interactions. Furthermore, factors of significance were represented in a way that could be easily assessed in clinical practice.

Research evidence that is generated with an insensitivity to whether variables and assessments are practical for nurses to use runs the risk of creating theories and models that require further development before they can be used in practice.

Is There Research Evidence to Support the Theory? One influential source of information for deciding whether a theory can be used in practice is research evidence, as noted in the example of Barnard's work. Sometimes a theorist, when presenting the theory, provides research evidence to support the initial theoretic formulation. If the evidence is convincing and attracts sufficient attention in the discipline, the professional literature will report research that either confirms or validates the initial theoretic relationships or that does not support the theory. Research that reports findings in theory confirmation and validation studies often suggests limits on the range of contexts in which the theory can be used or flaws in the initial theoretic construction that are based on the research evidence generated.

Because theories are not unequivocally supported by research evidence, practitioners have the responsibility to determine whether the evidence is sufficient to justify the use of the theory in practice. This judgment is best made on the basis of several research studies. If there is little or no research evidence to justify the use of the theory in practice, but most of the other concerns have been satisfied, you can be reasonably comfortable about using the theory. In this case, give particular attention to observing and recording relevant information about corresponding theoretic and situational variables and the limits and outcomes of the theory's use in practice.

How Will the Use of This Theory Influence the Practical Function of the Nursing Unit? Before using a theory in practice, you need to consider the ways in which this

BOX 10-2	Questions to Consider Before Confirmation and Validation of Theory in Practice

Do nursing personnel need to be oriented to the theory and its application?

Does the approach require adjustments in the function or processes of the nursing unit?

Does the approach require additional time or an adjustment in the allocation of time for nurses and other unit personnel?

Will the approach require new equipment or other material resources?

What practical arrangements and materials are needed to enhance the ease and accuracy of making and recording observations?

Are administrative personnel supportive of the approach being used?

How will the trial application affect other activities in the setting?

Are special provisions needed for gathering and storing information?

How will patients be informed of the approaches that will be used?

How will the data that are obtained be assessed and analyzed?

If the theoretic goal is attained or not attained, how will the results be explained or accounted for?

Have alternative explanations been projected to provide sufficient information to make a judgment about outcomes?

How will the results of the experience be compiled to be communicated to others?

approach will affect the functioning of the nursing unit and to assess the potential for observing and recording factors relevant to the theory's application. Because confirmation and validation will be disruptive, the support of administrative personnel is important. The successful use of a theory in practice depends on planning for the changes that are required, including the changes that will be needed to gather the required research data. Box 10-2 provides questions to be addressed when planning for theory use. If each of these questions can be answered in such a way that makes the research seem feasible and desirable, theory confirmation and validation processes should proceed.

METHODOLOGIC APPROACHES TO CONFIRMATION AND VALIDATION OF RELATIONSHIPS AND OUTCOMES

Methods that are used in the confirmation and validation of theory are drawn from evaluation research (Posavac & Carey, 2006; Schroeder & Maibusch, 1984; Smeltzer, Hinshaw, & Feltman, 1987). These methods depend on knowing what outcomes you want to achieve and on having a well-planned approach for achieving your goal. Evaluation research methods depend on having some means for assessing pertinent circumstances that exist before the deliberative confirmation and validation of a theory and then reassessing those same circumstances for changes after the confirmation and validation of the theory. Factors associated with the outcomes are usually identified and assessed before theory confirmation and validation are begun and again after the approach has been in place for a specified period. The following sections describe quality-related outcomes that you may consider when planning for the confirmation and validation of theoretic relationships.

EXPECTED OUTCOMES THAT FLOW FROM THEORETIC REASONING

At the heart of the confirmation and validation of theory is the idea that the theory suggests goals or outcomes that the profession values and that the fundamental purpose for using the theory is to achieve these goals. The outcomes that are identified as flowing from theoretic reasoning are likely to represent key concepts of the theory that require sound empiric indicators and operational definitions. Your choice of empiric indicators and operational definitions may come from prior research, in which case you need to determine their adequacy for your purposes. If existing empiric indicators and operational definitions are not readily available, you will need to invest preliminary time and effort to develop your own. It is important to choose or create empiric indicators that can be assessed or that are likely to be assessed easily within the nursing context for theory confirmation and validation.

Scientific Competence of Nurses

Although the primary aim when deliberatively using theory in practice is improving the outcomes of those who are receiving care, it is also important to verify that the scientific competence of nurses is enhanced. This latter outcome serves to ensure that the positive benefits of using the theory in practice can be sustained over time.

Standards of nursing practice accepted by your nursing practice unit can contribute to your choice of ways of assessing nurse scientific competence. However, if your standards of care reflect only minimum acceptable practice, you may need to consider what extensions of the standards are implied within the theoretic reasoning. For example, a key element of your theory could be specific nursing care actions that signify the concept of *caring*. If your standards of care do not reflect or require these actions as part of minimum acceptable practice, you will need to integrate empiric indicators for these actions and plan a way to assess these nursing actions as an outcome.

Functional Outcomes

Nursing goals are sometimes defined in terms of how efficiently the work of nursing is done, how cost-effective it is, or how smoothly the work of each individual coordinates with others' work. If environmental factors that impede nurse efficiency have been identified as needing improvement for a particular unit, the environmental changes needed and the factors indicating improvement need to be clearly specified and assessed before a theory can be used to improve nursing effectiveness. After the baseline data are obtained and the approach based on the theory has been in place for a time, the measures of functional effectiveness are obtained and compared.

Nurse Satisfaction

Satisfaction with respect to nursing job responsibilities in nursing can be closely related to functional outcomes. The job satisfaction of nurses can be assessed by factors such as working conditions, relationships with colleagues, personal fulfillment, various types of perceived benefits, and perceived dissatisfactions. A premise that underlies the selection of this type of outcome is that, if nurses are satisfied with their work situations, the quality of care they provide will improve.

Quality of Care Perceived by Those Who Receive Care

People who receive care can be interviewed or surveyed to ascertain their perceptions of the quality of their care. Aspects of perceived quality of care that can be assessed include satisfaction with specific dimensions of care, perceived benefits obtained from the care, and perceived dissatisfactions. If your nursing approach is guided by a particular theory, consider asking specific questions based on the practices, ideas, goals, and processes that the theory directs you to use.

IMPLEMENTING A FORMAL METHOD OF STUDY

The approaches used to confirm and validate theory in practice can draw on traditional research methods, but they often shift to include the methods of evaluation and quality assurance research (Posavac & Carey, 2006). In this type of research, the method is designed to provide evidence of the effect of theoretic knowledge on the overall well-being of people who receive care, on the scientific competence of those who practice nursing, and on the practice setting. Ideally, this type of investigation includes the measurement of key outcomes before the selected theory is applied in practice, to demonstrate what changes in practice occur after the theory has been applied.

For example, if the available research evidence suggests that you need to confirm and validate a theory of pain alleviation in practice, you might design a study that would first estimate the quality of nursing care and patients' experiences of pain before the theory is used in practice. Your assessment could include the perspectives of nurses, people receiving nursing care, and others involved in caring for people who experience pain. After you have this information, you would begin to use the theory in practice and over time continue to observe the same outcome indicators of quality of care. On the basis of your findings, you could make recommendations for practice and for revisions in the conceptualizations of the theory.

When it is not possible to obtain data before using the theory, alternative approaches include obtaining population or epidemiologic data related to selected outcomes or obtaining measures from a comparable population or group of people. You then compare your outcomes with the population statistics. This approach is useful in many types of situations. One such circumstance is nursing care that is directed toward the prevention of a negative health experience, such as child abuse. If you have selected a theory that you project will influence the parenting abilities of mothers who are at risk for abusing their children, you are unlikely to be able to obtain reliable measures of the outcomes you are seeking to achieve. The mothers that you are working with may not have had prior parenting experience, or you may not have been involved in their care before they were identified as high-risk parents. You can obtain population statistics regarding the incidence of child abuse, monitor the incidence of abusive behaviors among the mothers for whom you are providing care, and compare your outcomes with the population statistics. You may also identify a group of mothers who are receiving a different type of care so that you can compare your outcomes with those of a different group.

Think About It

1. As you work in nursing, consider the various ways in which you might use, confirm, and validate theory or how others might do this. What possibilities does the workaday world allow for these activities?
2. Consider what makes theories, formal empiric descriptions, and other types of empiric research useful. When these are not useful, why is that the case?
3. Search for the best evidence regarding some nursing problem or situation you have encountered. Was the information useful to you? What in particular made it useful? How generalizable was the evidence?

REFLECTION AND DISCUSSION – SUPPLEMENT ⊝

References

American Association of Colleges of Nursing. (2006). *The essentials of doctoral education for advanced nursing practice.* Retrieved from http://www.aacn.nche.edu/DNP/pdf/Essentials.pdf.

Armola, R. R., Bourgault, A. M., Halm, M. A., Board, R. M., Bucher, L., Harrington, L., et al. (2009). AACN levels of evidence: What's new? *Critical Care Nurse, 29*(4), 70–73.

Barnard, K. E. (1981). An ecological approach to parent-child relations. In C. C. Brown (Ed.), *Infants at risk: Assessments and interventions.* Madison, CT: Johnson & Johnson Pediatric Round Table.

Barnard, K. E. (1996). Influencing parent-child interactions for children at risk. In M. J. Guralnick (Ed.), *The effectiveness of early intervention* (pp. 249–265). New York, NY: Brookes.

Barnard, K. E., Eyres, S., Lobo, M., & Snyder, C. (1983). An ecological paradigm for assessment and intervention. In T. B. Brazelton & B. M. Lester (Eds.), *New approaches to developmental screening of infants* (pp. 199–218). New York, NY: Elsevier.

Carpenito-Moyet, L. J. (2012). *Handbook of nursing diagnosis* (14th ed.). Philadelphia, PA: Lippincott, Williams & Wilkins.

DiCenso, A., Guyatt, G., & Ciliska, D. (2005). *Evidence based nursing: A guide to clinical practice.* St. Louis, MO: Mosby-Elsevier.

Ellis, R. (1969). The practitioner as theorist. *American Journal of Nursing, 69,* 1434–1438.

Fineout-Overholt, E., Mazurek-Melnyk, B., & Shultz, A. (2005). Transforming health care from the inside out: Advancing evidence-based practice in the 21st century. *Journal of Professional Nursing, 21*(6), 335–344.

Fox, N. J. (2003). Practice-based evidence: Toward collaborative and transgressive research. *Sociology, 37*(1), 81–102.

Horn, S. D., & Gassaway, J. (2007). Practice-based evidence study design for comparative effectiveness research. *Medical Care, 45*(10), S50–S57.

Leeman, J., & Sandelowski, M. (2012). Practice-based evidence and qualitative inquiry. *Journal of Nursing Scholarship, 44*(2), 171–179.

Melnyk, B. M., & Fineout-Overholt, E. (2010). *Evidence-based practice in nursing and healthcare: A guide to best practice.* Philadelphia: Lippincott, Williams & Wilkins.

Porter, S. (2010). Fundamental patterns of knowing in nursing: The challenge of evidence-based practice. *ANS Advances in Nursing Science, 33*(1), 1–12.

Posavac, E. J., & Carey, R. G. (2006). *Program evaluation: Methods and case studies* (7th ed.). Englewood Cliffs, NJ: Prentice-Hall.

Schroeder, P. C., & Maibusch, R. M. (1984). *Nursing quality assurance.* Rockville, MD: Aspen.

Simons, H., Kushner, S., Jones, K. D., & James, D. (2003). From evidence-based practice to practice-based evidence: The idea of situated generalization. *Research Papers in Education, 18*, 347–364.

Smeltzer, C., Hinshaw, A., & Feltman, B. (1987). The benefits of staff nurse involvement in monitoring the quality of patient care. *Journal of Nursing Quality Assurance, 1*, 1–7.

Thorne, S. E., & Sawatzky, R. (2014). Particularizing the general: sustaining theoretical integrity in the context of an evidence-based practice agenda. *ANS Advances in Nursing Science, 37*(1), 1–10.

Glossary

This glossary contains definitions that we have created for the purposes of this book. Some are common definitions that are consistent with the meanings that are generally found in the nursing literature. Other definitions are consistent with generally accepted meanings but adapted—we think appropriately—to suit our purposes and perspectives. We ask you to use the glossary with the understanding that we are not the final authority with regard to meanings. Our definitions are reasonable and carefully formulated, but other nuances of meaning for many of these terms are possible.

abstract concept Mental image derived largely from indirect evidence that is not easily presented by a specific empiric indicator.

accessibility Trait of theory that is useful for questioning and clarifying the degree to which concepts have indicators in observable reality and, subsequently, how attainable the outcomes, goals, and purposes of the theory are.

aesthetic criticism Form of knowledge within the aesthetics pattern that is a discursive representation of meaning for expressions of aesthetic knowledge; criticism is formed from aesthetic methods that are designed to deepen shared meanings for aesthetic knowing.

aesthetics Fundamental pattern of knowing in nursing related to the perception of deep meanings that call forth inner creative resources to transform experience into what is not yet real but is possible; expressed as knowledge through works of art and criticism and integrated in practice as transformative art/acts.

allies Persons who are not directly affected by a particular disadvantage, injustice, or unfair practice but who join those who are affected; allies honor the perspectives of the disadvantaged while they assist with efforts to rectify injustices and create more equitable situations.

appreciation Process of focusing and reflecting on aesthetic knowledge as it is understood and valued by members of the discipline; interacts with the process of inspiration to challenge and authenticate aesthetic knowledge.

assumption Structural component of theory that is taken for granted or thought to be true without systematically generated empiric evidence; theoretic assumptions may be value statements or may have the potential for empiric testing, but are assumed to be true within the theory because the assumptions are reasonable.

atomistic theory Theory that deals with a narrow scope of phenomena; the term often implies an assumption that the whole may be understood from a study of the parts.

authentication Processes within each of the patterns of knowing for evaluating and assessing the soundness of knowledge that is formally expressed; each pattern requires specific approaches for authentication that reflect the pattern's form of expression and knowing.

axiom Type of premise used in deductive logic that is often not tentative but relatively firm; axioms as premises are used for deducing theorems, especially in mathematics.

centering Process that involves a deliberate focus on inner feelings, perceptions, and experiences and that involves contemplation and introspection to form deep inner personal meaning from life experiences; interacts with the process of opening to create personal knowledge.

245

clarifying [values] Process that involves a deliberate focus on understanding the values under-girding ethical decisions and dilemmas and on bringing to full understanding those actions that are right and good; interacts with the process of exploring [alternatives} to create ethical knowledge.

clarity Trait of theory that is useful for questioning and understanding the degree to which a theory is semantically and structurally lucid and consistent.

codes Form of knowledge expression within the ethics pattern; codes are shorthand expressions of prescribed professional behaviors that are generally accepted as right and good; codes primarily describe behaviors that represent the nurse's accountability as expressed in rights, duties, and obligations.

components of theory Features of theory that are useful for describing theory and that form a template for critically reflecting theory; components include purpose, concepts, definitions, relationships, structure, and assumptions.

concept Complex mental formulation of experience; concepts are a major component of theory and convey the abstract ideas within the theory.

conceptual framework Logical grouping of related concepts or theories that is usually created to draw together several different aspects that are relevant to a complex situation, such as a practice setting or an educational program; term used synonymously with *theoretic framework;* knowledge form within the empiric pattern.

conceptualizing General process within the empiric pattern that focuses on identifying, defining, and creating meaning for concepts within theory; conceptualizing includes but is not limited to the focused process of creating conceptual meaning.

conclusions Relationship statements that are derived from premises in a deductive logic system; conclusions are a type of proposition and may take the form of a theorem or hypothesis.

confirmation In qualitative research, the processes of establishing the validity of empiric theory and research; in some qualitative methods, confirmation may be assumed as a result of the methodology used; confirmation may also require the theory and research to be used in additional settings.

consistency Theory trait related to clarity; consistency may be semantic or structural and refers to the general agreement, harmony, and compatibility of components within the theory.

construct Type of highly abstract and complex concept; constructs are formed from multiple less abstract or more empiric concepts.

creating conceptual meaning Theory development process of identifying, examining, and clarifying the mental images that comprise the elements, variables, or concepts within a theory; process that conveys the thoughts, feelings, and ideas that reflect the human experience of the concept.

criteria for concepts Essential features of a concept formed by examining conceptual meaning; criteria are designed with reference to the purposes for which the concept is being used and should be useful to identify the concept and to differentiate it from other concepts.

criteria for nursing diagnoses Essential features for a specific diagnosis to be used in a given instance or situation encountered in nursing practice.

critical analysis Form of formal expression of emancipatory knowledge; critical analyses illuminate meanings that would otherwise remain hidden and that can be informed by multiple perspectives, including feminist, liberal, poststructural, and postcolonial.

critical multiplism Approach to inquiry that integrates multiple methodologic processes within the research inquiry process; sometimes refers to the combining of qualitative and quantitative approaches to data collection to reduce bias.

critical reflection Process that questions the function, purposes, and value of empiric knowledge structures, especially theory, as reflected in the clarity, generality, simplicity, accessibility, and importance of the structure; the questioning process does not imply an expected response; for example, inquiring about clarity does not imply that clarity is desirable.

critical theory Broad term used to describe both the process and the product of analyses that take a historically situated and sociopolitical perspective; critical theory seeks to undermine dominant power structures that create inequities and that maintain oppression and other forms of social injustice.

critical thinking Deliberate use of clear, concise, and thorough thought processes that consider diverse elements of a broad array of existing problems with the intent of solving the problem; emancipatory knowing builds on critical thinking but focuses on problems related to social and political inequities; unlike critical thinking, emancipatory knowing requires the examination and understanding of how sociopolitical networks sustain unfair institutionalized practices.

critiquing Creative inquiry process for emancipatory knowing that exposes the hidden dynamics and meanings that are structured and institutionalized by social, cultural, and political practices and ideologies.

deconstruction Process of uncovering hidden and oppressive assumptions, ideologies, and frames of reference within text; deconstruction makes visible features of text that cannot be justified as a basis for truth; its purpose is to uncover conventions of language and social practices that promote and sustain inequities and injustices.

deduction Form of reasoning that moves from the general to the specific; in deductive logic, two or more premises as relational statements are used to draw a conclusion; in deductive research processes, an abstract theoretic relationship is used to derive specific questions or hypotheses.

definition Component of theory that indicates the empiric basis for a concept; definitions are statements of meaning that provide a link between theoretic abstractions and empiric indicators; may be relatively general or specific.

deliberative utilization and validation of theory Theory development process that refines and develops empiric knowledge in relation to practice; involves processes that refine conceptual meaning and validate theoretic relationships and outcomes within practice contexts.

demystification Process of making things visible, especially oppressive social practices; the open disclosure of that which was formerly hidden from understanding.

descriptive relationships Statements that provide an account of what something is; descriptive relationships provide an image or impression of the nature or attributes of a phenomenon.

dialogue Process of exchanging various points of view concerning what is right, good, or responsible; interacts with the process of justification to challenge and authenticate ethical knowledge.

discipline Group of individuals engaged in developing knowledge; the structured knowledge within an area of concern or a domain of inquiry.

discourse Interconnected systems or patterns of language, symbols, and human communications that create meanings and behavior.

discourse analysis Inquiry approach that focuses on understanding patterns of language as well as other symbolic systems of communication (e.g., television, artwork, advertisements) as constitutive of meanings and behavior; in discourse analysis, interconnected symbolic systems (i.e., discourses) are assumed to create historically situated meanings and behavior; critical discourse analysis focuses on decentering dominant discourses that perpetuate power and justice inequities.

emancipatory knowing Pattern of knowing that makes social and structural change possible; the ability to recognize barriers that create unfair and unjust social conditions and to analyze complex elements of the sociopolitical context to change a situation to one that improves people's lives; praxis, which is value-motivated and constant reflection and action to transform the world, is the fundamental process of emancipatory knowing.

empiric indicators Sensory experience linked to a concept; more empirically grounded concepts have more direct empiric indicators; abstract concepts require the construction of indirect measures or tools that provide an approximate empiric measurement of some feature of the phenomenon.

empiric-abstract continuum Means of visualizing or representing the extent to which concepts have a basis in empiric reality; empiric concepts have a direct reality basis and are more directly experienced, whereas abstract concepts have an indirect basis in empiric reality and are more mentally constructed.

empirics Fundamental pattern of knowing in nursing that is focused on the use of sensory experience for the creation of mediated knowledge expressions; expressed as knowledge with the use of theories and formal descriptions and integrated in practice as scientific competence.

empowerment Growing capacity of individuals and groups to exercise their will, to have their voices heard, and to claim their full human potential; addressing and changing conditions to remove barriers that thwart an individual's or a group's ability to claim his/her/its full potential.

envisioning Process of imagining forms, ways of being, actions, and outcomes into a possible future; interacts with the process of rehearsing to create aesthetic knowledge.

epistemology Pertaining to the "stem" or basis of knowledge; perspectives regarding how knowing becomes knowledge or how knowledge is created.

ethics Fundamental pattern of knowing in nursing that focuses on matters of moral and ethical significance; expressed as knowledge by principles and codes and integrated in practice as moral and ethical comportment.

evidence-informed nursing practice Nursing practice that integrates empiric evidence that is appropriate for a specific situation, but that is also guided by ethical, personal, aesthetic, and emancipatory knowing and is responsive to the unique, particular situation and the people involved; this conceptual definition regards all sources of knowing as equally important in shaping nursing practice and differs from the concept of evidence-based nursing practice, which places empiric knowledge at a higher value than other sources of knowing.

explaining Statements that provide an account of how something came to be; explanatory relationships provide an image or impression of how the nature or attributes of a phenomenon interrelate.

explanatory relationships Statements that provide ideas about how events happen and that indicate how related factors affect or result in certain phenomena.

exploring [alternatives] Approach to understanding and analyzing the values inherent in situation as well as the various actions that flow from those values; a process that cultivates awareness of alternatives to personal values and facilitates recognition of the merits and pitfalls of different approaches to moral and ethical decision making; exploring interacts with the process of clarifying to create ethical knowledge.

fact Objectively verifiable event, object, or property; a phenomenon that is experienced and named similarly by others in a similar context.

feminism Philosophic perspectives and methods that focus on the oppression of women as a class; a perspective that values women and women's experiences; actions of feminist scholars and activists who are committed to a variety of social and political changes that improve women's lives and in turn the lives of all people.

formal descriptions Expressions of knowledge within the empiric knowing pattern; a rigorous and confirmable accounting of perceptions, inferences, and understandings expressed in a variety of written formats; some formal descriptions may not be structured as theory, but may reflect the components of theory.

formal expressions of knowledge Written documents that convey in systematic ways what is known, and that have content that can be examined and authenticated; each pattern of knowing has specific forms of expression that are appropriately suited to that pattern.

general definition Statement of the meaning of a term or concept that sets forth characteristics of the phenomenon or indicates with what the phenomenon is associated; by contrast, a specific definition states particular characteristics or indicators that name what the phenomenon is.

generality Trait of theory that is useful for questioning, clarifying, and understanding the range of phenomena to which the theory applies; generality in combination with simplicity yields parsimony.

generalizability Extent to which research findings can be applied to or used as a basis for making decisions in like situations; generalizability is affected by the soundness of the conceptualization process, the research design, and the analysis of the data.

genuine Self Form of nondiscursive knowledge expression within the personal knowing pattern; refers to the whole and entire Self as understood by the Self and others.

grand theory Theory that deals with broad goals and concepts that represent the total range of phenomena of concern within a discipline; this term may be used to imply macro theory and molar and wholistic theory.

grounded theory Theory that is generated from inductive research processes; the source of data is empiric evidence.

hegemony Interconnected network of dominant views, values, assumptions, ideologies, and patterns of thought that benefit privileged groups; hegemonic structures are taken to be "the way things are" without question while they unfairly separate and continue to disadvantage certain groups; hegemony is difficult to challenge because of its institutionalization in the social order.

hermeneutic inquiry Inquiry approach for interpreting text (language based) that considers the historical situation in which the text was produced; approaches to hermeneutic inquiry vary but in general require movement between text and the historical context for the researcher to understand embedded meanings.

holism See *wholism.*

holistic theory See *wholistic theory.*

hypothesis Tentative statement of relationship between two or more variables that can be empirically tested; the term *hypothesis* generally is used to refer to a relationship statement that is tested with the use of specific research methods.

ideology Ideals and values that dominate the discourses of a culture or society, that are often unfair and unjust, and that typically go unquestioned.

imagining Creative development process for emancipatory knowing; focuses on envisioning and communicating how social and political structures must change to remove conditions of injustice and inequity, thereby creating conditions that enable full human potential.

importance Trait of theory that is useful for questioning, clarifying, and understanding the extent to which a theory is clinically significant or has value for the profession.

induction Form of reasoning that moves from the specific to the general; in inductive logic, a series of particulars are combined into a larger whole or set of things; in inductive research, particular events are observed and analyzed as a basis for formulating general theoretic statements (often called *grounded theory*).

inspiration Process of responding to aesthetic knowledge to imagine new possibilities and directions; interacts with appreciation to challenge and authenticate aesthetic knowledge.

interpretive research General inquiry approach that assumes that "truth" is constructed from the frame of reference of the knower, including both the research participants and the researcher; interpretive research approaches can be contrasted with objectivist research approaches, which assume that there exists an independent reality with truth values that are independent of the knower.

intersectionality Perspective that recognizes multiple sources of oppression and disadvantage based on sociopolitical factors (e.g., race, religion, gender, sexual and gender identities, economic status) and views these as multiplicative, not additive, when more than one factor are involved in a situation.

isolated research Research that is completed without recognized reference or linkage to theory.

justification Process of developing explicit descriptions of the values on which an ethical ideal rests and the line of reasoning toward which an ethical conclusion flows; justification interacts with the process of dialogue to challenge and authenticate ethical knowledge.

knowing Individual human processes of perceiving and understanding the Self and the world in ways that can be brought to some level of conscious awareness; not all that is comprehended during the processes of knowing can be shared or communicated, but what is shared, communicated, and expressed in words or actions becomes the knowledge of a discipline.

knowledge Awareness or perception acquired through insight, learning, or investigation expressed in a form that can be shared; knowledge is a reasonably accurate accounting of the world as it is known and shared by members of a discipline; it is a representation of knowing collectively judged by shared standards and criteria.

law Relationship between variables that has been thoroughly tested and confirmed; laws are said to be highly generalizable and relatively certain.

logic System of reasoning that deals with the form of relationships among propositions without specific regard to their content.

macro theory Theory that deals with a broad scope of phenomena; this term may be used to imply grand, molar, or wholistic theory.

manifesto Type of formal expression of emancipatory knowledge; action-oriented and impassioned portrayals of that which is problematic, descriptions of the ideals envisioned, and actions required to effect change.

metatheory Theory about the nature of theory and the processes for its development.

metalanguage In general, language that encompasses or transcends other language; in nursing, the broad concepts of nursing, person, society, environment, and health often referred to as *nursing's metaparadigm.*

methodolotry Idolization or "worship" of methodology in research; the adherence to rules of method as being primary without regard to the value or utility of a methodology for answering questions of importance to a discipline; methodolotry stands in contrast to other techniques for blending methodologies in relation to research questions.

micro theory Theory that is relatively narrow in scope or that deals with a narrow range of phenomena; this term may be used to imply atomistic or molecular theory.

middle-range theory Relative classification for theory that embodies concepts, relationships, and purposes that reflect limited aspects of broad phenomena; concepts in middle-range theory can be more easily linked to perceptible events and situations.

model Symbolic representation of empiric experience in words, pictorial or graphic diagrams, mathematic notations, or physical material (e.g., a model airplane); when represented in written language, models are a form of knowledge within the empiric pattern.

modernism In knowledge development, the period that began during the early 1900s after the widespread abandonment of metaphysical and religious explanations of knowing; modernism is characterized by the rise of traditional science with a focus on objectivism and a reliance on reason for the creation of knowledge.

molecular theory Theory that is relatively narrow in scope or that deals with a narrow range of phenomena; this term may be used to imply micro theory or atomistic theory.

moral distress Distress that results when ethically significant moral behavior is blocked (e.g., by institutional or legal factors).

moral and ethical comportment Expression of ethical knowledge and knowing in nursing practice that is integrated with emancipatory, personal, aesthetic, and empiric knowledge and knowing.

morals, morality Expression of ethical precepts in behavior and actions; ontologic or behavioral expression of what is good and right.

multivocality Use of many "voices" for methods, data sources, and interpretations in research and knowledge development; the gleaning of different interpretations from the same data set to form multiple understandings rather than a single "correct" interpretation.

narrative analysis Research approach that typically makes use of a story that is told chronologically as data; narrative analysis focuses on the meanings of interrelationships among elements in the story.

nursing practice Experiences that a nurse encounters during the process of caring for people, including those of the person receiving care, the nurse, others in the environment, and their interactions.

objectivity, objectivism Assumption on which methods of science are based in which truth is thought to exist apart from or outside of the person who knows; based on a dualistic view of the rational mind that involves the existence of a reality that is separate from the person who knows.

ontology Pertaining to ways of being in the world; perspectives on the existence and experience of being.

opening Process that involves the taking in of experience fully and with conscious awareness; interacts with the process of centering to create personal knowledge.

operational definition Statement of meaning that indicates how a term or concept can be assessed empirically; operational definitions are inferred from theoretic definitions and specify as exactly as possible the empiric indicators used to observe, assess, or measure the concept empirically; the standards or criteria to be used when making observations.

paradigm Worldview or overarching frame of reference directing knowledge development; a paradigm implies standards or criteria for assigning value or worth to both the processes and the products of a discipline as well as the methods of knowledge development.

parsimony Trait of theory that incorporates degrees of both simplicity and generality; a highly parsimonious theory is one that has a broad range or generality and that is stated in very simple terms.

patterns gone wild Distortion of understanding that occurs when one pattern of knowing is not critically examined and integrated with the whole of knowing; overemphasis on one pattern without integration leads to uncritical acceptance, narrow interpretations, and partial use of knowledge.

personal knowing Fundamental pattern of knowing in nursing that is focused on the inner experience of becoming a whole, aware Self; expressed as knowledge through autobiographic stories and the genuine Self and integrated in practice with other patterns as the therapeutic use of the Self.

personal stories Tangible expressions of personal knowledge that are discursive in form and that can be shared within the discipline.

philosophy Form of disciplined inquiry for the purpose of discerning general traits of reality and principles of value.

postcolonialism Approach to understanding the relationship between culture and imperialistic colonization (i.e., takeover and domination of the powerless by the powerful); generally, postcolonial thought is concerned with reversing the effects of political or ideologic colonization.

postmodernism Period after modernism in which confidence in the achievement of objective knowledge through reason was eroded; postmodernism generally rejects universal truths and the idea that truth is possible and instead embraces multiple approaches to knowledge generation.

poststructuralism In linguistics, the view that language is not reflective but rather constitutive of meaning; for poststructuralists, there is no reality or truth, and the humanist idea of an autonomous knower is rejected; to these thinkers, we do not have language but instead language "has us" in the sense that it constructs our experiences and understandings.

practice-based evidence Evidence that comes from the validation of clinically used approaches and techniques that are known to be effective for promoting health-related goals; emphasizes investigating and confirming what seems to be effective in practice as a way to generate research evidence.

praxis Expression of emancipatory knowing and knowledge in nursing practice; value-grounded, thoughtful reflection and action that occurs in synchrony and that integrates ontology and epistemology; a value-motivated process that changes nursing practice and the larger sociopolitical environment to end injustices and inequities; praxis creates conditions in which all people can reach maximum well-being and full potential, and is integrated with ethical, aesthetic, personal, and empiric knowledge and knowing in nursing practice.

predicting Process used for the creation of empiric knowledge; prediction involves a focus on interrelating concepts and variables to create an understanding of when and how phenomena and events will occur and recur; used in conjunction with explaining.

predictive relationships Set of statements that interrelates variables so that a specified outcome can be expected when the theory is used.

premises Relationship statements that are used in deductive logic as a basis for forming a conclusion; in logic, the form of the argument must be valid, regardless of how sound the premises are; examples of types of premises are hypotheses and axioms.

principles Forms of knowledge expression within the ethics pattern; principles are general statements that reflect general and fundamental precepts of value or truths that are adhered to when providing nursing care, such as "do no harm."

problem solving Process of identifying a discrete difficulty or dilemma and finding situation-specific corrections or solutions.

processes for theory development In a practice discipline, the processes for theory development include creating conceptual meaning, structuring and contextualizing theory, refining and validating concepts and theoretic relationships, and deliberatively using and validating theory.

profession Vocation that requires specialized knowledge, provides a role in society that is valued, and uses some means of internal regulation of its members.

proposition Statement of a relationship between two or more variables; the term *proposition* is a general category that includes postulates, premises, suppositions, axioms, conclusions, theorems, and hypotheses; when a distinction in meaning is made among these various terms, it reflects the form or purpose of logic used or the context in which the proposition occurs; for example, the term *hypothesis* is generally used in the context of a research study, whereas the terms *axiom* and *theorem* are used to refer to the relationship statements that are made as part of a particular type of deductive logic.

purpose Component of theory that establishes the reasons that underlie a theory's development; the outcome or outcomes expected to emerge if the relationships of the theory are valid; the purpose of the theory also suggests the range of situations in which the theory is expected to apply.

qualitative methods Methods of data collection and analysis that depend on talk, language expressions of talk, or observations expressed in language, with interpretations presented by non-numeric (usually language) means.

quantitative methods Methods of data collection and analysis that depend on measurement and that are expressed in numeric terms.

reductionism Philosophic stance that the whole can be partitioned and understood through generalizations that are made from a study of the parts.

refining concepts and theoretic relationships Process for linking research and theory that focuses on the correspondence between the ideas of the theory and the accessible experience that involves both qualitative and quantitative approaches; includes validating empiric indicators for concepts, grounding emerging relationships empirically, and validating relationships with the use of empiric methods.

reflection Process that requires integrating a wide range of perceptions to realize what is known within the Self; interacts with the process of response to challenge and authenticate personal knowledge.

reflective practice Necessary component of best practices that requires practitioners to thoughtfully consider and adopt ways to improve practice over time; part of the process of praxis, but praxis requires bringing oppressive social and political practices to the center of concern when transforming practice to end injustices and inequities.

rehearsing Process of creating and re-creating narrative, body movements, gestures, and actions in relation to an anticipated situation; interacts with the process of envisioning to create aesthetic knowledge.

relationship statement Any statement that sets forth a connection or association between two or more phenomena; this general term is used to denote both tentative and confirmed types of statements, such as propositions, laws, axioms, and hypotheses; as a more general term, it does not imply a particular form of logic or a particular context in which the statement is used.

relationships Component of theory that refers to the interconnections among concepts.

replication Process that draws on methods of science to determine the extent to which an observation remains consistent from one situation or time to another; interacts with the processes of validation and confirmation to challenge and authenticate empiric knowledge.

research Application of formalized methods of obtaining confirmable and valid knowledge about empiric experience.

response Process of interacting with one's own Self and others to provide insight regarding the meanings that are conveyed in experience; interacts with the process of reflection to challenge and authenticate personal knowledge.

science As a product, the knowledge forms generated by the use of rigorous and precise empirically based methods (e.g., facts, formal descriptions, models, theories); as a process, the use of empirically based methods to generate theories, models, and descriptions of reality.

scientific competence Expression of empiric knowledge and knowing in nursing practice that is integrated with emancipatory knowing and knowledge, ethics, aesthetics, and personal knowing and knowledge.

simplicity Trait of theory used in critical reflection for questioning, clarifying, and understanding the degree to which a theory reduces complexity by utilizing a minimum number of descriptive components, especially concepts, to accomplish its purpose; simplicity in combination with generality yields parsimony.

situation-specific theory Theory that is developed with the sensitive consideration of context; assumes that theory (even middle-range formulations) generally cannot be used without taking into account important differences across populations; draws attention to the variables that significantly affect the successful use of theory.

social equity Criterion for the authentication of emancipatory knowledge; the demonstrable elimination or reduction of conditions that create disadvantage for some and advantage for others.

specific definition Statement of the meaning of a term or concept that names the associated object, property, or event and assigns it particular characteristics, as opposed to saying what the concept is like or associated with in reality.

structuralism In linguistics, the view that the meanings of words and language are not universally understood but rather derived from the language structure within which the words are found; more broadly, language practices are structured by the context of use and reflect the broader social and political environments.

structure Component of theory that refers to the overall morphologic arrangement of specific elements, especially concepts, within the theory.

structuring Process that involves forming empiric concepts into formal expressions, such as theories, models, and frameworks; interacts with the process of explaining to create empiric knowledge.

structuring and contextualizing theory Theory development process of forming relationships between and among concepts in a unique, creative, rigorous, and systematic way that is consistent with the purposes of the theory; this process also includes identifying and defining the concepts, identifying assumptions, clarifying the context of the theory, and designing relationship statements.

substantive middle-range theory In nursing, theory that tends to cluster around a concept (usually clinical) that is of interest to nursing; theories of pain alleviation, fatigue, or uncertainty represent theory in the middle range.

sustainability Criterion for the authentication of emancipatory knowledge; establishes how well the envisioned and implemented social change survives and thrives.

theoretic definition Statement of meaning that conveys essential features of a concept in a manner that fits meaningfully within a theory; a theoretic definition specifies conceptual meaning and implies empiric indicators for concepts; this term may be used synonymously with *conceptual definition.*

theoretic framework Logical grouping of related concepts that is usually created to draw together several different aspects that are relevant to a complex situation, such as a practice setting or an educational program; this term is used synonymously with *conceptual framework;* a knowledge form within the empirics pattern.

theory Expression of knowledge within the empirics pattern; the creative and rigorous structuring of ideas that project a tentative, purposeful, and systematic view of phenomena.

theory-linked research Research that is designed with reference or linkage to a theory; theory-linked research may be theory testing or theory generating; theory-testing research ascertains how accurately existing theoretic relationships depict reality-based events, whereas theory-generating research is designed to discover and describe relationships by observing empiric reality and then constructing theory on the basis of the empiric data observed.

therapeutic use of Self Expression of personal knowledge and knowing in nursing practice that is integrated with emancipatory, ethical, empiric, and aesthetic knowledge and knowing.

transformative art/act Expression of aesthetic knowledge and knowing in nursing practice that is integrated with emancipatory, empiric, aesthetic, and personal knowing and knowledge.

translational research Research designed to move evidence into the clinical arena by evaluating outcomes in the practice setting; research to connect basic discoveries with patient/client care.

validation Process that draws on the traditional methods of science to substantiate the accuracy of conceptual meanings in terms of empiric evidence; interacts with replication to challenge and authenticate empiric knowledge; may also refer to newer methods for establishing the credibility or truth value of knowledge structures within the empiric pattern.

wholism Perspective that is based on the assumption that a whole is emergent and cannot be reduced to discrete elements or be analyzed without consideration of the sum of its parts; may also refer to an emphasis on the value of the whole but with consideration for discrete parts that are interrelated.

wholistic theory Theory that deals with a broad scope of phenomena; often implies an assumption that the whole is greater than the sum of its parts; this term may be used to imply macro or grand theory.

work of art Tangible expression of knowledge within the aesthetic patterns that is not discursive in form and that can be communicated and shared within the discipline; includes aesthetic expressions such as poetry, drawings, music, dance, and other forms that are generally understood to be art.

Index

Page numbers followed by *b, t,* and *f* indicate boxes, tables, and figures, respectively.